CO-ORDINATED SCIENCE

GCSE Book 1

Christopher Lale, Ann Daniels, Mark Duke

Series Editors:
Ken Dobson and Chris Sunley

Collins Educational

An Imprint of HarperCollinsPublishers

Collins Educational, an imprint of HarperCollins*Publishers*
77–85 Fulham Palace Road, Hammersmith, London W6 8JB.

© HarperCollins*Publishers* / Suffolk County Council 1996

First Published 1996

ISBN 0 00 327850 6

Designed by Derek Lee
Picture research by Marilyn Rawlings
Artwork by Tom Cross, Barking Dog Art, Peter Harper, Martin Shovel, Pantek Arts,
Gay Galsworthy, John Booth, Ray Burrows, Jeremy Gower
Index by Julie Rimington
Production by Mandy Innes
Edited by Alan Trewartha
Printed and bound by Rotolito Lombarda Spa. (Italy)

Contents

How to use this book

This book has been written to support a *co-ordinated* science GCSE course – that is a course that includes physics, chemistry and biology. The chemistry part of the course also includes some earth science.

The course is divided into units and each unit is covered by one chapter. This book covers nine units. There are three physics units (chapters 1–3), three chemistry units (chapters 4–6) and three biology units (chapters 7–9).

The book also includes a Revision chapter, an Extension tasks chapter and a Reference Section. The Revision chapter gives you some ideas on how to revise as well as some past examination questions with sample answers. The Extension tasks include a variety of activities and more detailed questions.

The Reference Section (the grey edged section at the back) contains a Glossary and gives background information which will help you to understand the work covered in each chapter. It also gives details of some of the important practical techniques you will be using in your experimental and investigative work.

The chapters also include a number of special features to help you with your learning of science.

Key Words

Science sometimes seems to have a vocabulary all of its own! Quite a lot of technical terms are used by scientists and you will need to understand what these mean if you are to make good progress. The first time an important technical term is used in a chapter, it will be written in **bold type**. A detailed explanation of what the term means can be found in the Glossary.

> holidays in the sun. Scientists are also worried that the ozone layer of the atmosphere does not protect us as well as before. People with fair skins are more at risk. The skin tries to get some protection by tanning.
>
> Ultraviolet rays can damage your eyes. You can buy sunglasses with special uvA and uvB filters to protect your retina from different frequencies of ultraviolet radiation.
>
> Gamma rays are even more dangerous than X-rays. They have even higher frequencies and photon energies. Radioactive elements give out gamma rays when they decay. The **nucleus** inside each atom changes and produces a gamma ray.
>
> *R p208*
>
> Visible light is a radiation too. A photon of visible light does not have enough energy to affect your skin cells. It does have enough energy to trigger special sensitive cells in the retina at the back of your eyes. This is why you can see light. Infrared photons do not have enough energy to stimulate your retina cells because of their low frequency. This is why infrared radiation is invisible.

The word 'nucleus' has been written in bold type. This means that if you look in the Glossary you will find out precisely what it means.

A list of the most important, or 'key words', introduced in the chapter is also given at the end of the chapter. If you are not clear about what these words mean when you reach the end of a chapter, you have missed something fairly important. You should go back to find out what the words mean and look them up in the Glossary.

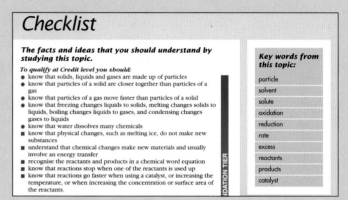

Checklist

The facts and ideas that you should understand by studying this topic.

To qualify at Credit level you should:

- know that solids, liquids and gases are made up of particles
- know that particles of a solid are closer together than particles of a gas
- know that particles of a gas move faster than particles of a solid
- know that freezing changes liquids to solids, melting changes solids to liquids, boiling changes liquids to gases, and condensing changes gases to liquids
- know that water dissolves many chemicals
- know that physical changes, such as melting ice, do not make new substances
- understand that chemical changes make new materials and usually involve an energy transfer
- recognise the reactants and products in a chemical word equation
- know that reactions stop when one of the reactants is used up
- know that reactions go faster when using a catalyst, or increasing the temperature, or when increasing the concentration or surface area of the reactants.

FOUNDATION TIER

Key words from this topic:

particle
solvent
solute
oxidation
reduction
rate
excess
reactants
products
catalyst

The key words for chapter 4.

Links to the Reference Section

Where you see this icon in the left margin, it means that you can look in the Reference Section for more details or background information.

Sound waves

R p203

Human ears are able to detect a huge variety of sound waves. You may already know how sound gets to your ear – it is carried as a wave through the air as tiny variations in air pressure. A peak is where the air is slightly more compressed, and a trough is where the air is slightly more expanded (rarefied). High **pitch** sounds have a short wavelength. Low pitch sounds have a long wavelength. Loud sounds have a large amplitude and quiet sounds have a small amplitude. Loudness is measured in **decibels**.

R p204

This icon tells you that there is some more information in the Reference Section if you turn to page 204.

The decibel scale

The decibel scale measures the loudness of sound as it reaches your ear. A loudness of 140 dB causes pain.

Loudness	Sound you hear	Sound level (dB)
silence	limit of your hearing	0
quiet	faint whisper	20
moderate	ordinary conversation	50
loud	busy street traffic	80
extremely loud	jet plane taking off	110

Questions and Practice

As you work through each chapter you will come across sections titled *Questions and Practice*. These will give you the chance to put into practice some of the ideas that you have just encountered. They should tell you very quickly whether you have understood the work and are able to continue through the chapter. If you find the questions difficult you should go back and read through the information in the chapter that leads up to the questions.

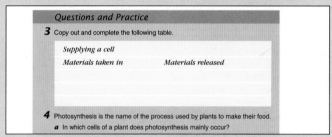

Questions and Practice

3 Copy out and complete the following table.

Supplying a cell	
Materials taken in	*Materials released*

4 Photosynthesis is the name of the process used by plants to make their food.
a In which cells of a plant does photosynthesis mainly occur?

If you can't answer these questions then you probably haven't read chapter 7 yet!

Examination Questions

These come near the end of each chapter. They test your knowledge and understanding of the work covered in the whole chapter. The questions have been taken from past examination papers and are graded at the three levels of difficulty: Credit, Merit and Special.

Checklists

At the end of each chapter a checklist gives you the facts and ideas that you should have learned by studying the chapter. These are also set out in the three levels of difficulty: Credit, Merit and Special. They list what you must know, be able to do, and understand in order to be successful in the GCSE Foundation and Higher Tier examinations.

Some of things on the checklist are 'key ideas' which are needed for other chapters and in the second year of your GCSE course. These are identified by a square icon.

To qualify at Merit level you should:
- be able to draw the arrangement of particles in a solid, liquid and gas
- be able to describe the changes of the movement and arrangement of particles during freezing, melting, boiling and condensing
- know that a solution is made up of a solute and a solvent
- know that in a solution, solvent particles surround particles in the solid and remove them from the solid structure
- be able to construct a word equation, knowing the reactants and the products
- know that a collision between particles must take place for a chemical change to happen
- know that an increase in concentration makes particles more crowded
- know that small amounts of catalysts can be used to speed up reactions
- be able to interpret graphs of reaction rates.

GCSE FOUN
GHER TIER

The ideas marked ● will only be tested in the Year 10 GCSE Examination. Those marked ■ will be tested in both the Year 10 and Year 11 Examinations.

The numbers in square brackets indicate the maximum number of marks given for each part of the question.

Examination Questions

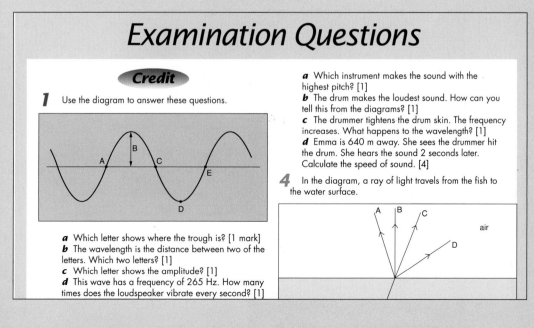

Credit

1 Use the diagram to answer these questions.

a Which letter shows where the trough is? [1 mark]
b The wavelength is the distance between two of the letters. Which two letters? [1]
c Which letter shows the amplitude? [1]
d This wave has a frequency of 265 Hz. How many times does the loudspeaker vibrate every second? [1]

a Which instrument makes the sound with the highest pitch? [1]
b The drum makes the loudest sound. How can you tell this from the diagrams? [1]
c The drummer tightens the drum skin. The frequency increases. What happens to the wavelength? [1]
d Emma is 640 m away. She sees the drummer hit the drum. She hears the sound 2 seconds later. Calculate the speed of sound. [4]

4 In the diagram, a ray of light travels from the fish to the water surface.

CHAPTER 1

Waves in Action

▲ Waves carry energy. The enormous energy in sea waves can be very destructive.

You can see this page because of light waves. The paper reflects more light than the ink. Some of the light waves bouncing off the page reach your eye. Light waves are responsible for eighty per cent of the signals reaching your brain.

Your brain also gets a lot of information from sound waves. You rely on sound waves when you talk to someone or listen to music. Much of the telephone system uses infrared waves to carry messages along fibre-optic cables. Radio and television (including satellite TV) are broadcast using radio waves.

You cook your food using infrared waves or microwaves.

Waves can cause problems too. Large ocean waves carry so much energy that they can sink ships and wear away the coastline. Ultraviolet waves damage your skin. X-rays and gamma rays are waves. They can cause damage inside your body.

Your life would be *totally different* without waves. Imagine what it would be like without radio and television, without light or sound. Could you survive?

▲ The dishes receive messages from satellites by microwaves.

▲ Remote controls use infrared light waves.

◄ This mobile phone depends on invisible radio waves.

▲ Space is a very quiet place. Astronauts who are space-walking talk to each other by radio.

Types of wave

Transverse waves

Throw a stone into the middle of a pond. The stone makes the surface of the water move down and then up again. The water keeps on moving up and down for a little while after the stone has sunk. The result is ripples (water waves) with **crests** and **troughs**.

At first, the water in the middle of the pond is moving up and down quite a lot. After a short time the water in the middle is calm, but water at the edge of the pond has started to move up and down. This means that energy – movement energy – has been transferred. The waves carried the energy from the middle of the pond to the edge. You can watch the wave travel along the surface of the pond, but the water particles move only up and down.

Water waves are an example of **transverse waves**. The particles of the **medium** move to and fro *across* the direction of the wave – at right angles to the wave's direction.

Longitudinal waves

Sound waves are **longitudinal waves**. The particles of the medium vibrate backwards and forwards *along* the direction of the wave. The wave does not have crests and troughs. It is made up of compressions and rarefactions (expansions). The particles are squashed together in a **compression** and stretched apart in a **rarefaction**.

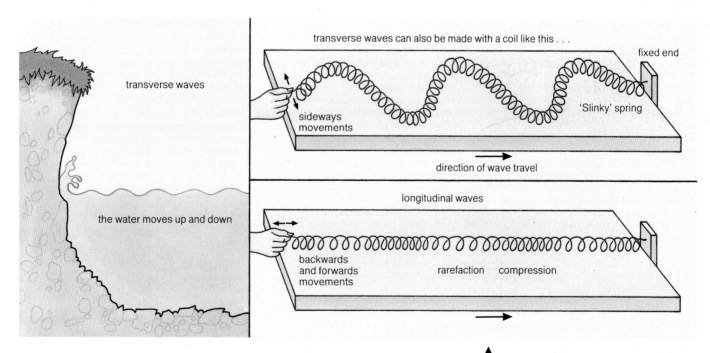

▲
Transverse and longitudinal waves are made by different types of vibrations.

What is a wave?

There are many types of wave. Sound waves, water waves and electromagnetic waves (such as radio waves and light waves) are all different from each other. Even though they are different, all waves have some things in common.

● Waves travel at a certain wave speed. The wave speed depends on the substance that the waves are travelling through. This substance is called the *medium*.

● Waves carry energy without moving material along.

● Waves have a repeating shape or pattern.

● Waves have a **frequency**, a **wavelength** and an **amplitude**.

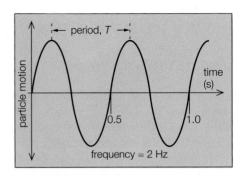

Frequency

Frequency is the number of repeated patterns per second. You can measure the frequency of a wave by counting the number of waves passing any point in one second. Frequency is measured in Hertz (Hz).

Wavelength

Wavelength is the length of the repeating pattern. You can measure the wavelength of a wave by measuring the distance from one crest to the next (or from one trough to the next).

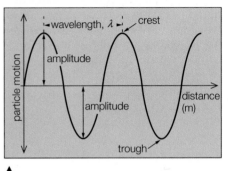

▲
The features of wave motion.

Amplitude

Amplitude is the maximum change of the medium from the rest position. For a water wave the amplitude is the height of a crest above – or the depth of a trough below – the rest position. The height of a crest above a trough is *twice* the amplitude of the wave.

███ *Measuring waves – the wave equation*

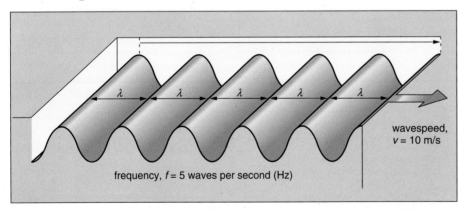

◄
After one second, five waves have been produced. All five waves have the same wavelength.

The frequency of waves affects the wavelength. If you make waves more frequent, they bunch up tightly together and their wavelengths are shorter. The wave speed does not change. For example, sound waves with a frequency of 170 Hz have a wavelength of 2 m. The wavelength of 340 Hz sound waves is only 1m. Waves with double the frequency have only half the wavelength. Both these waves travel at the same speed of 340 m/s.

   Suppose that a machine makes some water waves. You switch the machine on and in 1 second it produces 5 full waves each with a wavelength of 2 metres. This means that the first wave has travelled $5 \times 2 = 10$ metres in 1 second. So its speed is 10 m/s. This can be written as an equation in symbols or words:

$$v = f \times \lambda$$

wave speed = frequency × wavelength

Where v = wave speed, f = frequency, λ = wavelength (λ is the Greek letter 'lambda').

Worked example

A loudspeaker makes sound waves with a frequency of 200 Hz. The waves have a wavelength of 1.7 m. Calculate the speed of the sound waves.

Write down the formula: $v = f \times \lambda$

Put in the numbers: $v = 200 \times 1.7$

Write down the answer and the unit: $v = 340$ m/s

Worked example

Light waves have a very high speed and a very high frequency. Light speed is 300 000 000 m/s (3×10^8 m/s). The frequency of green light waves is 500 000 000 000 000 Hz (5×10^{14} Hz). Calculate the wavelength of green light.

Write down the formula: $v = f \times \lambda$

Rearrange the formula so that the subject is λ: $\lambda = \dfrac{v}{f}$

Put in the numbers: $\lambda = \dfrac{3 \times 10^8}{5 \times 10^{14}}$

Write down the answer and the unit: $\lambda = 6 \times 10^{-7}$ m

The wavelength of light is very small. A wavelength of 6×10^{-7} m is 0.0000006 m or 0.0006 millimetres. There would be more than 6000 wavelengths across the head of a pin!

Questions and Practice

1 The wavelength of a water wave is 20 metres. Its frequency is 0.2 Hz. Calculate the speed of the wave.

2 A sound wave has a frequency of 2000 Hz. It travels through a piece of iron. Its wavelength is 2.5 metres. Calculate the speed of sound in iron.

3 A radio wave has a frequency of 600 kHz (600 000 Hz). Radio waves are part of the electromagnetic spectrum. The speed of electromagnetic waves is 300 000 000 metres per second (3×10^8 m/s). Calculate the wavelength of the radio wave.

4 The speed of sound in air is 340 m/s. An organ pipe is 1.3 metres long. It makes a sound wave that is four times its own length. Calculate the frequency of the sound it makes.

5 The wavelength of ultraviolet radiation is 4×10^{-7} m. Ultraviolet radiation is part of the electromagnetic spectrum. The speed of electromagnetic waves is 300 000 000 metres per second (3×10^8 m/s). Calculate the frequency of ultraviolet radiation.

Controlling waves

If you want to use waves you must be able to control them. Waves can be controlled by **reflection** and **refraction**.

Changing direction – reflection

The easiest way to change the direction of a wave is to put a barrier in its way. Engineers make models before they build expensive harbours. They can change the shape of the walls to control the waves. The harbour wall reflects sea waves. You can use a flat cliff to reflect sound waves or a mirror to reflect light waves.

Suppose that you make a wave in a tank of water. When a wavefront hits a barrier at an angle, it reflects off at the same angle. The angle of reflection is the same as the angle of incidence.

p206

Echoes

All kinds of waves can be reflected. You can hear an echo of your voice if you shout in front of a cliff (or a big wall). The cliff reflects the sound waves back to you. If you stand closer to the cliff, the echo reaches you much sooner.

You can often hear the effect of echoes in large sports halls. The walls reflect the sound waves backwards and forwards several times. This makes it difficult to talk to a friend on the other side of a hall because the sound waves mix together. Architects design concert halls to cut down troublesome echoes. They avoid large, flat surfaces and use soft materials. They do not get rid of all the echoes or the music would sound dull and lifeless. The echo effect is called reverberation.

Earthquakes

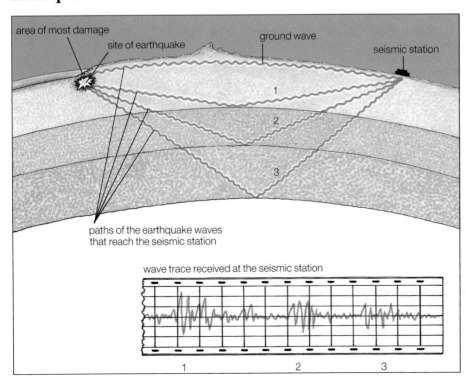

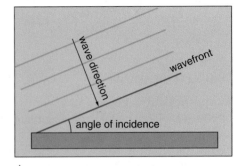

▲ Waves hit a barrier. The angle between a wavefront and the barrier is the angle of incidence.

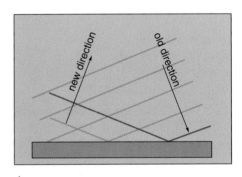

▲ The waves bounce off, bit by bit, like a ball hitting a wall.

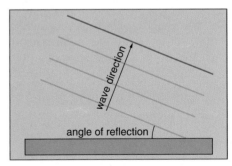

▲ The angle of reflection is the same size as the angle of incidence.

◄ Geologists can detect transverse seismic waves caused by earthquakes a long distance away. Waves arrive at different times because they are reflected by different layers. Geologists can work out how thick the layers are. They can even work out what kind of rock the layers are made of.

Earthquakes make waves that travel right through the Earth. These waves are called **seismic waves**. There are longitudinal seismic waves (called P-waves) and transverse seismic waves (called S-waves). The waves travel through rock. They are reflected at places where the type of rock changes. Special instruments called seismometers detect the reflected waves. They arrive at different times because they travel different distances. This provides geologists with evidence that the Earth is made up of layers of rock.

Changing speed causes refraction

The speed of a wave changes when it travels from one medium to another medium. When ripples travel from deep water to shallow water, their speed changes. They travel more slowly in shallow water. This makes them bunch up. Their wavelength gets shorter. Light waves travel faster in air than in glass.

There are two effects when wave speed changes: the wavelength changes and the direction of the waves may change.

Wavelength

Suppose that a wave travels into a medium where it travels more slowly. Its frequency stays the same, so its wavelength gets shorter.

You can sometimes see this effect when rows of soldiers are marching to a drum beat. The frequency of the beat stays the same. The rows bunch up when the soldiers march from a fast surface (hard, clean concrete) to a slow surface (soft, sticky mud).

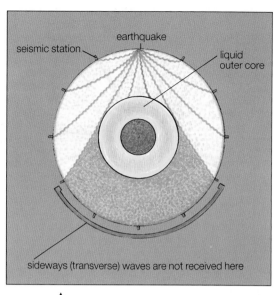

▲
Transverse S-waves can travel through solid rock but not through liquid. Longitudinal P-waves can travel through solid and liquid rock. A seismic station on the opposite side of the Earth from an earthquake detects only P-waves. This provides geologists with evidence that part of the Earth's core is liquid.

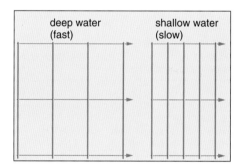

▲
When waves move from a fast medium to a slow medium, their wavelength gets shorter.

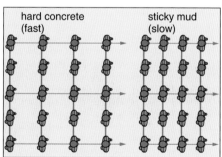

▲
When rows of marching soldiers have to slow down, they take shorter steps.

Direction

When waves travel into a new medium at an angle, the direction of travel changes. This is called refraction.

You can see this effect with marching soldiers too. Suppose a soldier at one end of a row marches with short steps and the soldier at the other end marches with long steps. The whole row changes direction. This is how rows of soldiers march around corners.

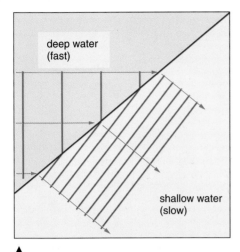

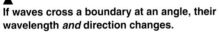

deep water
(fast)

shallow water
(slow)

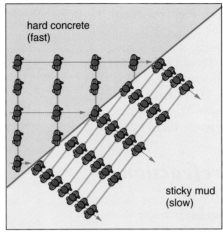

hard concrete
(fast)

sticky mud
(slow)

▲
If waves cross a boundary at an angle, their wavelength *and* direction changes.

▲
When rows of soldiers march from one type of surface to another at an angle, their direction changes because, one by one, they have to take shorter steps.

Questions and Practice

6 You are standing on a beach in front of a cliff. You shout 'Hello!' to a friend who is standing a distance further along the beach. Explain exactly what your friend will hear, and why.

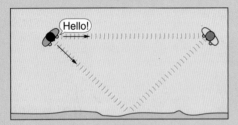

7 You are standing 340 m from a large brick wall. You clap your hands once. You hear the echo exactly 2 seconds later.

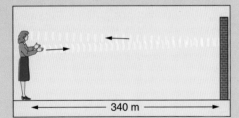

340 m

a How far does the sound wave travel from your hands, to the wall and back to your ear?

b Write down the formula you use to calculate speed from distance and time.

c Calculate the speed of sound in air.

8 You are standing in a valley between two cliffs. You clap your hands once. You hear more than one echo. Draw a diagram and use it to explain why this happens.

9 What does 'refraction' mean? Describe the two ways that waves change because of refraction. Draw a diagram to show the changes happening.

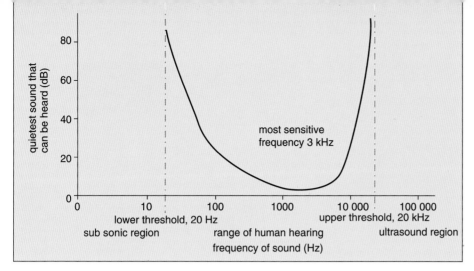

Sound waves

Human ears are able to detect a huge variety of sound waves. You may already know how sound gets to your ear - it is carried as a wave through the air as tiny variations in air pressure. A peak is where the air is slightly more compressed, and a trough is where the air is slightly more expanded (rarefied). High **pitch** sounds have a short wavelength. Low pitch sounds have a long wavelength. Loud sounds have a large amplitude and quiet sounds have a small amplitude. Loudness is measured in **decibels**.

The speed of sound

Sound waves travel fast. The speed of sound in air is about 340 m/s. When you listen to a friend talking, you hear the sound straight away. If you listen to something that is further away you may notice a delay. If you are at one end of a large car park and a car door slams at the other end, you will see the door close before you hear the sound. Light from the door reaches your eyes before the sound reaches your ears. This is because light travels very fast indeed – much faster than sound. The speed of light is about 300 000 000 m/s.

Thunder is the sound caused by lightning. You see the light from the lightning flash straight away. The thunder travels to you at the speed of sound (about $1/3$ kilometre per second). You can work out how far away the lightning is. When you see the lightning flash, start counting in seconds. Stop counting when you hear the thunder. Divide the number of seconds by three to find the number of kilometres that the sound has travelled.

Sound waves travel faster through liquids than through air. Sound travels fastest through solids. This is because the particles in a solid are linked most strongly. Sound cannot travel through a vacuum because there are no particles to vibrate.

Material	Speed of sound (m/s)
steel	6000
concrete	5000
rubber	1600
water	1500
air	330
vacuum	0

The speed of sound in different materials.

Ultrasound

You cannot hear low pitch notes below about 20 Hz or high pitch notes above about 20 kHz (20 000 Hz). On average, women and young people can hear higher pitch sounds than men or old people.

The range of hearing varies for different animals. Some dog owners use special whistles to call their dogs. Humans cannot hear the dog whistle because its frequency is too high. It works because dogs can hear sounds with a frequency higher than 20 kHz. The name of high frequency sound that people cannot hear is **ultrasound.**

Echo sounding

Echo sounders are fitted to ships. They tell the captain how deep the water is. The echo sounder sends out ultrasonic waves. The waves travel down to the bottom of the sea. The sea bed reflects them back to the echo sounder. The echo sounder measures the time the waves take to travel from the ship to the sea bed and back. A computer works out the depth using the time and the speed of sound. This echo sounding system is called SONAR (short for SOund NAvigation and Ranging). SONAR can also be used to find submarines and wrecks on the sea bed.

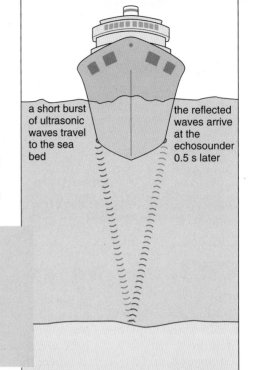

a short burst of ultrasonic waves travel to the sea bed

the reflected waves arrive at the echosounder 0.5 s later

speed of sound in water	=	$\dfrac{\text{distance travelled by ultrasonic wave}}{\text{time taken}}$
distance travelled by ultrasonic wave	=	speed of sound in water × time taken
	=	1500 × 0.5
	=	750 metres
depth	=	half distance travelled
	=	375 metres

As blind as a bat?

Bats hunt for food at night. They fly fast in the dark without crashing into anything. They do not *see* where they are going, they *hear* using ultrasound.

A bat sends out short bursts of ultrasonic waves that have a frequency of about 50 000 Hz. Trees, rocks and even insects reflect the waves back to the bat. The bat can tell what is in the way and how far away it is. The bat homes in on its prey and sends out bursts of ultrasound more frequently – up to 170 bursts per second. It can detect insects as small as a gnat. The bat's system of using ultrasound is called echo location.

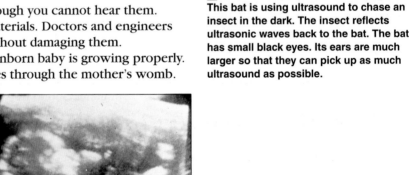

This bat is using ultrasound to chase an insect in the dark. The insect reflects ultrasonic waves back to the bat. The bat has small black eyes. Its ears are much larger so that they can pick up as much ultrasound as possible.

Using ultrasound in hospitals

Ultrasonic waves can be very useful even though you cannot hear them. Ultrasonic waves can travel through solid materials. Doctors and engineers can use ultrasound to look inside objects without damaging them.

Doctors use ultrasound to check that an unborn baby is growing properly. They send a narrow beam of ultrasonic waves through the mother's womb.

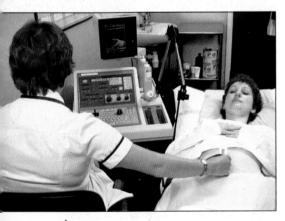

▲
This woman is having an ultrasound scan. The midwife can check the position of the baby before it is born.

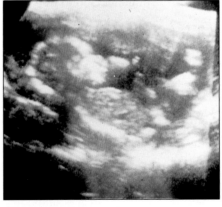

▲
This is an ultrasound scan of an 18-week old fetus. The dense parts (like the heart and the bones) show up in white.

Some of it is reflected back. Dense tissue, like bone, sends back more ultrasound than lighter tissue. A computer uses the information from the reflections to make a picture called an *ultrasound scan*. Doctors also use ultrasound to measure how well blood flows through blood vessels.

Some people build up hard, chalky 'stones' in their kidneys. Kidney stones cause a lot of pain. In the past, doctors had to cut them out during an operation. Today, they can use ultrasonic waves to break up the stones.

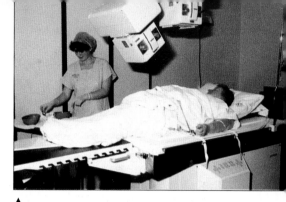

▲
Kidney stones can be removed without an operation. The machine focuses ultrasonic waves on to the kidney with a lens made of metal. The waves shatter the stones into small pieces. Urine carries the pieces out of the body.

Questions and Practice

10 During a thunderstorm you see a flash of lightning. Five seconds later you hear thunder. This is the sound from the lightning. The speed of sound is 330 m/s. How far away was the lightning?

11 How is ultrasound different from normal sound?

12 Describe one way that ultrasound is used in hospitals.

13 A ship uses an ultrasonic echo sounder to find the depth of the sea bed. The speed of ultrasonic waves in the sea water is 1500 m/s. The echo sounder sends out a burst of ultrasonic waves which arrives back two seconds later.

   a Draw a diagram to show what is happening.

   b Calculate the depth of water under the ship.

▲
This prism is refracting a beam of white light. The beam is split into the spectrum of light. This spreading out of colours is called dispersion. The second white beam is caused by total internal reflection.

◀
The radiation from the Sun.

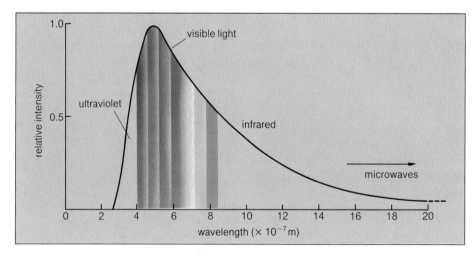

The electromagnetic spectrum

The electromagnetic spectrum is a family of different kinds of waves. The waves are made when particles with electric charge stop, start, slow down or speed up - in other words, when they **accelerate** or **decelerate**. For example, light is made when a negative electron jumps down from one place to another inside an atom. Electromagnetic waves all travel at the same speed in a vacuum. They travel at the speed of light: 300 000 000 m/s.

The spectrum of sunlight

You can use a prism to split white sunlight into different colours. The 'rainbow' of colours is called a **spectrum**. The great scientist Sir Isaac

▲
Ultraviolet radiation makes certain chemicals glow (fluoresce). Safety clothing for motor cyclists is made using fluorescent dyes. The material appears much brighter than normal, especially at dusk.

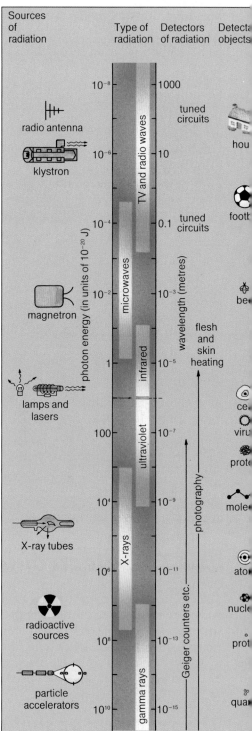

◄
Anything that is warm or hot gives out infrared radiation. People trapped in a collapsed building are warmer than the rubble. Rescue workers use infrared detectors to search for survivors.

Newton thought he could see seven different colours in the spectrum (red, orange, yellow, green, blue, indigo and violet) though the colours all blend smoothly together. Scientists call this the *visible spectrum* of white light. He did the experiment in a room that he had made dark by closing wooden shutters across the window. By making a hole in the shutters, he got a narrow beam of sunlight to shine through the prism.

Much later, scientists discovered some invisible parts of the spectrum. **Ultraviolet** waves have a shorter wavelength than violet waves.

Infrared waves have a longer wavelength than red waves. TV remote controls use invisible infrared (IR) radiation to carry signals from the handset to the television. Electric cookers have hot-plates. They glow and give out red light. They also emit invisible infrared rays. The infrared radiation – not the red light – heats up the food.

The whole **electromagnetic spectrum** contains radio (and TV) waves, microwaves (and radar), infrared, visible, ultraviolet, X-rays and gamma rays.

Radio and TV

Radio waves are made when electrons race up and down inside an aerial. They are the electromagnetic waves with the longest wavelengths and the lowest frequencies. Scientists knew about radio waves as long ago as the 1890s. In 1901, Gugliemo Marconi sent the first radio message across the Atlantic Ocean. He sent radio waves from England to Newfoundland in Canada. They only got there because they could bounce off the ionosphere like a mirror.

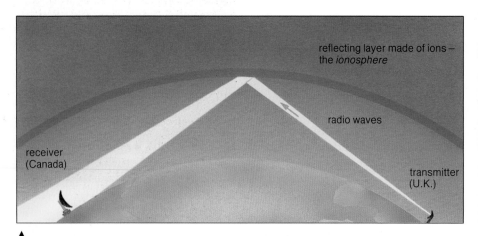

▲
Marconi was lucky. Most radio waves just shoot off into space. The kind Marconi was using reflected off the ionosphere. The ionosphere is a layer of ions (charged atoms).

▲
The full electromagnetic spectrum.

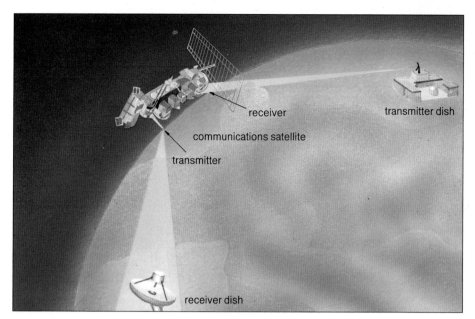

◄ A communications satellite receives TV, radio or telephone signals carried by high frequency radio waves. Modern satellites are better than mirrors. They collect the signals, amplify them and send them back to Earth.

High frequency radio waves can carry a lot of information. Very High Frequency (VHF) waves are used to carry FM radio broadcasts. Ultra High Frequency (UHF) waves are used to carry TV broadcasts. These high frequency radio waves pass straight through the ionosphere. You can still pick up television signals from other parts of the world if they are bounced off a communications satellite.

Microwaves and radar

You can cook food with **microwaves**. Microwaves have wavelengths that are shorter than radio waves, but longer than infrared. Water and fat molecules absorb the energy carried by the microwaves. The molecules move about faster and the water or fat gets hotter. Microwave ovens produce microwaves at just the right frequency for this to happen (2.45 gigahertz, or 2.45 thousand million hertz). Normal cookers heat the outside of the food. Molecules one or two centimetres below the surface absorb microwaves. This helps the food to cook quickly.

Radar uses microwaves with higher frequencies than microwave ovens (about 10 gigahertz). Metal objects reflect the waves very strongly. The radar machine works out the position and speed of cars, ships and aeroplanes from the reflections.

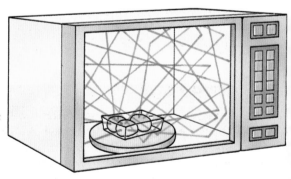

▲ A microwave oven is lined with metal which reflects microwaves. Microwave radiation passes right through glass and plastic. It carries energy to about 1 cm below the surface of the food.

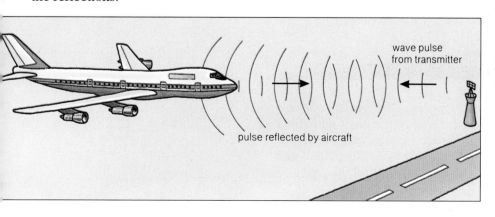

◄ A radar dish aerial sends out bursts (pulses) of microwaves. The aerial picks up the microwaves reflected by an aircraft. The radar machine measures the time taken by the burst of microwaves to travel there and back. The distance between the radar machine and the aircraft can be worked out because microwaves travel at the speed of light.

Looking right through you: X-rays

Konrad Röntgen discovered **X-rays** in 1895. X-rays are sometimes called Röntgen rays. He was doing an experiment with a fluorescent plate (like a TV screen) and a beam of fast electrons in a tube. By accident he found that the fluorescent plate glowed even when it was a long way from the electron tube. He put his hand in front of the fluorescent plate and saw the first X-ray picture. He saw the bones of his hand because the electron tube was making mysterious, invisible 'X- rays'.

X-rays are electromagnetic waves with shorter wavelengths than ultraviolet waves. Doctors use X-rays to look at broken bones inside your body. Diseased parts of lungs and bits of metal or stone that people have swallowed also show up on X-ray photographs. Dentists use X-rays to look at teeth inside your gums. They shine X-rays through your teeth on to a special photographic film. The film is developed like a black and white negative.

People who work with X-rays every day must take special precautions. They wear lead-lined aprons that stop X-rays from constantly damaging their bodies.

Gamma rays

Gamma rays have so much energy that they easily pass through your body without being affected. They have the shortest wavelengths, and the highest frequencies, of all the electromagnetic waves. Radioactive substances like Cobalt-60 and Caesium-137 emit gamma radiation. Doctors use the gamma rays to kill cancer cells. This treatment is called *radiotherapy*. Engineers use gamma rays to look for cracks in pipes and aircraft parts. They penetrate better than X-rays.

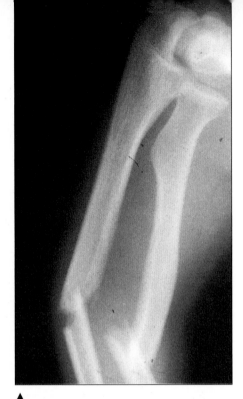

▲
X-ray pictures 'see' straight through skin and bone. X-rays make the film turn black when it is developed. Solid bones stop the X-rays from reaching the photographic film. These bits stay clear when the film is developed.

◀
A radiologist uses gamma rays from this machine to treat a cancer patient. The radiologist must calculate the dose carefully. The dose must kill cancerous tissue and leave healthy tissue alone.

Doctors also use radioactive substances as **tracers**. They put the tracer inside a patient's body and follow (trace) where it goes. A patient with lung problems can breathe Xenon-133. Xenon-133 is a gas that emits gamma rays. A special gamma camera uses the rays to build up a picture. The patient only gets a small dose of radiation because they soon breathe out all the gas.

Wave energy or particle energy?

All parts of the electromagnetic spectrum are kinds of **radiation**. They travel in straight lines or *rays*. Light waves can behave like particles. How can this be? One of the great mysteries of physics is that electromagnetic radiation can behave as both waves *and* particles. The particles are called **photons**.

Radiation with a high frequency has photons with a high energy. A photon of X-radiation carries 5000 times as much energy as a photon of yellow light. This is enough to kill or badly damage a living cell. Ultraviolet radiation has a lower frequency, so the photons carry less energy. Ultraviolet radiation is less dangerous than X-radiation. The photons can still kill skin cells but they cannot get so far into your body.

They cause sunburn and trigger skin cancer. Sunbathing can be dangerous. In recent years, skin cancer has become a serious problem in countries from Australia to Scotland. These days, people are much more likely to take holidays in the sun. Scientists are also worried that the ozone layer of the atmosphere does not protect us as well as before. People with fair skins are more at risk. The skin tries to get some protection by tanning.

Ultraviolet rays can damage your eyes. You can buy sunglasses with special uvA and uvB filters to protect your retina from different frequencies of ultraviolet radiation.

Gamma rays are even more dangerous than X-rays. They have even higher frequencies and photon energies. Radioactive elements give out gamma rays when they decay. The **nucleus** inside each atom changes and produces a gamma ray.

Visible light is a radiation too. A photon of visible light does not have enough energy to affect your skin cells. It does have enough energy to trigger special sensitive cells in the retina at the back of your eyes. This is why you can see light. Infrared photons do not have enough energy to stimulate your retina cells because of their low frequency. This is why infrared radiation is invisible.

Questions and Practice

14 Write down one use for each of these electromagnetic waves: gamma rays; infrared; microwaves; UHF waves; ultraviolet; X-rays.

15 Copy the table and fill in the gaps.

Part of electromagnetic spectrum	Wavelength in metres
Radio	0.01–10 000 (longest)
Microwaves	
Visible light	10^{-6}
	10^{-8}–10^{-12}
	10^{-12}–10^{-16} (shortest)

16 Write a short description of the dangers of these types of radiation: gamma radiation; ultraviolet radiation; X-radiation.

17 What do all parts of the electromagnetic spectrum have in common?

18 Write down the colours of the spectrum of visible light. Which colour has the longest wavelength?

Reflection of light

It is hard to work with light waves because they are so small. The wavelength of visible light is about 5×10^{-7} m. This is much too small to see individual waves. Even so, scientists believe that light is a wave because of the way it behaves.

Mirrors and the normal line

When you investigate the reflection of a ray of light, measure the angle between the ray and an imaginary line that is at right angles to the mirror. The angle is called the *angle of incidence*, and the imaginary line is called the **normal**.

A light ray shining along the normal reflects back on to itself, so it can be found even on a curved surface. This is why it is so useful. It is difficult to measure the angle between a ray of light and the surface of a curved mirror. The *angle of reflection* is the angle between the reflected ray and the normal.

Whenever a mirror reflects light:

the angle of incidence, i = the angle of reflection, r.

This is called the *law of reflection*.

What do you see in a mirror?

p206

If you look at yourself in a mirror, you see an **image** of yourself. Everything looks normal, but when you raise your left hand, your image raises its *right* hand. This effect is called *lateral inversion*. It is the reason why a photograph of yourself sometimes looks strange to you but normal to your friends. Your face is not truly symmetrical and you are used to seeing it laterally inverted in a mirror.

Using mirrors

Plane mirrors

You can use a flat (plane) mirror to see into awkward spaces. For instance, you can look underneath floorboards or inside a car's engine compartment. Dentists use a mirror with a handle to look inside your mouth. Police use a larger version to see underneath lorries during roadside safety checks. You can use two mirrors to reflect light around two corners. The instrument for doing this is called a periscope.

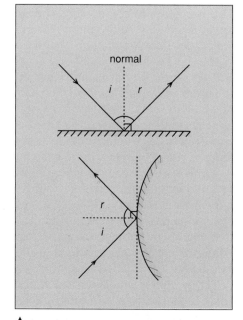

▲
The angles of incidence and reflection are the same when a mirror reflects light. This is true when the mirror is flat (plane) and even when the mirror is curved. This curved mirror is called a convex mirror because it bows out in the middle.

▼
A periscope is useful for seeing over the heads of people in a crowd. The mirrors are angled so that the first mirror reflects light from the object on to the second mirror, and the second mirror reflects it into your eye.

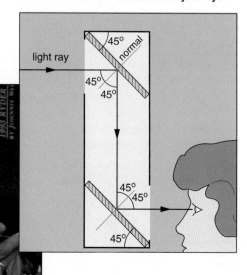

◄ Shaving mirrors and make-up mirrors are often concave.

Curved mirrors

A concave mirror curves in at the middle. If you look at yourself in a shallow concave mirror, you see a magnified reflection.

You can use a strongly curved concave mirror to focus light. The reflector behind a torch bulb is often a concave mirror. Reflecting telescopes use a concave mirror to focus light from distant stars.

A convex mirror bows out at the middle. If you look at the inside of a room with a convex mirror, you can see more of the room than you would with a plane mirror. It brings in light rays from a wider area. The image is smaller and slightly distorted. Convex mirrors are useful because of their wide field of view. They are used inside buses and shops for security, and for car wing mirrors.

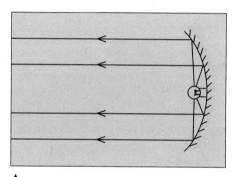

▲ Torches and car headlights use concave mirrors to focus light into a narrow beam.

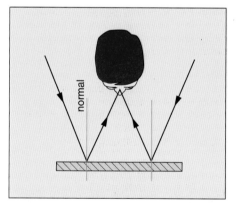

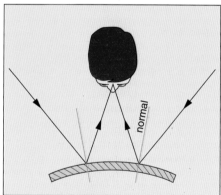

◄ A convex mirror gathers light from a wider area. When you look at something using a convex mirror you have a wider field of view.

◄ Drivers find it difficult to judge distances using only convex mirrors, so at least one rear-view mirror is normally a plane mirror.

21

Questions and Practice

19 Write down the law of reflection of light.

20 What is the normal line?

21 The diagram shows a ray of light hitting a plane mirror.

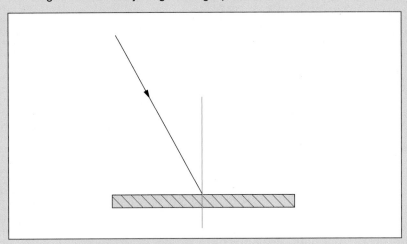

a Measure the angle of incidence.

b What will be the size of the angle of reflection?

c Copy the diagram and draw the reflected ray accurately.

22 Write down two uses for each of the following mirrors: a plane mirror; a concave mirror; a convex mirror.

Refraction of light

Bending light

Light waves slow down when they travel from air into a medium like glass or plastic. This can cause refraction: rays that go into a medium at an angle change direction. Rays that travel out of the medium are deflected the opposite way. You should use the normal line when you measure angles of refraction - just as you do for reflection with mirrors.

Prisms

A prism is a glass or plastic block. You can use a triangular prism to produce a spectrum of white light (see page 15). Light slows down in glass causing refraction. Blue light slows down more than red, so it is refracted more. This spreading out of the white light into colours is called **dispersion.**

Lenses

Lenses are like prisms but they have curved surfaces. Different parts of a lens refract different amounts.

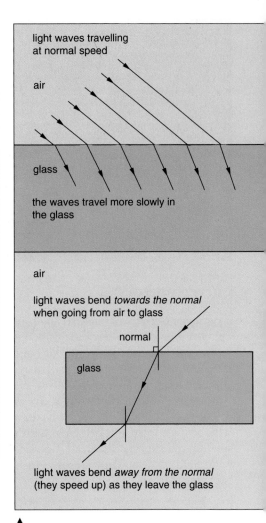

light waves travelling at normal speed

air

glass

the waves travel more slowly in the glass

air

light waves bend *towards the normal* when going from air to glass

normal

glass

light waves bend *away from the normal* (they speed up) as they leave the glass

▲
Refraction of light rays. The rays show the direction of the light waves. The waves themselves are too small to see.

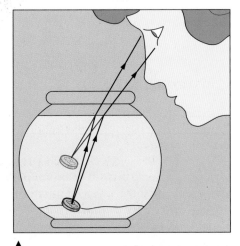

▲
Refraction of light produces some interesting effects. Water appears shallower than it really is. You do not see any bends – the rays appear to come straight from an imaginary coin higher in the water.

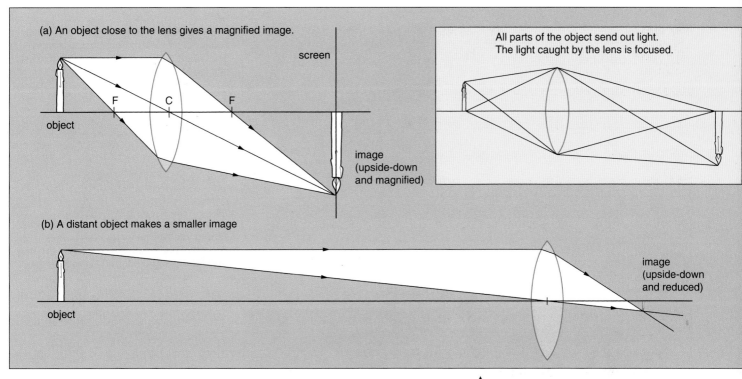

(a) An object close to the lens gives a magnified image.

screen

F C F

object

image
(upside-down
and magnified)

All parts of the object send out light.
The light caught by the lens is focused.

(b) A distant object makes a smaller image

object

image
(upside-down
and reduced)

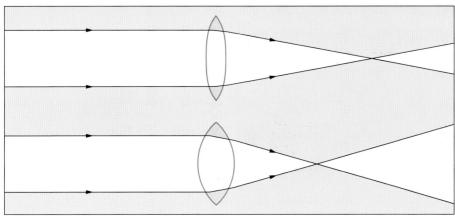

▲
How a lens makes an image of an object.

◄
**Lenses use refraction to focus light. A lens
with a deep curve has a large effect on a
beam of light. It is a strong lens. A lens with
a shallow curve has less effect.**

▼
**You can focus a camera on a nearby object
by moving the lens further away from the
film.**

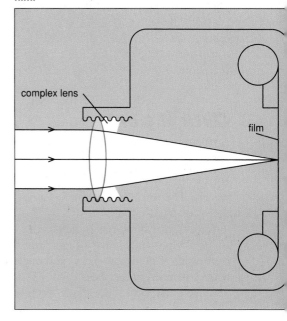

complex lens

film

Converging lens

Converging lenses have a convex shape. They are sometimes called positive
lenses. They are fatter in the middle. They are useful for focusing light or
making images.

A camera uses a lens to make an image on a film that is very close to the
lens. The object that you photograph is much further away from the lens.
This means that the image is much smaller than the object (and upside
down). The same effect happens in your eye.

Diverging lens

Diverging lenses have a concave shape. They are sometimes called negative
lenses. They are thinner in the middle and are useful for making light spread
out.

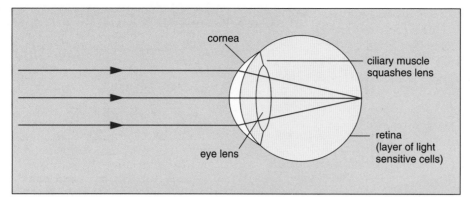

The lens in your eye changes shape. You focus on a nearby object by making the lens fatter. Special ciliary muscles squash the lens to make it more powerful.

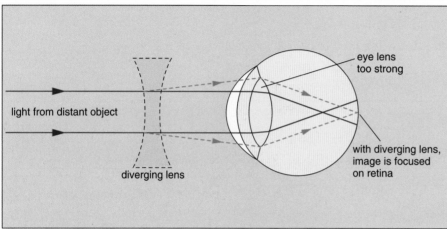

If your ciliary muscles in your eye are too strong you cannot focus on far away objects. This is called short sight. You can correct this fault using a diverging lens.

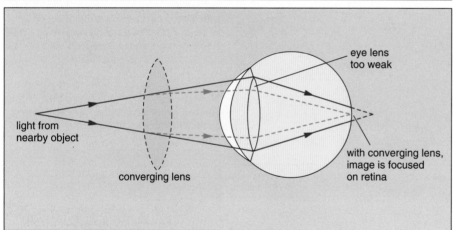

If your ciliary muscles are too weak you cannot focus on nearby objects. This is called long sight. You can correct this fault by wearing spectacles or contact lenses made from converging lenses.

Optical fibres

The direction of a light ray changes when it goes from one medium to another. The refracted ray makes a smaller angle to the normal line when it goes from a less dense medium (like air) into a more dense medium (like water). The refracted ray makes a larger angle to the normal line when it goes the other way.

Rays that make large angles to the normal line, travel quite close to the surface when they leave a dense medium. If the angle is too large the ray cannot leave at all. It is reflected back into the dense medium. This is called **total internal reflection**.

Fibre optic cables are made from bundles of long glass fibres. Each fibre is

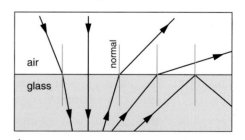

Total internal reflection happens when a ray tries to leave the glass. All the light is reflected back inside if the angle between the ray and the normal line is greater than a certain angle called the *critical angle*.

only as thick as a hair. The cables can bend to fit around corners. Light can travel around the corners because of total internal reflection.

Some modern telephones and televisions get their signals through fibre optic cables. These cables do not use electricity. They carry infrared rays from tiny laser chips in electronic circuits. Signals from fibre optic cables are very clear because they are not affected by electrical interference.

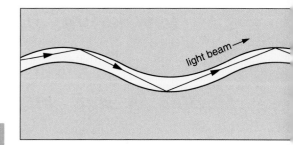

▲ **Light rays travel in straight lines along an optical fibre. Light does not escape from the fibre, even on the bends, because of total internal reflection.**

Questions and Practice

23 Light is refracted when it travels into air from a fish tank full of water.

  a Write down the effect on the rays.

  b The refraction alters the way things appear. Give an example.

24 Draw a diagram showing a ray of light going into a glass block at an angle.

  a Draw in the normal line and label it.

  b Label the angle of incidence.

  c Show what happens to the ray after it is refracted.

25 The ciliary muscles in your eye relax when you look at a far away object. Explain why.

26 The diagram shows how you can make a simple lens from two glass prisms and a glass block.

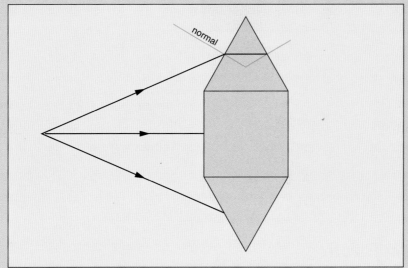

Copy the diagram measuring the angles carefully. Show how the three rays come to a focus. Use normal lines to help you draw the rays.

27 The diagram shows three light rays travelling from water towards air. The first ray travels towards the air at the critical angle. Copy the diagram and show what happens to the other two rays.

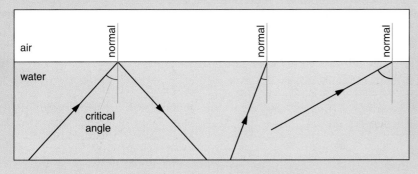

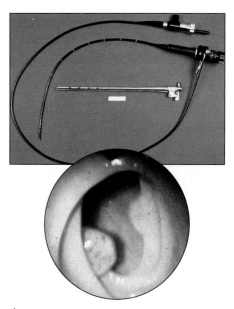

▲ **An endoscope is used to look inside your body. It is made from a fibre-optic cable. Light shines into the body through some of the optical fibres on to the parts you want to see. A video camera takes pictures through the other fibres.**

How waves behave

Diffraction and interference are two important effects of waves.

Meeting an edge – diffraction

You stand underneath an umbrella when it rains. The rain drops travel straight down on either side and you stay dry. The umbrella works because the rain drops are particles. Particles travel in straight lines even when they go past the edge of something.

Waves also travel in straight lines, but when they go past an edge, part of each wave spreads out in a new direction. This is called **diffraction**.

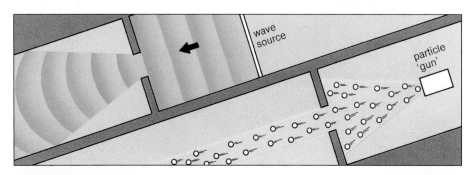

◄ Waves spread out after going through a gap. Particles do not spread out.

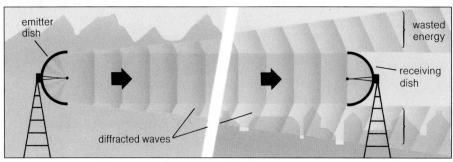

◄ Diffraction is a problem for communications. Concave reflectors (dishes) send and receive television and telephone signals. It is difficult to keep waves in a narrow beam because of diffraction. Not all the energy transmitted gets into the receiving dish.

Meeting other waves – interference

Snooker balls act like particles. They bounce off each other when they collide. Waves are different. They pass through each other. When the crest of one wave meets the crest of another wave, they 'add' to make a large crest.When a crest meets a trough they 'add' to make nothing. This is called **interference**. When light interferes it can produce areas of bright light (a crest plus a crest) and total darkness (a crest plus a trough).

▼ Waves pass through each other causing interference.

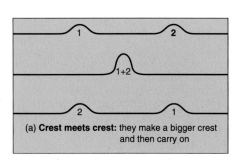

(a) **Crest meets crest:** they make a bigger crest and then carry on

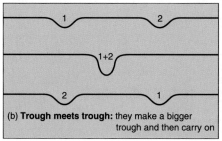

(b) **Trough meets trough:** they make a bigger trough and then carry on

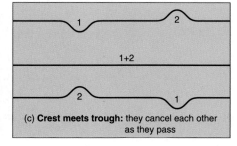

(c) **Crest meets trough:** they cancel each other as they pass

Sometimes diffraction and interference happen together. You can see dark and bright stripes when you look at a light bulb through two small slits. The stripes are called fringes. They happen because the wave diffracted by one slit interferes with the wave diffracted by the other slit.

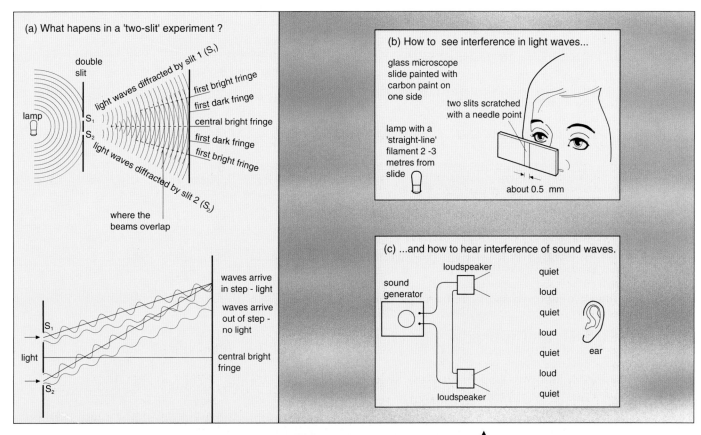

(a) What hapens in a 'two-slit' experiment ?

double slit

light waves diffracted by slit 1 (S₁)

lamp

S₁

S₂

light waves diffracted by slit 2 (S₂)

first bright fringe
first dark fringe
central bright fringe
first dark fringe
first bright fringe

where the beams overlap

S₁

light

S₂

waves arrive in step - light

waves arrive out of step - no light

central bright fringe

(b) How to see interference in light waves...

glass microscope slide painted with carbon paint on one side

two slits scratched with a needle point

lamp with a 'straight-line' filament 2 -3 metres from slide

about 0.5 mm

(c) ...and how to hear interference of sound waves.

sound generator

loudspeaker

loudspeaker

quiet
loud
quiet
loud
quiet
loud
quiet

ear

▲
Seeing and hearing the effects of interference.

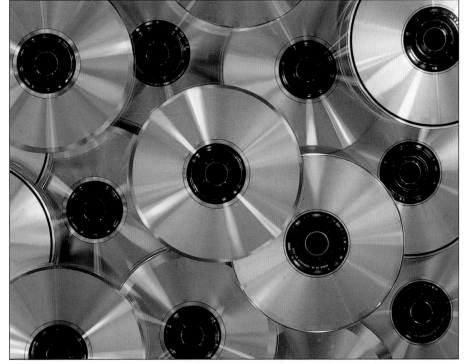

◄
The coloured fringes on these CDs are caused by interference. Light waves are reflected from the grooves but they spread out because of diffraction and interfere with each other. The bright fringes have different colours because some colours are diffracted more than others.

27

Examination Questions

Credit

1 Use the diagram to answer these questions.

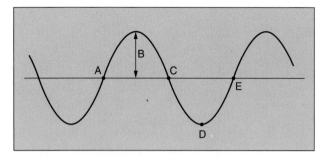

a Which letter shows where the trough is? [1 mark]
b The wavelength is the distance between two of the letters. Which two letters? [1]
c Which letter shows the amplitude? [1]
d This wave has a frequency of 265 Hz. How many times does the loudspeaker vibrate every second? [1]

2 Look at the list. Each uses one kind of electromagnetic radiation. Radio; getting a suntan; cooking; fibre-optics; looking for cracks in aircraft; remote control for a TV. Choose from the list to fill in the gaps in these sentences.
a Ultraviolet radiation is used in … [1]
b Gamma rays are used in … [1]
c Microwaves are used in … [1]

Merit

3 Emma is a sound engineer. She listens to the sound of a concert. She studies the sound waves with an oscilloscope (CRO).

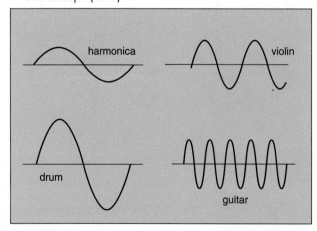

a Which instrument makes the sound with the highest pitch? [1]
b The drum makes the loudest sound. How can you tell this from the diagrams? [1]
c The drummer tightens the drum skin. The frequency increases. What happens to the wavelength? [1]
d Emma is 640 m away. She sees the drummer hit the drum. She hears the sound 2 seconds later. Calculate the speed of sound. [4]

4 In the diagram, a ray of light travels from the fish to the water surface.

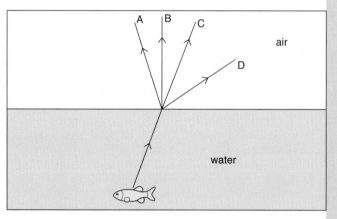

a Which line shows the correct path of the light ray after it leaves the water? Choose from lines in A, B, C or D. [1]
b Explain your answer. [2]

Special

5 Ranjit feels the vibrations of a drum through the ground. The frequency of the drum note is 100 Hz. Its wavelength in the ground is 10 m. Calculate the speed of sound through the ground in m/s. [3]

6 Visible light and X-rays are part of the electromagnetic spectrum.
a Write down one use for X-rays. [1]
b Explain why X-rays are used instead of visible light. [1]
c Write down one practical use of total internal reflection. [1]

[Adapted from the Periodic Examination, July 1995 and the Terminal Examination, June 1994.]

Checklist

These are the facts and ideas that you should have learned by studying this topic.

Key words from this topic:

longitudinal

transverse

amplitude

wavelength

frequency

reflect

refract

diffract

electromagnetic spectrum

To succeed at Credit level you should:

- ● know that sound is a wave that travels slower than light
- ■ know that waves can be reflected
- ■ recognise these things in transverse waves: crest, trough, amplitude, wavelength, frequency
- ● recognise longitudinal waves in a spring
- ● know that converging lenses focus light by refraction
- ● know that light travels along optical fibres
- ■ know about the parts of the electromagnetic spectrum (radio waves, microwaves, infrared, visible light, ultraviolet, X-rays, gamma rays)
- ● know that X-rays can be used to look inside the human body
- ● know what plane mirrors and curved mirrors are used for
- ● be able to draw simple ray diagrams
- ● know that you can see objects because they reflect light.

To succeed at Merit level you should:

- ■ know that waves can be refracted
- ■ know what these things mean (they are all to do with transverse waves): crest, trough, amplitude, wavelength, frequency
- ● know that sound travels as a longitudinal wave
- ● know that waves transfer energy, *not* matter
- ■ know what happens to the frequency of waves when their wavelength increases or decreases
- ● be able to draw diagrams of light rays being refracted and know what happens to light rays refracted by a lens
- ● know that the frequency of ultrasound is too high to hear
- ● know how ultrasound is used in medicine
- ● know about seismic waves travelling through the Earth
- ■ know the order of the regions of the electromagnetic spectrum and how they depend on wavelength
- ● know about the uses of electromagnetic waves and the dangers of ultraviolet, X-rays and gamma rays
- ● know that gamma rays can be used to treat cancer
- ● be able to draw diagrams of light rays being reflected by plane and curved mirrors (including the normal line).

To succeed at Special level you should:

- ■ know about waves, such as light, being diffracted
- ■ know what these things mean: longitudinal, transverse, crest, trough, amplitude, wavelength, frequency, compression, rarefaction
- ■ know and use the wave equation $v = f\,\lambda$
- ● understand how lenses work in cameras and the human eye
- ● know about optical fibres and how total internal reflection happens and be able to draw ray diagrams
- ● know that seismic waves provide evidence of the Earth's structure
- ■ know the effects of different parts of the electromagnetic spectrum, what they are used for and why
- ● understand the use of tracers in medicine
- ● understand everyday examples of relection in plane mirrors and curved mirrors.

GCSE FOUNDATION TIER

GCSE HIGHER TIER

CHAPTER 2

ENERGY AT HOME

In cold weather you heat the rooms in your home. You also use quite a lot of hot water. Think of all those hot showers and baths. The hot water for these is usually stored in a special tank until you need it. You cook much of your food before you eat it. All this heating relies on transferring energy.

Most energy gets into your home by electricity or by burning fuels. Electricity is clean and easy to use – you just turn on a switch.

You do not make gases or ashes when you use electricity. Of course, most power stations that produce electricity burn fossil fuels – coal, oil or natural gas. These power stations produce waste and pollute the air with gases.

You can use fossil fuels at home. This is not always as convenient as using electricity. You need grates, stoves or boilers to burn the fuel. You need chimneys or flue pipes to carry away the dangerous waste gases. You also

need somewhere to store the fuel. Then you have to get rid of the ashes and soot!

Energy also gets out of your home. You pour hot water down the drain when you empty a sink or a bath or a washing machine. Energy escapes from a warm house through the floor, the windows, the walls and the roof. You cannot stop this escape, but you can slow it down by insulating your house.

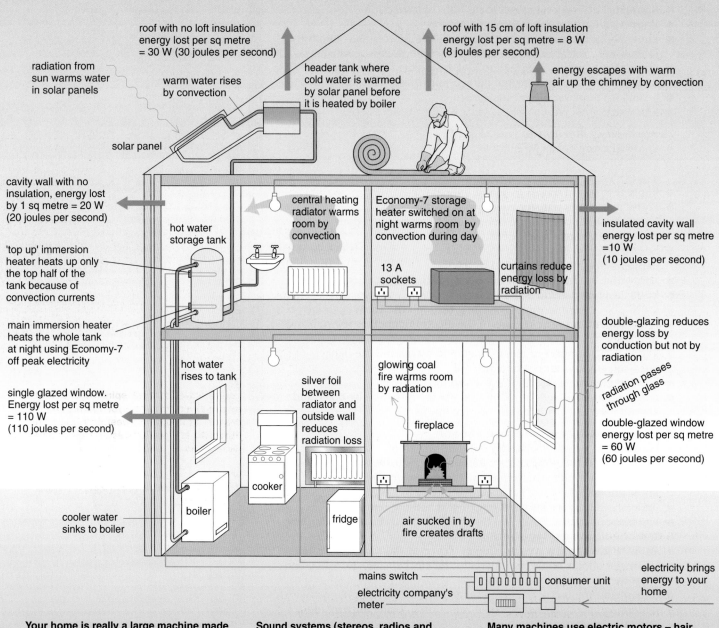

roof with no loft insulation energy lost per sq metre = 30 W (30 joules per second)

roof with 15 cm of loft insulation energy lost per sq metre = 8 W (8 joules per second)

radiation from sun warms water in solar panels

warm water rises by convection

header tank where cold water is warmed by solar panel before it is heated by boiler

energy escapes with warm air up the chimney by convection

solar panel

cavity wall with no insulation, energy lost by 1 sq metre = 20 W (20 joules per second)

hot water storage tank

central heating radiator warms room by convection

Economy-7 storage heater switched on at night warms room by convection during day

insulated cavity wall energy lost per sq metre =10 W (10 joules per second)

'top up' immersion heater heats up only the top half of the tank because of convection currents

13 A sockets

curtains reduce energy loss by radiation

main immersion heater heats the whole tank at night using Economy-7 off peak electricity

double-glazing reduces energy loss by conduction but not by radiation

radiation passes through glass

single glazed window. Energy lost per sq metre = 110 W (110 joules per second)

hot water rises to tank

silver foil between radiator and outside wall reduces radiation loss

glowing coal fire warms room by radiation

fireplace

double-glazed window energy lost per sq metre = 60 W (60 joules per second)

cooker

fridge

air sucked in by fire creates drafts

cooler water sinks to boiler

boiler

mains switch

electricity company's meter

consumer unit

electricity brings energy to your home

Your home is really a large machine made from many smaller machines. Whenever you use a machine, energy is transferred. Most of the machines use electricity.

Sound systems (stereos, radios and televisions) get their electricity from batteries or the mains supply. Telephone lines supply electricity direct to your telephone. The lighting in your home is probably electrical.

Many machines use electric motors – hair dryers, vacuum cleaners, washing machines and refrigerators.

Transferring energy

A cup of hot coffee has a higher temperature than a cup of cold coffee. It also has more heat energy. Many people use the words 'heat' and 'temperature' to mean the same thing. They are not the same in science. A bath full of warm water has a *lower temperature* than a cup full of hot coffee – only the hot coffee will scold you. But starting with cold water, you have to transfer *more energy* when heating a warm bath than when heating a cup of coffee.

- Energy is measured in joules
- Energy flows from high temperatures to low temperatures – this is called *thermal transfer*
- Temperature is measured in degrees Celsius
- Temperature tells you about the direction of energy flow

Energy can be transferred in four main ways when you heat something: by **conduction**, **convection**, **radiation** and **evaporation**. In chapter 3 you will learn about another form of energy transfer called **work**.

Conduction

Metal saucepans let heat through to the food inside them very quickly. This is because metals are good **conductors** of heat. Energy transfers from the cooker to the food very easily by **conduction**.

Saucepan handles are usually made from wood or plastic. These materials are good **insulators**. They do not conduct heat very well. They can only transfer energy slowly. This means that you do not burn your hand when you pick up the saucepan.

Many materials make use of air as an insulator. Air is an excellent insulator.

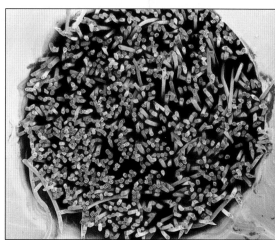

▲ **Polyester fibres in a sleeping bag. Through an electron microscope you can see that there is air trapped between and inside the fibres. Air is a good insulator. It cuts down conduction.**

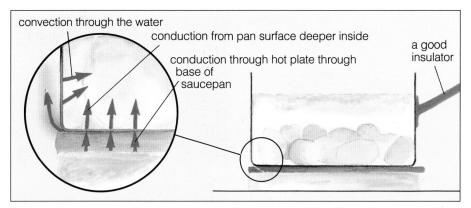

convection through the water

conduction from pan surface deeper inside

conduction through hot plate through base of saucepan

a good insulator

◄ **Conduction plays an important part when you cook food.**

Air can reduce heat lost to surroundings due to **conduction**. The material has to trap the air to get the best results. This is to avoid warm air escaping and taking the energy with it. Your hair traps air that insulates your head. Ovens and refrigerators are insulated with a fire-proof fibre, such as rock wool or fibreglass. The fibre fills the space between the outer case and the inner liner. Air fills the gaps between the fibres. You can save money on heating bills by lagging your hot water pipes with foam containing trapped air.

Conduction – the particles' story

p208

A metal saucepan is a good conductor. The metal in a saucepan is made from very small particles, called **atoms**. The particles are joined together. Scientists call the forces that glue them together **bonds**. The bonds behave like springs. When the saucepan is hot, the metal particles vibrate very fast. They still hold together but they have **kinetic energy** because of their movement.

A fairly still atom in a cold part of the metal can pick up vibration from an atom in the hot part of the metal. This is because the springy bonds join the atoms together. The energy is transferred from one particle to another very quickly. Soon, particles much further away have more and more kinetic energy.

When you iron a shirt, the hot iron touches the cold cloth. The fast-moving iron particles bump into the slow-moving cloth particles. The cloth particles gain kinetic energy and the cloth warms up. The hot iron has lost some energy so it cools down. We say that energy has been transferred from the iron to the shirt. There is a special switch inside the iron called a **thermostat**. The thermostat switches on the electricity when the iron cools below a certain temperature.

Liquids and gases do not conduct as well as solids. The particles are not connected together by strong bonds. They can only pass on kinetic energy by the much slower method of bumping into each other. Conduction cannot happen without any particles. This means that a **vacuum** is the perfect insulator.

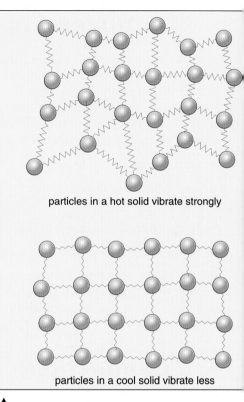

particles in a hot solid vibrate strongly

particles in a cool solid vibrate less

▲
Conduction in a solid. Particles in a hot part of a solid vibrate further and faster than particles in a cold part. The vibration of a particle soon passes to its neighbours because of the springy bond that connects them. The neighbouring particles cause *their* neighbours to vibrate too. Very soon all the particles vibrate vigorously and the whole solid feels hot.

Questions and Practice

1 Some take-away shops sell hot food in foam containers. Explain why these containers are useful.

2 If you stand on a bath mat, your bare feet feel warmer than if you stand on a vinyl floor, even though both the mat and floor are at the same temperature. Why is this?

3 An electric iron has a metal base plate and a plastic handle.

   a Why is the handle made from plastic?

   b Describe what happens to the metal particles as energy is transferred from the heating element to the clothes.

Convection

Convection only happens in liquids or gases. Liquids and gases are sometimes called **fluids** because they can flow. In convection, hot fluids rise and cold fluids sink.

The best place to put a radiator or other heater is near the floor. The coolest air in a room sinks to the floor by convection. The radiator heats the air and the hot air rises. Then the rising air 'sucks in' cool air behind it ready to be heated. This means that the air circulates around the room in a **convection current**.

▶
This special photograph shows convection currents of air warmed by a person's body. The warm air flows upwards around his body. You can see the air rising above his head very clearly.

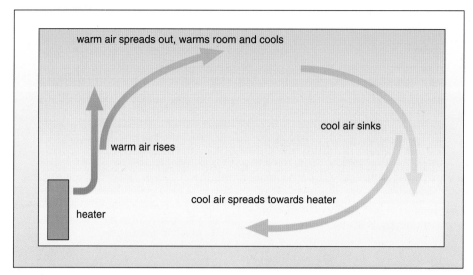

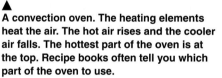

▲
A convection oven. The heating elements heat the air. The hot air rises and the cooler air falls. The hottest part of the oven is at the top. Recipe books often tell you which part of the oven to use.

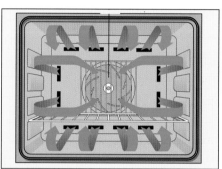

▲
Fan assisted ovens use forced convection to give faster cooking and even distribution of temperature.

▼
A hot water system for a house. Convection currents transfer energy from the boiler to the hot water in the storage tank. Hot water expands. The expansion pipe allows extra space for the expanded water.

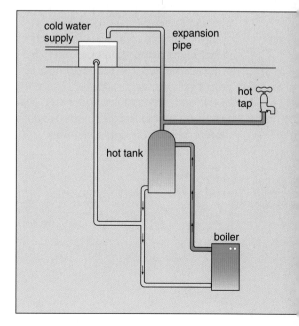

If you have a coal or wood fire in a grate, the air is not recycled in this way. You lose the hot air that rises up the chimney. Cold air is drawn in across the floor to replace the heated air. This can create draughts because air is sucked in through gaps in windows, doors and floors.

Convection currents are important in heating systems. Suppose an architect is designing a house. Should the hot water storage tank be upstairs or downstairs? Hot water rises so it is sensible to put the storage tank higher than the boiler. This way you will not need such a strong pump.

Cold things can cause convection too. Inside a refrigerator or freezer, the cooling unit is at the *top*. It cools the air which sinks to the bottom. Any warm air rises to the cooling unit. This means that the bottom of a refrigerator or freezer is the coldest part. If you made a refrigerator with the cooling unit at the bottom, the warm air at the top would never get cold.

Convection – the particles' story

The particles in a fluid (a liquid or gas) move all the time. When you heat a fluid, energy is transferred to the particles. The particles move faster and get further apart, so the heated part of the fluid expands. This makes the heated

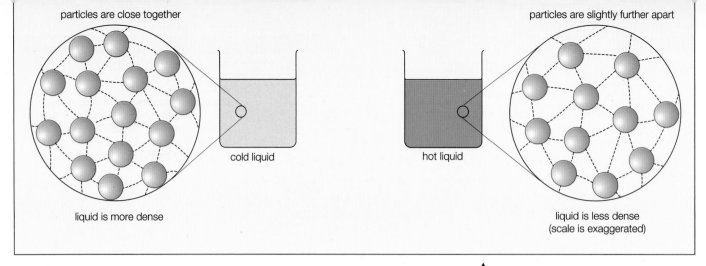

particles are close together

cold liquid

liquid is more dense

particles are slightly further apart

hot liquid

liquid is less dense
(scale is exaggerated)

fluid less **dense** than the unheated fluid. Because it is less dense, the warm fluid floats above the cool fluid, taking its extra energy with it.

▲
A change in density causes convection. Hot fluid is less dense and rises above cold fluid, which is more dense.

Questions and Practice

4 a Why is the heating element of an electric kettle at the bottom?

b Why is the cooling unit of a freezer at the top?

5 Draw diagrams and use them to describe the convection currents in a warm room caused by:

a a hot radiator;

b a cold window.

6 When you heat water in a saucepan, the hot water at the bottom of the saucepan expands and rises. Explain what happens to the water particles to cause this.

Radiation

Radiation is completely different from conduction and convection. It does not need particles at all.

p204

Every object sends out **infrared** radiation. Hot objects give out more infrared radiation than cool ones. Infrared radiation is part of the **electromagnetic spectrum**, like visible light, but you cannot see it with your eyes. Infrared radiation has many of the same properties as other parts of the electromagnetic spectrum: it is reflected by shiny surfaces; it is absorbed by black and rough (matt) surfaces; it can pass through transparent materials and through a vacuum.

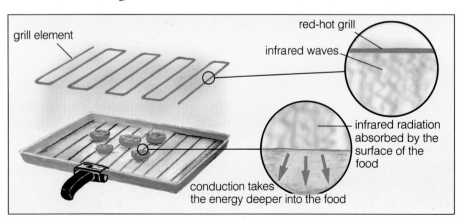

grill element

red-hot grill

infrared waves

infrared radiation absorbed by the surface of the food

conduction takes the energy deeper into the food

◄
Grilled food cooks by infrared rays. The grill element glows with a red light which does not cook the food. The invisible infrared radiation cooks the food.

34

Coffee or tea stays hot in a vacuum flask (thermos flask) partly because of the reflective lining. The lining is made from glass coated with a thin layer of aluminium. Infrared rays cannot escape from the liquid. The shiny, silver surface reflects infrared radiation back into the liquid.

You can also use a vacuum flask to stop cold drinks getting warm. The silver surface reflects the rays from hot objects outside the flask so that they do not transfer energy to the liquid. Silver surfaces and smooth, white surfaces are bad at absorbing radiation.

Did you know that you can keep baked potatoes hot by wrapping them in aluminium cooking foil? This might seem strange when you think that aluminium is a good conductor. The reason is that the foil stops infrared rays escaping. Even though the wrapped potato is very hot, it does not emit much radiation because its surface is silver.

> Silver surfaces and smooth, white surfaces are bad at absorbing and bad at emitting radiation.

What about black surfaces? It turns out that black surfaces are good at both these things. Car radiators are painted black to help them cool more quickly by emitting infrared radiation. On the other hand, solar panels are painted black to make them good at absorbing radiation.

> Black surfaces and rough (matt) surfaces are good at absorbing and good at emitting radiation.

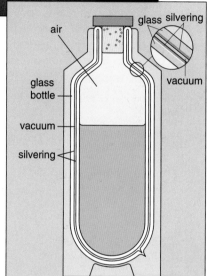

▲ A vacuum flask is made from hollow glass. It keeps hot drinks hot, or cold drinks cold, for hours. There is hardly any air inside the hollow part and the insides of the glass are coated with silvery aluminium. The nearly perfect vacuum reduces energy transfer by conduction to almost nothing. The shiny, silver surface stops most energy transfer by radiation.

▲ These solar panels have transparent tops and black bases. This lets the infrared radiation in and absorbs it. Water flows over the hot, black base, providing cheap hot water.

Questions and Practice

7 Which cools more slowly: a shiny, silver teapot or a brown, ceramic one? Explain why.

8 If you draw your curtains on a cold night, your room stays warmer. Explain why.

9 Suppose you have a central heating radiator on an outside wall as shown. You can save money by putting silver foil on the wall behind the radiator. How does this work?

10 Why are solar panels coloured black?

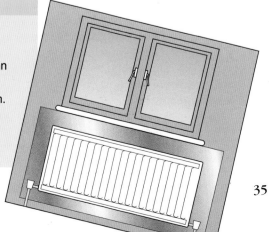

Evaporation

You can boil a saucepan of water more quickly if you put a lid on it. When you heat a liquid some of it turns into gas even when the liquid is below the boiling point. Scientists call this evaporation. Energy is transferred from the liquid water to water vapour in the air as the liquid evaporates. The saucepan lid cuts down the evaporation of water. This means that less energy is transferred from the liquid, so it heats up more quickly.

Your body uses evaporation to keep you cool on a hot day. Special glands make your skin wet with sweat. The sweat evaporates taking the unwanted energy with it. The result is that your skin temperature drops.

A refrigerator transfers energy from inside to outside by evaporation. A pipe inside the refrigerator contains a liquid called freon. A pump sucks the liquid freon into the cooling unit. This lowers its pressure and makes the freon evaporate. Evaporation needs energy, so it is transferred to the freon from the air inside the refrigerator. This means that the air gets colder. Then the pump pushes the freon into the outside pipe. This raises the vapour's pressure so that it turns back into a liquid and transfers energy to the outside pipe.

▲ These athletes are evaporating sweat and radiating heat too quickly! The aluminium coated blanket stops both of these unwanted energy transfers.

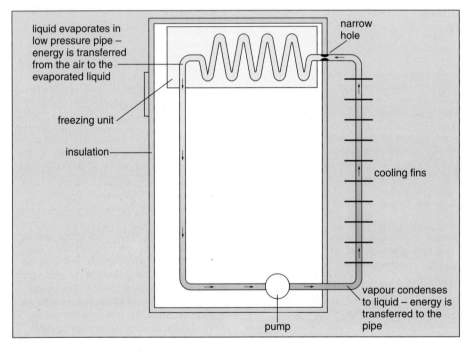

liquid evaporates in low pressure pipe – energy is transferred from the air to the evaporated liquid

narrow hole

freezing unit

insulation

cooling fins

vapour condenses to liquid – energy is transferred to the pipe

pump

◄ The refrigerator transfers energy from inside to outside by conduction, convection, radiation *and* evaporation. Convection currents inside the refrigerator transfer energy to the liquid in the pipe. The liquid evaporates. The pipe is made from metal because it is a good conductor. The pipe is painted black at the back to emit radiation well. The fins increase the surface area which helps radiation and convection.

Evaporation – the particles' story

The particles in a liquid stick together, but much more weakly than particles in a solid. The particles move about and constantly bump into each other. They are said to have kinetic energy. Some particles will receive so much energy during the collisions that they can escape from the liquid. These escaped particles have so much kinetic energy that they move as fast as particles in a gas. During the process, energy is transferred from the liquid to the gas because only the most energetic particles escape. As a result, the liquid gets cooler.

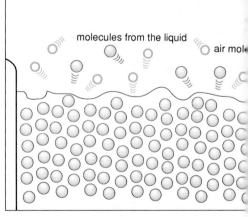

molecules from the liquid

air mol

▲ Evaporation. The particles in a liquid keep bumping into each other. Occasionally a particle will get several hard bumps in a row all in the same direction. If this happens to a particle near the surface it can break away from the attraction of the other particles and escape.

Saving energy costs

Energy is expensive. One way of saving the cost of energy is to use only the amount you need and no more. You can control the temperature of the things that you heat. Convection ovens, hot water systems, central heating systems and electric irons all have **thermostats** that control temperature.

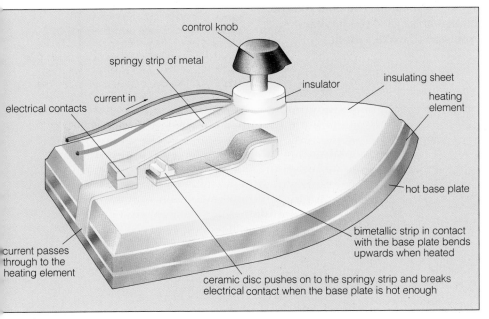

▲
Electric irons use bimetallic strips as thermostats. You set the control to turn the iron off as soon as it reaches a certain temperature. This means that you can have a cool iron for synthetic fabrics that would scorch if you used a hot iron.

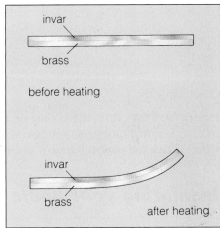

▲
A bimetallic strip is made from two sheets of metal – brass and invar. When you heat it, brass expands more than invar. The brass is firmly welded to the invar. The only way the brass can expand is by bending the whole strip. Electric kettles that switch off automatically use bimetallic strips.

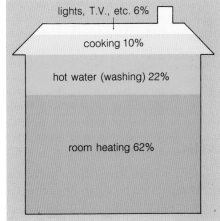

▲
Energy used in an average UK home. This chart shows that we use 90% of the energy we take into our homes for heating.

Another way of saving money is to waste less energy. Wasting energy usually means letting energy go to places where you do not want it. Most of the energy you use at home is for heating. You want to heat your home, *not* the air outside. Unfortunately, energy is always transferred from your home to the outside. This is because the inside has a higher temperature than the surroundings outside. Insulating your home will save energy because it slows down this energy transfer.

You will be better off if the money you save on your heating bill is more than the money you spend on insulating your home. This may take a few

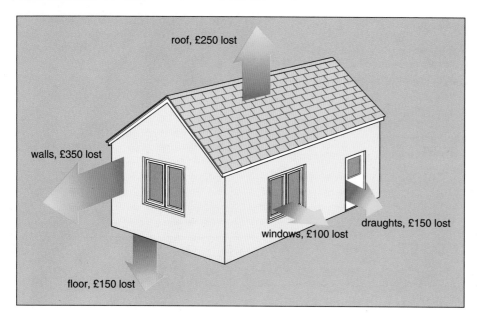

◀
The typical cost of the energy transferred out of an uninsulated house in one year. The total energy cost wasted is £1000. You can reduce your energy costs by insulating your home.

months or a few years depending on the type of insulation. The time you take to save as much money as you spend on insulation is called the **payback time**. When the payback time is finished you start to make a profit.

Insulating your home

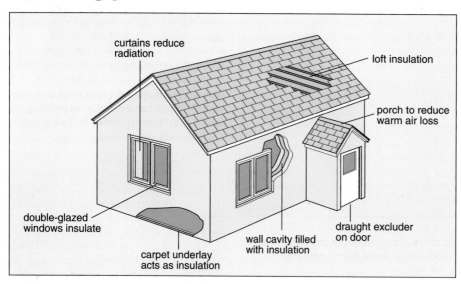

◀
How to reduce your heating bill.

Walls

Modern houses have *cavity walls*. Each wall is made from two single-brick walls separated by a gap or cavity. The air in the cavity is a good insulator, but convection currents can transfer energy out of the cavity through the top of the wall. Builders can fill the gap with glass fibre when they build the wall. This is called *cavity wall insulation*. The fibres trap the air and stop convection currents. You can also inject foam into existing cavity walls. The payback time for cavity wall insulation is between three and six years.

Roof

The space in your roof is called the loft. *Loft insulation* reduces energy transfer through your roof. You can use glass fibre or rock wool which trap air between their fibres. Remember that air is a good insulator and the fibres reduce convection currents. The payback time for loft insulation is about one or two years.

Floors

Modern houses are built with foam blocks under the floor. The trapped air in the foam is a good insulator. Carpets and underlay also help to insulate your floors.

Windows

Energy is transferred through glass by conduction and by radiation. You can insulate your windows by **double-glazing**. A double-glazed window has two panes of glass with insulating air trapped between them. Double-glazing reduces conduction but it does not stop radiation. You can reduce the radiation by simply drawing your curtains!

Double-glazing has other advantages. It reduces condensation on windows, which is important in kitchens and bathrooms. It also helps to cut down **noise** from outside. It stops draughts getting in through window frames. Double-glazing has a long payback time. It might take you ten or twenty years to recover the cost of a cheap DIY system. A professional system has a longer payback time.

Draughts

The quickest way that you can save money is by **draught-proofing**. The payback time is usually less than a year. Draughts of cold air get into your home through gaps between your doors and their doorframes. Draughts also get in through gaps in your window frames. You can buy cheap, foam tape that sticks around the door or window frame.

Saving electricity costs

Most power stations use fossil fuels to make electricity. The world is running out of fossil fuels. They will last longer if you use less electricity. Insulating your home will make a big difference, but there are other things you can do. Remember to switch off lights and televisions when you do not need them. Set the thermostat on your water heater a few degrees lower. Make sure that you insulate your hot water storage tank.

You can also buy power-saving appliances. Some washing machines use lower temperature hot water. You can replace your ordinary light bulbs with fluorescent lighting. Fluorescent light tubes and energy-saving light bulbs (compact fluorescent bulbs) save energy. They are more expensive to buy, but they last longer and use less electricity. Almost anything that saves energy will save you money in the long run too.

You can also use **off-peak** electricity. The electricity companies record the amount of electricity that you use at off-peak times. The next section takes a closer look at how this is done.

▼
Loft insulation. You can buy insulation fibre in rolls. You put it on top of your ceiling between the wooden joists.

▲
Draught-proofing saves money. The squashy tape fills the gap between the closed door or window and the frame.

▲
Both these light bulbs have the same light output. The ordinary bulb on the left has a power of 100 watts. It transfers 100 joules of energy each second – much of it as heat. The other one is a compact, fluorescent light bulb. It only takes 20 watts from your electricity supply – 20 joules every second.

Questions and Practice

14 Choose from walls, floor, roof, windows. Which part of a house:

  a loses most energy;

  b is most expensive to insulate;

  c is cheapest to insulate;

  d has the longest payback time when you insulate it;

  e has the shortest payback time when you insulate it?

15 What would you do to reduce energy transfer:

  a through your roof;

  b through your windows;

  c from your hot water system?

Keeping track of electricity

Energy and power

Suppose that you want to buy an electric kettle. One thing you might want to know is how much electricity the kettle will use. The kettle takes energy from the electricity supply while it is switched on. The company that made the kettle do not know how long you leave your kettle switched on! What they do know is how much energy the kettle will transfer to the water each second. The amount of energy transferred per second is called the **power** and it is measured in watts (W) or kilowatts (kW). 1 kW = 1000 W.

You can work out how much energy your kettle will transfer in one minute (60 seconds), 1 hour (3600 seconds) or any other time. Just multiply the power (in watts) by the time (in seconds) to get the energy (in joules).

You can write this down as a formula:

$$\text{Energy transferred (joules)} = \text{power of appliance (watts)} \times \text{time taken (seconds)}$$
$$E = P \times t$$

▲
All your electrical appliances have information like this attached to them near the flex. The two most important pieces of information are the *supply voltage* and the *power*. In this case the voltage is 240 V and the power is 350 W. The symbol with one square inside another means that the appliance is double insulated.

Method	Power used (W)	Time taken (minutes)	Energy supplied (kJ)
microwave	650	8	312
boiling	about 100	120	720
conventional oven	about 700	90	4000
pressure cooker	about 50	20	60

◄
There is more than one way to cook a chicken. The table shows the energy cost for four different methods. Which one would you recommend?

Worked example

The power of your kettle is 2 kW (2000 W). How much energy does it transfer to the water in 5 minutes?

There are 60 seconds in 1 minute, so the time is 5 × 60 = 300 seconds.

R
p202

Write down the formula: $\qquad$ $E = P \times t$

Put in the numbers: $\qquad$ $E = 2000 \times 300$

Write down the answer and the unit: $\quad E = 600\,000$ J

This is over half a million joules just for using the kettle once! What would be the total for everything you use in a whole day, or a week, or a month? The numbers get so large that companies sell electricity using a bigger unit – the kilowatt-hour (kWh). One kilowatt-hour is the energy transferred by a 1 kW appliance in 1 hour. For example, if you use a 2 kW kettle for a total of 6 hours, you have to buy $2 \times 6 = 12$ kWh units of electricity. You can write this down as a formula. It is the same formula as before but with different units:

Energy (kWh) = power of appliance (kW) × time (h)

Off peak electricity

Power stations cannot be switched off at night. They carry on producing electricity. This might waste energy because people are asleep and not using electricity at home or at work. You can save money by buying this **off-peak electricity.** Off-peak electricity is cheap, but you do need a special white meter instead of the normal black one. The electricity company will fit one for you. They will charge you less than half price for the electricity you use between midnight and 7 a.m.

You can run immersion water heaters and automatic washing machines and dishwashers on time switches. The time switches turn on the appliances after midnight and off again before 7 a.m. You can heat your rooms with electric storage that uses off-peak electricity.

▲
An off-peak white meter has two displays. The lower display shows the number of kWh units you have used at the standard rate. The other one is for off-peak electricity.

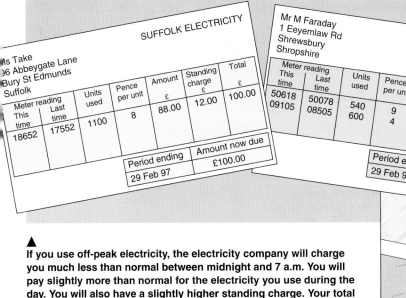

SUFFOLK ELECTRICITY

Ms Take
96 Abbeygate Lane
Bury St Edmunds
Suffolk

Meter reading		Units used	Pence per unit	Amount £	Standing charge £	Total £
This time	Last time					
18652	17552	1100	8	88.00	12.00	100.00

Period ending	Amount now due
29 Feb 97	£100.00

SHROPSHIRE ELECTRICITY

Mr M Faraday
1 Eeyemlaw Rd
Shrewsbury
Shropshire

Meter reading		Units used	Pence per unit	Amount £	Standing charge £	Total £
This time	Last time					
50618 09105	50078 08505	540 600	9 4	48.60 24.00	15.00	63.60 24.00

Period ending	Amount now due
29 Feb 97	£87.60

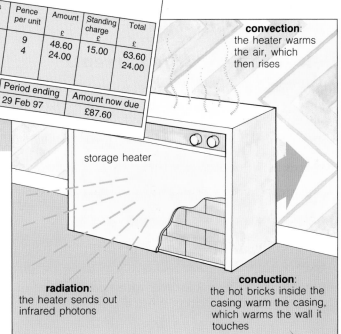

convection:
the heater warms the air, which then rises

storage heater

radiation:
the heater sends out infrared photons

conduction:
the hot bricks inside the casing warm the casing, which warms the wall it touches

▲
If you use off-peak electricity, the electricity company will charge you much less than normal between midnight and 7 a.m. You will pay slightly more than normal for the electricity you use during the day. You will also have a slightly higher standing charge. Your total electricity bill will only be cheaper if you can use at least one third of your electricity between midnight and 7 a.m.

▶
Storage heaters use off-peak electricity. They have special bricks inside which heat up during the night. The hot bricks transfer energy to the air during the day without needing any more electricity.

Questions and Practice

16 A 3 kW immersion heater transfers energy to water for 10 minutes (600 seconds).

    a What is the power of the heater (i) in kilowatts, (ii) in watts?

    b How much energy, in joules, does the heater transfer (i) in one second, (ii) in 600 seconds?

17 How much energy is transferred in kilowatt-hour units:

    a by a 1 kW heater running for 1 hour;

    b by a 1 kW heater running for 8 hours;

    c by a 100 W (0.1 kW) lamp running for 25 hours?

18 In a certain part of the country, a kilowatt-hour unit of electricity costs 10p. How much would it cost to use the following appliances:

    a a 2 kW kettle used for one hour;

    b a 10 W radio for 6 hours;

    c a 500 W vacuum cleaner for 30 minutes?

Using electricity safely

You probably use mains electricity every day without thinking, but it can be dangerous. The mains voltage in the UK is 230 **volts**. This is more than enough to kill you. Engineers have designed your appliances so that you cannot touch any live parts. Most accidents happen when people tamper with appliances, plugs or wiring in their own home. If you have a problem, get an electrician to look at it. Do not try and fix it yourself.

The major danger when something goes wrong is that the electric **current** gets too large. A large electric current makes conductors get hot. All your appliances connect to the mains using flexible cables, or 'flex', covered in plastic. The plastic melts if the current gets too large. The live electric wires become bare and you can easily get an electric shock. The plastic can also burn and start a fire.

▲
On January 1st 1995 the UK mains voltage officially dropped to 230 volts. Most European countries have increased their mains voltage to match.

How large is a safe current?

You can find out how much current your appliances can use safely. All your appliances have the mains voltage and the **power rating** printed or stamped on them. You can use the voltage and the power to calculate how much electric current your appliance uses when it is working normally. The current is the power (in watts) divided by the voltage (in volts). It is measured in **amperes** (A) or 'amps' for short. You can write this as a formula:

current (amperes) = power (watts)/voltage (volts)

$$I = P/V$$

Worked example

Suppose you have a tumble dryer with a power rating of 2.3 kW (2300 W). You can calculate the current it will use:

Write down the formula: $I = P/V$

Put in the numbers: $I = 2300/230$

Write down the answer and the unit: $I = 10A$

The tumble dryer uses a 10 A current quite safely.

The fuse

When your 2.3 kW tumble dryer is working, it uses a 10 A current. Suppose that something goes wrong inside your tumble dryer. For example, a **short circuit** makes the electric current bigger than 10 A . The large current might cause serious damage or even a fire. Fortunately, you can stop this happening by fitting the right **fuse** in the plug.

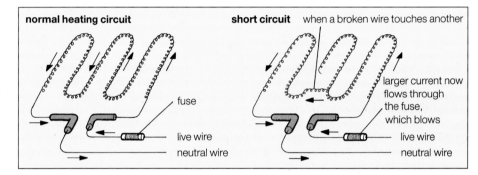

The design of an electric plug means that electric current flowing into the appliance along the **live wire** has to go through the fuse. The fuse is actually a thin wire inside a ceramic (pottery) or glass tube. When too much current flows through the fuse wire, it gets hot and melts. This breaks the circuit and stops any dangerously large current flowing. This protects the appliance and prevents the flex from heating and possibly starting a fire.

You must use the right fuse. If you use a fuse that is too low in value, it will 'blow' (break) straight away and the appliance will not work. If the fuse's value is too large, it may not blow even when there is a fault. This can be very dangerous. You can normally get three values of fuse for a 13A mains plug: 3A, 5A and 13A. There are two rules for choosing the correct value:

Rule 1. The value of the fuse must be larger than the appliance's normal safe current

Rule 2. The value of the fuse must be as small as possible

The tumble dryer's normal safe current is 10A. A 3A fuse and a 5A fuse are too small because of rule 1. This leaves only one choice: a 13A fuse.

Example

Suppose a food processor has a supply voltage of 230 V and a power of 690 W. What size fuse should you fit in the plug?

First you must work out the normal safe current:

Write down the formula: $I = P/V$

Put in the numbers: $I = 690/230$

Write down the answer and the unit: $I = 3A$

◀ A short circuit can happen inside an appliance when part of it breaks. In this diagram, part of a wire heating element has broken away and fallen on to another part of the wire. This shortens the circuit and makes the current larger.

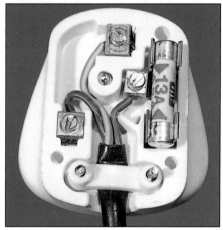

▲ The wiring inside a 13A three-pin plug. The 230-volt live wire is brown. The fuse fits between the brown wire and the pin. The other wires connect directly to the pins. The brown live wire and the blue neutral wire carry the electric current. The green-and-yellow striped earth wire is needed to make metal appliances safer. You cannot see any bare wire in a properly wired plug. The plug also has a cord-grip to stop the flex from pulling out.

▼ A fuse wire that has 'blown'. Fuses almost never blow unless you have a fault. You should always check for a fault before you put a new fuse in your plug. If you are not sure, check with an electrician.

According to rule 1, the fuse value must be *larger* than the normal current. This means that you cannot use a 3A fuse because it is the same size as the normal safe current for the food processor. This leaves a 5A fuse and a 13A fuse. Rule 2 says that the fuse must be as small as possible. You need a 5A fuse.

Using adapters

Quite often you want to connect two or three appliances to the mains, but you have only got one socket on the wall. You can buy an adapter that lets you do this. Using adapters can be dangerous. The socket is only safe up to 13A. The three appliances together might take more current than this. The wiring under your floor could overheat and cause a fire. You will be much safer if you do not use adapters. An electrician can put in more sockets for you.

▲ This adapter lets you use more than one appliance from a single 13A socket. This one has its own 13A fuse. The fuse stops you using a dangerously high current. Never use an adapter that does not have a fuse.

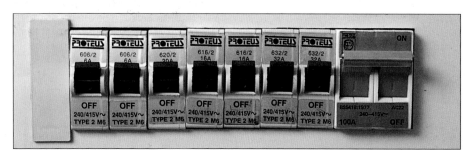

◄ Your consumer unit might have circuit breakers instead of fuses. They use an electromagnet to turn a switch off instead of having a wire that melts. They work faster than fuses. You reset them by pushing the switch back up.

Circuit breakers

Inside your home (or in a special cupboard outside) there is a fuse and meter that belong to the electricity company. This is where electricity comes into your home. You also have a 'consumer unit' that belongs to you. The consumer unit has a mains switch and a fuse box. Inside the fuse box are fuses or circuit breakers. The wires that join your sockets and lights to these fuses lie under your floors, above your ceilings and inside your walls. The fuses in the consumer unit protect the wires from overheating and causing a fire.

The outside of an appliance

Some faults do not make the current go up. If a piece of wire comes loose inside an appliance, it could touch other metal parts and make them 'live' (230 volts). You could touch the metal and get an electric shock.

The outside of a hair dryer is normally made from plastic. Plastic is an electrical insulator. The hair dryer is **double insulated**. This means that there are no metal parts on the outside which could become live. If there was an electrical fault inside you would still be safe as long as you put the right fuse in the plug. Double-insulated appliances need only two wires in the plug – the live wire and the neutral wire.

Many other appliances, like electric cookers and vacuum cleaners, have metal parts that you can touch. For example, almost all the outside of a washing machine case is metal. These appliances must have the **earth wire** connected in the plug. This wire joins the metal case of the appliance to water pipes buried in the earth. The earth can never become live – it always stays at 0 volts.

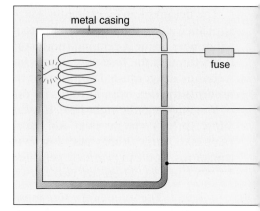

▲ The earth wire stops you getting an electric shock. The earthed parts cannot become live. If a fault happens, the current flows easily to the earth. A large current then flows which breaks the fuse. This means that the appliance is disconnected from the 230V supply. No more damage can happen and the appliance is safe to touch.

◄
When lightning strikes it could take a dangerous route. Lightning conductors help to disperse the electrical charge and lead it to earth safely.

Questions and Practice

19 Calculate the normal safe current for:

    a a 920 W kettle running at 230 V;

    b a 46 W light bulb running at 230 V;

    c a 2.3 kW washing machine running at 230 V;

    d a 460 W electric drill running at 230 V.

20 A 13A plug can have a 3A, 5A or 13A fuse. Choose the correct size fuse for each of the appliances in question 19.

21 Explain how a fuse in the plug makes your appliances safer to use.

22 What kinds of appliance need an earth wire? Explain what an earth wire does.

Examination Questions

Credit

1 Barry heats his house. Look at the diagram on p.38. It shows his house wasting £1000 of energy in a year.

a Which part of the house transfers most energy to the outside? [1 mark]

b What could Barry do to his walls to cut down his heating bills? [1]

c Barry insulates all his house. He wants to save even more money on his heating bills. He decides to use his heating more sensibly. Explain two ways he could do this. [2]

2 This question is about a fan heater that runs on a 10A current.

a You can work out how much it costs to use the fan heater. You need to know two things. One is the number of watts. What is the other thing you need to know? [1]

b Which fuse must be fitted in the plug of the fan heater? Choose from: 3A, 5A, 13A. Explain your answer. [2]

c You drop the fan heater on the floor. The live wire becomes loose and touches the metal case of the fan heater. The loose wire causes a problem. What is the problem? [1]

d What is the job of the earth wire? [1]

e What colour is the live wire? [1]

Merit

3 Energy can be transferred thermally in three ways: conduction, convection and radiation.

a Double glazing is better at keeping the heat in. One reason is that there is twice the thickness of glass. Another reason is the narrow air gap. Explain how this gap helps to keep heat in the house. [2]

b Jane buys a new gas fire. It has an input power of 5.0 kW. Its output power to the room is only 3.0 kW. What happens to the other 2.0 kW? [1]

c The fire has a shiny metal surface around the flames. This helps to heat the room even more quickly. Explain how the shiny surface does this. [1]

4 A family was trying to save electricity by reducing energy loss.

a They use their cooker for 1.5 hours a day. The cooker was rated at 6kW. Calculate the number of kilowatt-hours (kWh) used by the cooker in one day. [1]

Improvement to home	Cost	Year saving	Payback time
Double glazing	£3000	£60	50 years
Roof insulation	£320	£80	
Cavity wall insulation		£60	6 years

b Calculate the payback time for roof insulation and the cost of fitting cavity wall insulation. [2]

c Double glazing has a long payback time. Explain why so many people still choose to fit double glazing. [3]

Special

5 A 100 W light bulb cost 80p and lasts about 1000 hours. A 100 W fluorescent light tube costs £3.00 and lasts about 8000 hours. This diagram shows what happens to the energy every second.

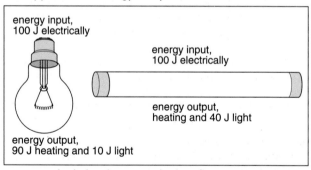

energy input, 100 J electrically

energy output, 90 J heating and 10 J light

energy input, 100 J electrically

energy output, heating and 40 J light

a The light tube is switched on for 1 second. How much energy is transferred as heat in joules? [1]
A school office needs some new lights. The office needs a light output of 80 joules.

b How many fluorescent tubes would be needed? [1]

c How many light bulbs would be needed? [1]

d Write down one advantage and one disadvantage of fluorescent tubes. [2]

[Adapted from the Terminal Examination, June 1994, and the Periodic Examinations, July 1994 and June 1995.]

Checklist

These are the facts and ideas that you should have learned by studying this topic.

To succeed at Credit level you should:
- know that hot objects cool down
- be able to tell which materials are good and bad thermal conductors
- know that air is a poor conductor and notice insulating materials that use air
- be able to see how to save energy costs in your home
- know about electricity bringing energy into your home
- be able to tell how expensive it is to use some electrical appliances by looking at their power (wattage)
- be able to see why you must use fuses or circuit breakers
- be able to identify the three wires in a mains cable
- know why metal parts that you can touch must be earthed and that you do not need to earth a double-insulated appliance.

To succeed at Merit level you should:
- know that energy is transferred from hot objects to cooler objects
- understand how energy is transferred through conduction, convection and radiation
- be able to calculate the costs and payback times of energy saving in the home
- be able to see the good and bad points of using electricity in your home compared to other sources of energy
- know that electricity companies use the kilowatt-hour (kWh) unit to measure the electricity you use at home
- be able to calculate the number of kWh units by multiplying the power in kilowatts by the time in hours
- know how electricity can be used for space heating, heating water and for cooking
- know that power is the energy transferred per second
- know that when something is connected to earth it cannot become live
- know what the neutral and earth wires are for
- know how a fuse works.

To succeed at Special level you should:
- be able to explain how conduction, convection and radiation affect your home and everyday objects
- know how energy is transferred in evaporation
- know that the kilowatt-hour is a measure of energy supplied
- be able to calculate the number of kWh units from power in watts and time in minutes
- be able to calculate power and time by changing the subject in the formula: kWh unit = power in kW × time in h
- understand the advantages and costs of off-peak electricity
- know the names of the three wires in a mains cable and what they do
- know why you must use fuses or circuit breakers and why metal parts that you can touch must be earthed
- know why you do not need to earth a double-insulated appliance
- know how a fuse or a circuit breaker can stop an appliance becoming damaged.

GCSE FOUNDATION TIER

GCSE HIGHER TIER

Key words from this topic:

conduction

convection

radiation

evaporation

conductor

insulator

current

ampere

joule

kilowatt-hour

3 MOVING AROUND

▲ The human body can *accelerate* more than a car. The top *speed* of a car is a lot faster though.

CARS cause a large number of road deaths. Car performance and condition, road, weather and the driver's experience are all important. Any damage to injured people is much worse at higher speeds. The damage at 40 mph is *four* times greater than the damage at 20 mph. Cars that do not work very well cause accidents, but many accidents are the driver's fault.

Drivers get tired, especially on motorways. They react more slowly and even fall asleep at the wheel. Drivers sometimes have a number of 'microsleeps', which only last a second or two, without even knowing it. Some drugs, especially alcohol, make you feel drowsy or make it harder to concentrate. Drivers often do not realise how badly they are affected. Any amount of alcohol will affect the ability to drive. It is safest not to drink alcohol at all if you are driving.

Of course cars are not the only way to travel. There are safer methods that use less fossil fuels, but no matter which way you move around, the science of movement applies. You need energy to move. Where can you get the energy from? If you want to stop as well, you also have to know how to transfer that energy somewhere else. Perhaps most importantly of all, the safety of travel is based on a knowledge of speed, forces and materials.

▶ **Cycling is an excellent form of personal transport. It is quicker and easier than walking because the bicycle supports your weight. It does not use fossil fuels or create pollution. If you cycle regularly you will improve your fitness and health.**

▶ **Deaths from transport accidents in the UK. More people die in motorcycle accidents than any other. Cars are often involved in motorcycle, bicycle and pedestrian accidents.**

▼ **It is illegal for a person to drive if they have drunk too much alcohol. This is likely to happen if they have had more than one alcoholic drink of any sort. Sometimes, just one drink takes you over the limit.**

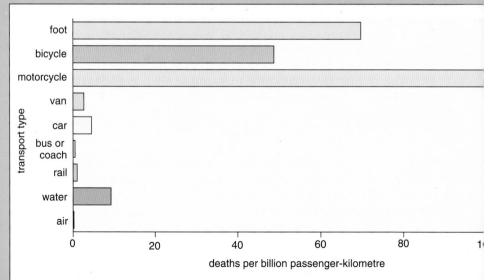

Graph: deaths per billion passenger-kilometre vs transport type (foot, bicycle, motorcycle, van, car, bus or coach, rail, water, air)

	m/s	km/h	mph
light (the fastest speed possible)	300 000 000	1 080 000 000	675 000 000
Earth in orbit around the Sun	29 790	10 724	6700
speed needed for rocket to escape from Earth	11 200	40 320	25 200
speed of typical Earth satellite	7 500	27 000	16 875
military jet aircraft	833	3 000	1 875
Concorde	648	2 333	1 500
Boeing 747	268	964	600
average speed of molecule in air	500	1 800	1 125
sound	340	1 224	765
fastest animal (peregrine in its swoop on to prey)	97	350	220
high speed train (French TGV)	92	315	200
high speed train (BR)	62.5	200	125
legal maximum, UK motorways (70mph)	31	112	70
fastest water animal (sailfish)	30	109	68
fastest land animal (cheetah)	28	100	60
legal maximum, UK towns	13.4	48	30
fastest Tour De France cyclist (B. Hinault, over whole course)	10.5	37.8	23.6
100 m sprinter	10	36	22.5
marathon runner	5.8	21	13
average walking speed	1.7	6	4
average speed of a snail	0.06	0.02	0.013

Speed and thinking distance

A normal driver takes two-thirds of a second to react. This is the time between seeing a problem and putting on the brakes. Suppose a car travels at 30 m/s (about 70 mph). The car travels 30 m in one second, or 20 m (2/3 × 30 m) in two-thirds of a second. The car travels a thinking distance of about 20 m at 70 mph while the driver is reacting. You can check this in the *Highway Code* chart of shortest stopping distances.

The UK national speed limit for cars on motorways is 70 mph. A car takes one hour to travel 70 miles at this speed. To a scientist, the speed of something is how far it travels in one second. Scientists normally measure distances in metres or centimetres. Speed is measured in metres per second or centimetres per second.

Average speed

You should be able to walk with an average speed of 6 kilometres per hour (km/h), which is 1.7 metres per second (m/s). This does not mean that you walk at a steady 6 km/h for the whole journey. It means that you will walk 30 km in 5 hours.

To calculate the average speed, you divide the total distance you travel by the time it takes. You can write this as a formula.

average speed = total distance travelled/time taken

$$v = s/t$$

v = average speed, s = total distance travelled, t = time taken

Worked example

Your friend takes 10 minutes (600 seconds) to walk to your house. Your house is 0.9 km (900 m) away. Calculate your friend's average speed.

Write down the formula: $v = s/t$

Put in the numbers: $v = 900/600$

Write down the answer and the unit: $v = 1.5$ m/s

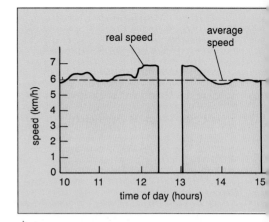

▲
Sometimes you walk slowly, sometimes you walk faster. Your average speed tells you how far you will get after a certain time.

Starting and stopping

Car drivers spend a lot of money on fuel to give their cars **kinetic energy**. This is the energy that cars have when they move. You have to take the energy away again to make cars stop. A fast car has more kinetic energy than a slow car. A parked car has no kinetic energy.

You can do experiments to measure kinetic energy at different speeds. Suppose that one car travels twice as fast as another identical car. You should find that it has four times the energy. Kinetic energy depends on the *square* of **speed**. Kinetic energy also depends on **mass**. A 1000 kg car has twice the kinetic energy of a 500 kg car travelling at the same speed.

You can describe these results in a formula:

kinetic energy = $\frac{1}{2}$ × mass × speed²

$$E_k = \frac{1}{2}mv^2$$

E_k = kinetic energy, m = mass, v = speed

Machine	Power
radio	3 W
light bulb	100 W
stereo sound system	130 W
food processor	600 W
electric kettle	2 200 W
car engine	50 000 W
lorry engine	200 000 W
aeroplane engine	500 000 W

▲
A lorry engine transfers 200 000 joules of energy in one second. This is enough to run a light bulb for over half an hour.

◄
Passenger trains can be faster than cars and buses, but slower than air travel. They use less energy per person than most other forms of transport.

Example

If you weigh 600 newtons, this means your mass is 60 kg. Your speed is 5 m/s when you are running. What is your kinetic energy?

Write down the formula: $E_k = \frac{1}{2}mv^2$

Put in the numbers: $E_k = \frac{1}{2} \times 60 \times 5^2$

Write down the answer and the unit: $E_k = 750\,J$

Getting kinetic energy

A car engine uses fuel to make the car move. The engine transfers the energy from burning fuel to kinetic energy of the car. A lorry engine transfers energy faster than a car engine. A lorry has a more powerful engine than a car. In science, **power** means the energy transferred in one second. A normal car engine can transfer 50 000 joules of energy every second. Its power is 50 000 watts.

Thinking, braking and stopping distances

Road safety depends on good braking and a good driver. The driver must react quickly if someone steps in front of the car. The car keeps moving while the driver is reacting. The distance the car travels while the driver is reacting is called the *thinking distance*. The driver then puts on the brakes. The distance the car travels while it is braking is called the *braking distance*.

▼
Shortest stopping distances for a car on a good, dry road. This information comes from the *Highway Code*. You must add the *thinking distance* and the *braking distance* together to find the overall *stopping distance*.

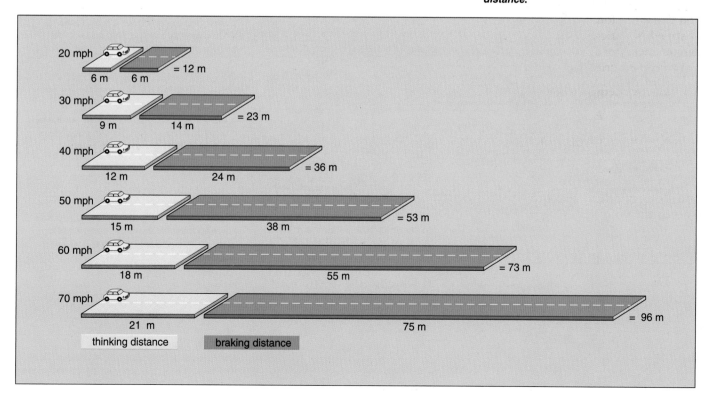

Braking distance and kinetic energy

The brakes get hot when a car slows down. Energy is transferred from the moving car to the brakes. If the car is *twice* as fast, it has *four* times the kinetic energy ($\frac{1}{2} \times$ mass $\times$ speed^2). The brakes have to transfer four times as much energy, so the car travels four times as far. If the car's speed is three times faster, the square of speed is nine times greater. This means that the braking distance is also nine times greater. You can check this in the *Highway Code* chart of shortest stopping distances. Look at the braking distances for 20 mph, 40 mph and 60 mph.

The *Highway Code* stopping distances are for cars. Heavy lorries take longer to brake because they have more mass. A lorry that has five times the mass of a car has to transfer five times more kinetic energy than a car at the same speed. Lorries have more powerful brakes than cars, but they still take longer to stop.

Friction

Friction is the force that tries to stop movement between touching surfaces. Friction between the brakes and the wheel slows down the wheel. Friction between car tyres and the road stops the car from sliding around. Water, sand or leaves on the road reduce friction. This means that drivers cannot brake as hard because the car will skid. The drivers must use less force on the brakes, so the braking distance is longer.

A car's braking system exerts a force on the car. A force does **work** when the force moves along. In science, work is the *amount of energy transferred*. You can calculate work using the formula:

p195

work (energy transferred) =   force × distance moved in direction of force

If you only use half the braking force, the braking distance doubles. If the distance did not double, the brakes would not transfer enough kinetic energy from the car to make it stop.

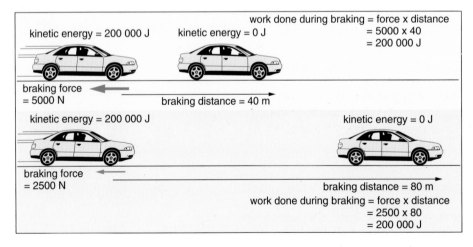

kinetic energy = 200 000 J   kinetic energy = 0 J

work done during braking = force x distance
= 5000 x 40
= 200 000 J

braking force = 5000 N

braking distance = 40 m

kinetic energy = 200 000 J   kinetic energy = 0 J

braking force = 2500 N

braking distance = 80 m
work done during braking = force x distance
= 2500 x 80
= 200 000 J

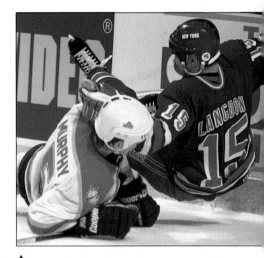

▲
In some situations it can be hard to get rid of your kinetic energy. Here's one painful way of doing it.

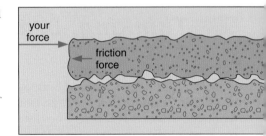

your force

friction force

▲
Rough surfaces cause friction. The roughness can be very fine so that you can only see it under a microscope. The tiny bumps make it hard for the surfaces to slide over each other. This causes the friction force.

◄
If you use a lower braking force, you still have to transfer away the car's kinetic energy. The result is a longer braking distance.

▲
There is a lot of friction between greyhound and track. The friction provides the large force that the dog needs to speed around corners. Without enough frictional force, the dog would skid and speed headlong in a straight line.

▲
Over-inflated tyres expand, reducing the surface area of the tyre in contact with the road. A reduced contact means a reduced friction between the car and the road, and that can mean losing control of the car. Tyres without treads are also likely to slip.

Questions and Practice

1 An electric kettle's power is 2200 W. You use it to heat some water. How much energy does it transfer:

a in 1 second;

b in 10 seconds;

c in 1 minute?

2 A car has a mass of 750 kg. How much kinetic energy does it have when it travels at:

a 10 m/s;

b 20 m/s?

Braking force

Car brakes use a large force to stop a car, but the driver only uses gentle pressure on the brake pedal. A **hydraulic** pressure system joins the pedal to the brakes. The hydraulic system of oil-filled pipes and cylinders multiplies the force.

What is pressure?

Suppose you and your friend walk across a damp lawn. You are about the same size and you weigh the same. Your **weight** is the force that pulls you to the ground. Your feet press onto the ground – they exert a **pressure** on the ground. You are wearing shoes with large, flat heels, but your friend's shoes have got narrow heels. The narrow heels sink into the ground because they have a smaller area. You both push on the ground with the same force, but your friend exerts more pressure because the shoe's area is smaller.

Doubling the area halves the pressure. Doubling the force doubles the pressure. You can write a formula that shows this:

53

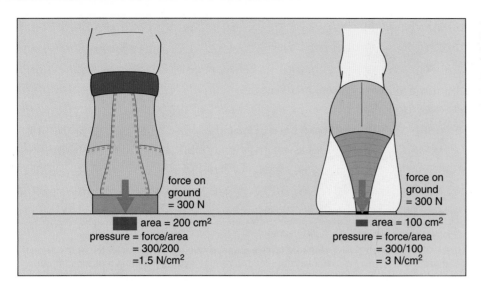

Shoes pressing on the ground. The shoe on the left does not sink into the ground. This is because the bottom of the shoe has a large area. The other shoe does sink into the ground. The bottom of this shoe has a smaller area, so it exerts more pressure.

pressure = force/area

$P = F/A$

P = pressure, F = force pushing on surface, A = area of surface

Worked example

The area of the bottom of a table leg is 10 cm². A table has four legs so the total area is 40 cm². The table weighs 320 N. What pressure does the table exert on the floor?

Write down the formula: $P = F/A$

Put in the numbers: $P = 320/40$

Write down the answer and the unit: $P = 8$ N/cm²

Hydraulic systems

If you get a puncture, you must take the wheel off the car. You must use a jack to lift the car up first. Garages use hydraulic jacks. A hydraulic jack has two cylinders full of oil. The cylinders are joined together. The cylinders are

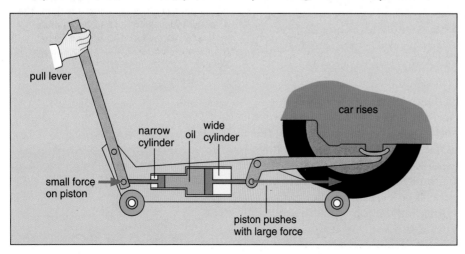

◄
Hydraulic car jack. The force on the narrow piston exerts pressure on the oil. The piston's area is small, so you only need a small force to push it. All the oil is under pressure because it is a fluid. It flows until the pressure is the same everywhere in the liquid. The pressure forces the wide piston to move outwards. The piston's area is large, so it pushes out with a large force.

different sizes. The narrow cylinder has a piston that you push to exert a pressure on the oil. The oil forces a piston in the wide cylinder to move outwards. The large piston pushes a lever that lifts the car.

All hydraulic systems rely on the fact that *pressure is the same in all parts of the fluid*. The pressure is the same for all piston sizes. Look at the diagram of two syringes joined together. The system is full of water.

The small piston's area is 2 cm^2. Suppose you push the small piston with a force of 10 newtons. You can work out the pressure on the end of the small piston:

Write down the formula: $P = F/A$

Put in the numbers: $P = 10/2$

Write down the answer and the unit: $P = 5$ N/cm^2

This makes the water's pressure 5 N/cm^2 too.

The pressure in the water is the same everywhere, so the large piston's pressure is also 5 N/cm^2. The large piston pushes out with a large force. The large piston's area is 12 cm^2. You can calculate the large piston's force: $P = F/A$, $F = PA$, $F = 5 \times 12$, $F = 60$ N.

The large piston produces six times as much force because it has six times the area.

A car's braking system works in exactly the same way. The pistons are connected together by pipes that can be bent around corners. Leaks can be dangerous. Air bubbles might get into the oil. Gases are much more squashy than liquids. You will squash the air bubbles rather than moving the wide pistons. Your brakes will not work at full strength. Your brakes will not work at all if the oil drains out of the pipes.

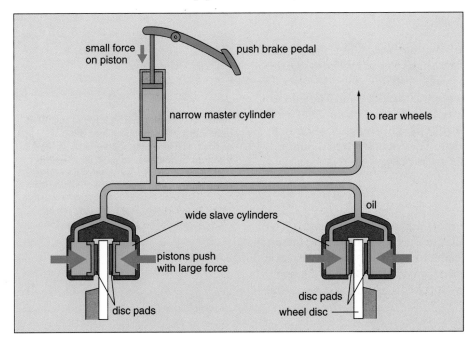

◄
Hydraulic disc brakes. The brake pedal pushes a piston in a narrow cylinder called the 'master' cylinder. Each wheel has two wide cylinders called 'slave' cylinders. The pipes connecting the cylinders are filled with a special oil called hydraulic fluid. The slave cylinder pistons push brake pads against a metal disc. The friction force between the pad and the disc slow down the car.

3 Two cars have the same size tyres. One car is heavier than the other – it weighs more.

  a Which car puts more pressure on the road surface – the heavy car or the light car?

  b Which car does more damage to the road?

  c You can reduce the problem by fitting wider tyres. Explain why.

4 You push a drawing pin into a notice board with a force of 5 N.

  a The head of the drawing pin has an area of 1 cm². Calculate the pressure between your thumb and the head of the drawing pin.

  b The point of the pin has one-hundredth of the area of the head (0.01 cm²). What is the pressure between the point of the pin and the board?

5 You have a hydraulic braking system in your car. The area of the piston in the master cylinder is 6 cm². You push the piston with a force of 600 N.

  a Calculate the pressure in the hydraulic oil.

  b The piston in a slave cylinder has an area of 24 cm². It pushes on the brake pads. Calculate the force it uses.

A safe stop

Stretching seat belts

Seat belts stop you moving when your car stops moving in a crash. Without a seat belt you would just keep moving at the car's original speed. You would crash into other parts of the car and be seriously injured. The seat belt also stretches. If it did not stretch in a crash, you could also be badly injured. The front of your body would stop as suddenly as the car. Your ribs might be cracked by the force of the seat belt.

Elastic and plastic

Seat belts are **elastic**. You can stretch an elastic material. When you let go, the material goes back to its original size and shape. Metals are also elastic. This is why you can make a spring out of steel.

Materials can also be **plastic** when you stretch them too far. They do not go back to their original size or shape. Plasticine is a good example of a plastic material. A car crash can damage seat belts. They stretch so far that they stop being elastic and start being plastic. They stay stretched out of shape after the crash. You must then fit new seat belts.

Plastics that aren't plastic

Washing-up bowls, pens and even car bumpers are made from materials we call 'plastics'. 'Plastics' are not plastic at all. They are ex-plastic. The materials are plastic when the bowls and pens are being made. They are easy to mould into shape because they are plastic. Then they are changed. They change chemically so that they become stiff. They stop being plastic and keep their shape for a long time.

▲ Testing seat belts in a 50 km/h crash. Seat belts stop you smashing into the windscreen in a crash. They also stretch so that you take longer to stop. This means that there is less force on you. A smaller force injures you less.

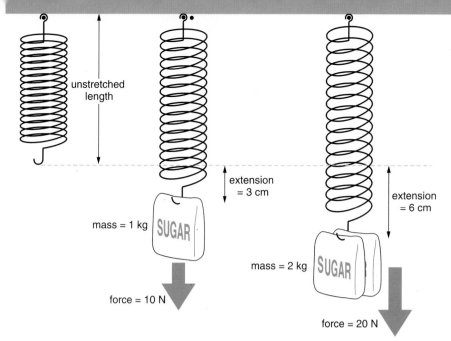

unstretched length

extension = 3 cm

mass = 1 kg SUGAR

force = 10 N

mass = 2 kg SUGAR

extension = 6 cm

force = 20 N

Hooke's law

Robert Hooke discovered a law for elastic materials in the seventeenth century. Hooke found that a small force stretched a spring a little and that double the force stretched it twice as much. Hooke's law is that the amount the spring stretches by is proportional to the stretching force. The amount the spring stretches by is called the **extension**.

Engineers use a number called the spring constant to describe how springy a spring is. The spring constant is the size of the force that stretches the spring by one centimetre. Using Hooke's law we can write:

force = spring constant × extension

$F = kx$

F = stretching force, k = spring constant, x = extension

Worked example

You have a 30 cm long spring. Its spring constant is 2 N/cm. You stretch it until it is 40 cm long. How much force do you use?

The extension is:	40 – 30 = 10 cm
Write down the formula:	$F = kx$
Put in the numbers:	$F = 2 \times 10$
Write down the answer and the unit:	$F = 20$ N

Passenger cages and crumple zones

Cars could be made very strong so that they do not bend very much in a crash. The cars would stop very suddenly when they crash. The passengers would decelerate very fast and be badly injured. Modern cars have crumple zones. The metal bends and buckles in a crash. It behaves like a plastic material. The car takes longer to stop, so it decelerates more gently. This means that the inside of a passenger's body is not shaken about so badly. Passengers are also less likely to damage themselves on their seat belt. The passenger compartment does not crumple. It is called the safety cage.

◄
The spring's extension is proportional to the force you use to stretch it. The extension doubles when you double the force.
The spring goes back to its original length if you take the force away. This is because the spring is elastic.
If you use too much force, the spring becomes plastic. It stays partly stretched when you take the force away.

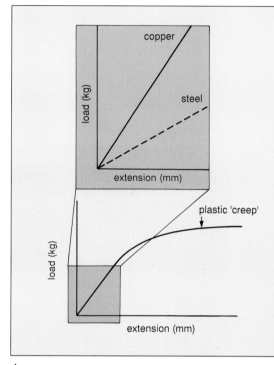

copper

steel

load (kg)

extension (mm)

plastic 'creep'

load (kg)

extension (mm)

▲
Metals obey Hooke's law up to a certain point. They start being plastic when you stretch them beyond this point. They stretch a lot with hardly any more force. Eventually they snap.

▼
Modern cars have crumple zones at the front and the rear.

Safety on two wheels

Motor cycle safety helmets work in a similar way to crumple zones on cars. The helmet protects your head from large forces in an accident. The helmet is made from expanded plastic foam. It is covered by a thin plastic shell. The foam gives way in a crash so that your head moves a bit further before it stops. The extra time for your head to slow down means that it decelerates more gently. Your brain smashes against the inside of your skull with less force.

▲
Your head is the most important part of your body to protect in an accident. A safety helmet works like a crumple zone. You must throw your helmet away after an accident even if you cannot see the damage inside. Leather overalls and boots cut down the amount of skin and flesh scraped off as you slide along the road.

◄
You should wear a helmet whenever you ride your bike. Nothing will protect you very well if you have a head-on collision with a car. A car is too massive – there is no contest! Fortunately, not many accidents are like this. Usually, a car knocks a cyclist off the bike. Banging your head on the road as you fall can be very dangerous.

You can fall off a pedal cycle very awkwardly, even at slow speeds. Many serious injuries can happen this way. A pedal cycle helmet works on the same principle as a motor cycle helmet. It is lighter and designed for lower speeds. You should not use a pedal cycle helmet when you ride a motor bike.

Air bags

Air bags stop front seat passengers hurting their heads and faces in a car crash. When a crash starts, the air bag quickly fills with a gas. Gas is squashy. It lets the driver's head stop more slowly. This means that there is less force to cause injury.

Gases are also elastic. If you squash them they bounce back. It would be very dangerous if the air bag made the driver's head snap back again. The air bag does not stay inflated. The force of the driver's head squeezes out some of the gas.

Air bags would also be dangerous if they went off by mistake. The built-in computer knows the car's own 'crash signature'. This is information about the car's deceleration in at least fifty test crashes. There is also a mass on a spring that detects deceleration. The air bag only goes off when both the computer and the mass on a spring detect a crash.

▲
An air bag helps to protect the driver's head in a crash. It is kept in the middle of the steering wheel. It bursts out if a built-in computer detects a crash at more than 12 mph (5 m/s). It takes 0.04 s (1/25th of a second) to do this – before the driver's head even starts to move forwards.

Boyle's law for a gas

p201

The main reason that the air bag works is that gases squash under pressure. When you put more pressure on a gas by squeezing it, its volume gets less. In the eighteenth century Robert Boyle discovered that pressure × volume always stays the same.

pressure × volume = constant

Suppose a fully inflated air bag contains 30 000 cm^3 of gas at 10 N/cm^2 pressure. What will the gas volume be when the pressure has gone up by three times to 30 N/cm^2? The volume will reduce to one third – the 'inverse proportion'. It will be 10 000 cm^3.

pressure × volume (at start) = pressure × volume (at end)

$$P_1V_1 = P_2V_2$$

P_1 = gas pressure at start, V_1 = gas volume at start

P_2 = gas pressure at end, V_2 = gas volume at end

▲
Measuring the volume of a trapped bubble of air at different pressures.

Worked example

Suppose a bicycle pump is full of air. The air's pressure is 10 N/cm^2 and its volume is 150 cm^3. You squash the air down to 50 cm^3 before any air escapes. What is the pressure of the air now?

Write down the formula:	$P_1V_1 = P_2V_2$
Put in the numbers:	$P_1 \times 50 = 10 \times 150$
	$P_1 = 1500/50$
Write down the answer and the unit:	$P_1 = 30$ N/cm^2

Impulse and momentum

Cycle helmets, crumple zones and air bags are valuable ways of reducing the damage during sudden changes of speed. They work because they increase the total time of impact. It then takes less force to come to a stop.

A small force acting for a long time can produce the same effect as a large force acting for a short time. This effect is called **impulse**. There is a formula for impulse:

impulse = force × time

$$I = Ft$$

Impulse measures the change of **momentum** in an object. Momentum is calculated by multiplying an object's mass by its speed:

momentum = mass × speed

So when you change speed you also change momentum and this requires an impulse. Momentum is a very useful quantity in the physics of movement. This is because the total amount of momentum always stays the same – just like energy.

Questions and Practice

6 When you stretch anything, it can be elastic or plastic.

a What does elastic mean?

b What does plastic mean?

7 Why must seat belts be stretchy, but not too stretchy?

8 Suppose a spring is 20 cm long.

   a You stretch it with a 5 N force. Its new length is 22 cm. How large is the extension?

   b You increase the force to 10 N. What is the spring's new extension? What is its new length?

9 An air bag fills with gas, then your head hits it hard.

   a What happens to the volume of the gas?

   b What happens to the pressure of the gas?

   c What happens to the movement of your head?

10 An air bag inflates to a pressure of 15 N/cm^2. Its volume is 40 000 cm^3.

   a A passenger's head hits the air bag. Will the pressure go up or down? Will the volume get larger or smaller?

   b If the gas pressure changes to 30 N/cm^2, what is the volume of the gas?

Acceleration

A car builds up speed as it moves off. This is called **acceleration**. Some cars have better acceleration than others. Suppose two cars start at the same time. They accelerate until they reach the speed limit. The car with more acceleration reaches the speed limit first. Every second, its speed goes up more than the other car. To a scientist, acceleration is how much the speed changes in one second.

Suppose a car starts from being at rest (0 m/s), and accelerates to a speed of 12 m/s in 6 seconds. Its overall speed increase is 12 m/s. Its speed increase in one second is 2 m/s. Its acceleration is 2 m/s every second. Scientists write this as 2 m/s^2. The formula for acceleration is:

      acceleration = change in speed/time taken

$$a = (v - u)/t$$

a = acceleration, u = speed at start, v = speed at end, t = time taken

Worked example

A car is standing still (0 m/s) when the traffic lights change to green. The car takes 5 seconds to reach 15 m/s. Calculate the car's acceleration.

Write down the formula:	$a = (v - u)/t$
Put in the numbers:	$a = (15 - 0)/5$
Write down the answer and the unit:	$a = 3$ m/s^2

Worked example

A car accelerates at a rate of 2.5 m/s^2. What is its change of speed after 8 seconds?

Write down the formula:	$a = (v - u)/t$

Change the subject to $(v - u)$: $\qquad$ $(v - u) = at$

Put in the numbers: $\qquad$ $(v - u) = 2.5 \times 8$

Write down the answer and the unit: $\quad$ $(v - u) = 20$ m/s

The change in speed is $(v - u)$. If the car starts at rest, it reaches a speed of 20 m/s. If the car was already moving at 15 m/s when it started to accelerate, it would have reached a final speed of 35 m/s.

Deceleration

If you calculate the acceleration when the car is slowing down, you get a negative number! This is not a mistake. Negative acceleration is called **deceleration**.

Graphing motion

You may find it easier to use graphs when you compare ways of moving around. The most useful graph for this is the speed-time graph. The simplest kind of motion graph is the distance-time graph.

Distance–time graph

Suppose you travel down a hill on your bicycle. You start a stopwatch when you begin your journey. You accelerate down the hill at first, but you stay at a steady speed by using your brakes. The diagram shows what the distance-time graph looks like.

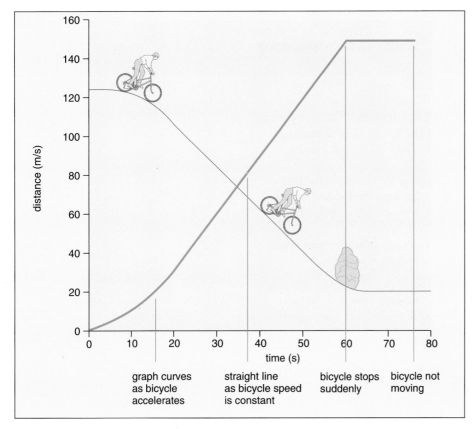

graph curves as bicycle accelerates

straight line as bicycle speed is constant

bicycle stops suddenly

bicycle not moving

◄
A distance–time graph for a bicycle travelling down a hill. The graph slopes when the bicycle is moving. The graph gets steeper when the bicycle gets faster. The graph shows distance going up the same amount every second when the bicycle's speed is constant. The distance goes up by 30 m every 10 seconds. This is 3 m every second, so the speed is 3 m/s. The graph is flat when the bicycle is at rest.

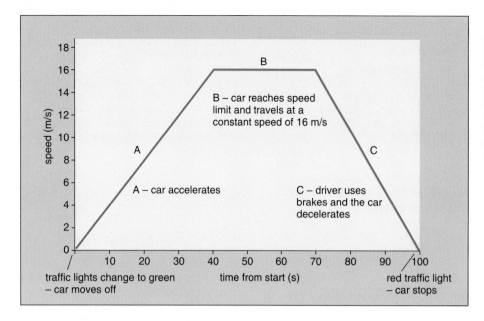

A speed–time graph for a car travelling between traffic lights. The first part of the graph slopes upwards. This shows that the speed is increasing, so the car is accelerating. The graph is flat when the car travels at a constant speed. The final downward slope shows deceleration. This slope is steeper than the acceleration slope. A steeper slope shows that the deceleration (or acceleration) is greater.

Speed–time graph

p201

You can get a lot of information from a speed-time graph if you know what to look for. You can find out the speed, the acceleration and even the distance travelled. Look at this example.

The first section of the speed-time graph (section A) shows that the speed goes up by 16 m/s in 40 seconds. You can use the formula to work out the acceleration.

$$a = (v - u)/t$$

$$= (16 - 0)/40 = 0.4 \text{ m/s}^2$$

If you calculate the graph's slope, the 'gradient', you get an interesting result:

slope = vertical rise/horizontal run

$$= (16 - 0)/40 = 0.4$$

The slope is the same as the acceleration. You can check that the slope gives you the right acceleration for the other parts of the graph. You should get 0 m/s² for the constant speed section (section B), and –0.8 m/s² for the deceleration (section C).

The area under the graph is the distance travelled by the car. The area under the graph for any slice of time is equal to the time multiplied by the speed, or average speed, and average speed × time = distance. You can see this by looking at the diagrams.

The area under the graph is in three parts. There are two triangles (each area = $\frac{1}{2}$ × base × height) and a rectangle (area = length × width).

	area of triangle when accelerating		area of rectangle when at constant speed		area of triangle when decelerating
total area =		+		+	
=	$\frac{1}{2}$ × 40 × 16	+	16 × 30	+	$\frac{1}{2}$ × 20 × 16
=	320	+	480	+	160
=	960 m				

The car travels 960 m during its journey.

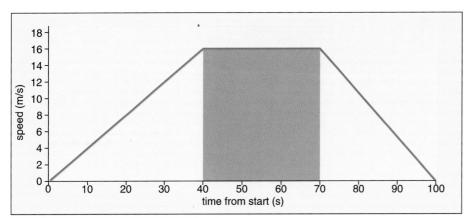

◀

Distance travelled by a car at constant speed. The car travels at a constant speed of 16 m/s between time = 40 s and time = 70 s. The time taken is (70 – 40) = 30 s. You can use the average speed formula to calculate the distance it travels: $s = vt = 16 \times 30 = 480$ m. The shaded rectangle has area = length $\times$ width = $16 \times 30 = 480$. This is the same as the distance travelled.

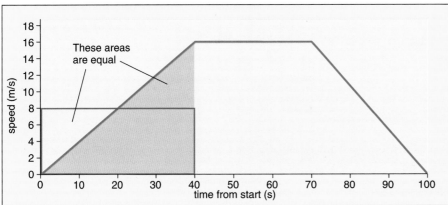

◀

Distance travelled by an accelerating car. The shading shows the area under the graph. The car's speed increases steadily from 0 m/s to 16 m/s between time = 0 s and time = 40 s. Its *average* speed is 8 m/s. The area of the purple rectangle is the distance it travels at its average speed. Area of rectangle = $8 \times 40 = 320$ m. The shaded triangle has the same area. If you chop off the top of the triangle it fits exactly in the unshaded part of the rectangle.

Questions and Practice

11 Your friend travels across a school playground on roller skates.

  a Write down two things you must measure to calculate your friend's average speed.

  b Explain how you would measure these two things.

12 A car travels 500 m along a road in 50 seconds. Calculate the car's average speed.

13 Look at the graph. It is a distance–time graph for a person walking down a street and looking in three shop windows.

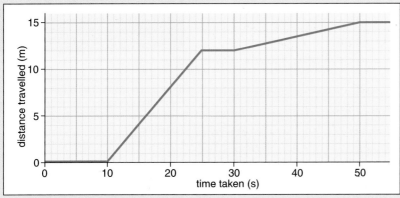

  a What is the person doing (i) between 0 s and 10 s, (ii) between 10 s and 20 s, (iii) between 20s and 30 s?

  b How far apart are the shops?

14

a You are sitting on your bike. It is standing still. You pedal hard for 4 seconds and reach a speed of 8 m/s. Calculate your acceleration.

Look at the graph. It is a speed–time graph of your motion.

b Calculate the slope (gradient) of the graph between 0 and 4 seconds.

c Calculate the slope of the graph between 4 and 6 seconds.

d Write down your deceleration.

e Use the area under the graph to find out how far you travelled all together.

15 Explain the meaning of thinking distance, braking distance and stopping distance.

Mass, force and acceleration

High performance cars accelerate very quickly. The cars are light, so they have a low mass. They also have powerful engines. The engine drives the wheels that push the car along with a large force.

Suppose a factory replaces the ordinary engine in a car with an engine that is twice as powerful. The new engine provides *twice* the force of the normal engine. The result is that the car will have *twice* the acceleration.

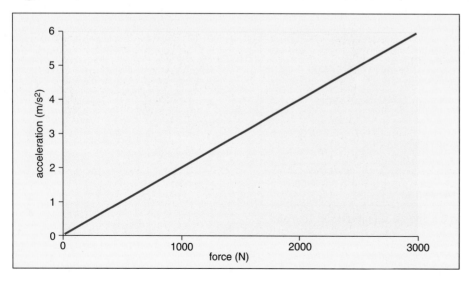

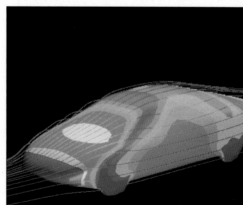

▲
Designing a high performance car. It must have a low mass. The engine and transmission exert a large force. The car is also shaped to reduce drag, or wind resistance.

◄

Acceleration depends on force. If you double force, the acceleration doubles. If you treble force, the acceleration trebles. Acceleration is *proportional* to force.

A light car can have quite a good acceleration. A massive car with the same engine will have a low acceleration. Tests show that a car with *half* the mass has *double* the acceleration.

Force and mass have opposite effects on acceleration. If you double force *and* double mass, the acceleration stays the same. There is a formula that shows this:

acceleration = force/mass

$$a = F/m$$

a = acceleration, F = force, m = mass

Scientists often want to find force from mass and acceleration. They change the formula to look like this:

force = mass × acceleration

$$F = ma$$

a = acceleration, F = force, m = mass

Worked example

A 600 kg car accelerates at 4 m/s². How much force do the wheels use to push the car?

Write down the formula:	$F = ma$
Put in the numbers:	$F = 600 \times 4$
Write down the answer and the unit:	$F = 2400$ N

With four people and some luggage, the car's total mass is now 1000 kg. The wheels push the car with the same force as before. What is the car's new acceleration?

Write down the formula:	$a = F/m$
Put in the numbers:	$a = 2400/1000$
Write down the answer and the unit:	$a = 2.4$ m/s²

Questions and Practice

16 A car pulls a caravan at 30 mph. It then accelerates to 50 mph.

a Is the acceleration higher or lower than for the car on its own?

b Give *two* reasons for your answer to a.

17 You and your bike have a total mass of 80 kg. You take 18 seconds to change your speed from 0 m/s to 9 m/s.

a Calculate your acceleration

b Calculate the force you use.

18 A car's mass is 1200 kg. Its braking force is 6000 N. Calculate the car's deceleration. (Deceleration is negative acceleration.)

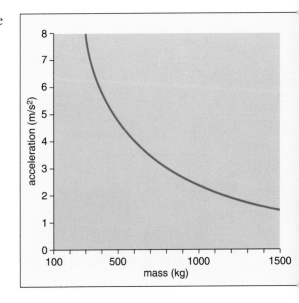

▲
Acceleration depends on mass. If you double mass, the acceleration halves. If you treble mass, the acceleration drops to one-third. Acceleration is *inversely proportional* to mass.

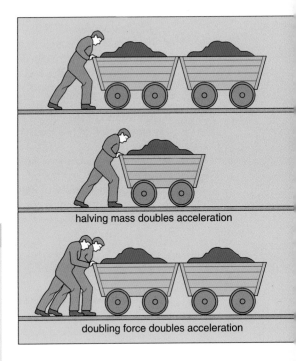

halving mass doubles acceleration

doubling force doubles acceleration

Examination Questions

1 Look at the diagram.

driving force = 2000 N

drag force = 500 N

a Which force is trying to make the lorry go slower? [1 mark]

b What is the lorry doing? Choose from: speeding up; going at a steady speed; slowing down. Explain your answer. [2]

c The driving force stays at 2000 N, but the drag force goes up to 2000 N. What is the lorry doing now? Choose from: speeding up; going at a steady speed; slowing down. [1]

d The lorry is now without its trailer. The driving force is still 2000 N. The lorry can reach its top speed more quickly. Why is this? Give two reasons. [2]

2 Jan is playing ice hockey.

a Jan wants to calculate the speed of her puck when it is moving. What *two* measurements does Jan need to take? [2]

b Jan hits two pucks with the same force. One puck has a mass of 100 g. The other puck has a mass of 200 g. The pucks move at different speeds. Jan wants them to move at the same speed. How can she do this? [1]

3 Cars often have safety features such as crumple zones and safety cages.

a In a crash, the crumple zones can help to save lives. Explain how. [2]

b The part of the car where the passengers sit is made of strong steel. It is called the safety cage. Explain how it can save lives in a crash. [1]

c A van travelling at 12 m/s crashes into the back of a car. Before the crash, the car is not moving. The van is slowed down by the crash and the car speeds up. This is a graph of the crash.

d Sketch a copy of the graph. Label the line for the van and the line for the car on your copy of the graph. [1]

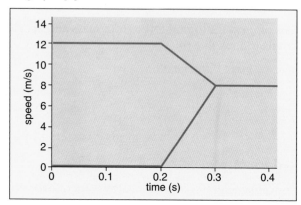

e Which vehicle has the biggest change in speed? Explain how you know this. [2]

4 A van travelling at 12 m/s crashes into the back of a car. Before the crash, the car is not moving. The van is slowed down by the crash and the car speeds up. Look at the graph of the crash in question 3.

a The deceleration of the van is 40 m/s². What is the acceleration of the car during the crash? [2]

b Calculate the force that causes the car to accelerate. [2]

c The driver in the van was wearing a seat belt. Some seat belts are wide and some are narrow. A wide seat belt would be safer. Explain why in terms of force, area and pressure. [2]

5 A rocket stands on a launch pad. The rocket has five engines. Each engine produces a force of 4 000 000 N (4×10^6 N). The mass of the rocket is 2 000 000 kg (2×10^6 kg).

a Calculate the acceleration produced at lift-off. [3]

b The force from the engines stays constant for the first 5 minutes of the flight. The acceleration of the rocket increases during this time. Explain why. [2]

[Adapted from the Periodic Examination, June 1995, and June and July 1994.]

Checklist

These are the facts and ideas that you should have learned by studying this topic.

To succeed at Credit level you should:
- know that you need to measure distance and time to find speed
- know how to measure distance and time
- be able to spot when a force speeds something up or slows it down
- know that you change speed when you accelerate
- be able to see why thinking distance and braking distance are important for road safety
- know that seat belts are stretchy and should be replaced after a crash
- know that gases can be squashed, e.g. in an air bag during a car crash
- know that the pressure of the liquid in a hydraulic system is the same everywhere
- know that when force or area is changed, the pressure will change.

To succeed at Merit level you should:
- be able to calculate speed using the formula $v = s/t$
- be able to draw and understand distance-time and speed-time graphs
- know what the steepness of distance-time and speed-time graphs represent
- know that acceleration is change in speed per unit time
- know that the same force accelerates a small mass more than a large mass
- know the things that affect a driver's thinking distance and braking distance
- know that some things (including seat belts) stretch further when they are pulled with more force
- know that some things will not return to their original size or shape when you stretch them beyond a certain limit
- know how a car's hydraulic brakes rely on the pressure in the liquid being the same everywhere in the liquid
- be able to calculate pressure from $P = F/A$.

To succeed at Special level you should:
- be able to calculate distance and time by using the formula $v = s/t$
- be able to measure speed, distance and time using distance-time graphs and speed-time graphs
- be able to calculate speed change and time taken by changing the subject in the formula $a = v/t$
- be able to calculate mass and acceleration using the formula $F = ma$
- be able to explain how friction, mass and speed affect braking distance
- be able to use the idea of acceleration to explain how braking force affects the time taken for a car to stop
- undertand that for certain materials force is proportional to extension
- know how volume is related to pressure in a fixed mass of gas at constant temperature and be able to use the formula $PV = k$
- know that a small force exerted over a small area can be transmitted through a liquid to produce a large force exerted over a large area
- be able to calculate force, pressure and area using $P = F/A$.

GCSE FOUNDATION TIER

GCSE HIGHER TIER

Key words from this topic:

acceleration

mass

force

power

pressure

hydraulic

extension

elastic

plastic

CHAPTER 4

Rates of Reaction

▲ A slow chemical change that is part of life on Earth.

The natural world is full of change. Plants grow and change. Animals can even take materials from their environment and change them in to new materials – bees create honey and silkworms create silk. Humans have studied these changes in order to create new, original materials – from life-saving drugs to hard-wearing fabrics, from liquid crystals to biodegradable plastic bags.

The change from one material to another is called a *chemical change*. Is the ripening of wheat a chemical change? Yes – unripe and ripe wheat are slightly different substances. It is a change that is helped by the Sun. Is the formation of clouds a chemical change? No – we call this a *physical change*. No new substance has been made.

▼ Encouraging tomatoes to ripen quicker. A greenhouse keeps the temperature high, and that makes changes happen quicker.

▲ Even the picture that she is taking depends on a controlled chemical reaction. The colours of the autumn leaves change quicker or slower according to the temperature.

In this chapter you will find out more about the differences between these changes.

Chemical changes, or *reactions*, happen at different speeds. Tomatoes ripen very slowly. Gardeners try to speed up this chemical change. How? They also put oil on their spades. Why? Which slow chemical reaction are they trying to stop?

Photography also depends on controlling chemical reactions. Light going in through the lens starts a chemical reaction that makes an image on the film. Developing the film is another chemical reaction. To get the best quality photograph, you need to carefully control the speed of that reaction.

You control many chemical reactions each time you prepare a meal. Heating changes food into new, more delicious substances. Cooling food slows down unwanted chemical reactions. What other ways are there of making a slow reaction go faster, or a fast reaction go slower?

▼ Is this your favourite chemical change?

◄ How to prevent rusting.

Making changes

Cooking fat, like all materials, is a chemical. You can buy it either as a solid or as a liquid (oil). You can change chemicals by melting or boiling them – they look different but can easily be changed back. You can also change chemicals more permanently. A **chemical reaction** can turn them into a new substance.

Changes that are not permanent

When you heat solid fat in a pan it will become liquid. If you heat it even more the fat will form a vapour. When this vapour cools down on a cold wall behind the cooker it will first form a liquid, then go back to being a solid. These changes happen when energy is supplied or taken away.

Solid, liquid and vapour are called *states of matter*. These changes from solid to liquid to vapour are called *changes of state*.

- When a solid changes to a liquid the process is called **melting**

- When a liquid changes to a vapour it is called **evaporation** – or **boiling** if it happens very quickly

- When a vapour changes to a liquid it is called **condensation**

- When a liquid turns to a solid it is called **freezing** (or fusion)

These changes of state can be reversed. They are **physical changes** - nothing new is made.

▲
A solid glass, liquid lemonade and gas bubbles.

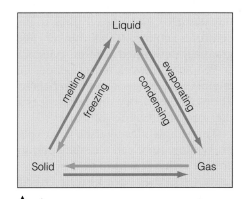

▲
The changes of state.

◄
Some solids change straight from a solid to a vapour. This is called *sublimation*. When solid carbon dioxide sublimes it can be used to create misty stage effects.

Questions and Practice

1 When water vapour from a kettle boils near a cold window, water droplets appear on the glass. What is this process called?

2 When we are hot, unwanted energy is transferred from our bodies as our sweat changes into a vapour. What is this process called?

3 A cooling liquid (coolant) runs through pipes around the inside and at the back of a freezer. For the freezer to work this liquid needs to evaporate into a vapour. Where does the liquid get the energy to do this?

Permanent changes

What happens if you heat liquid fat too much? It starts to change and give off nasty fumes. The fumes are new substances, new chemicals. **A chemical change**, or reaction, has happened. In this case the fat has broken down or **decomposed.**

Another change happens if the fat catches fire. **Burning** is a chemical change. The fat is hot enough to react with the oxygen in the air. Once the fat has burned, it is permanently changed, the reaction is not reversible.

The reaction of the fat with the oxygen will not be activated if it is too cold. There must be enough **activation energy** to get it started. The rate at which the oxidation reaction then happens depends on the temperature of the fat. The higher the temperature the quicker the reaction.

Why do chemicals behave like this? To explain this you need to look at the most important idea in science. An idea that needs a lot of imagination.

Imagining particles

Imagine that all matter, whether solid, liquid or gas, is made up of extremely tiny particles. Not an easy thing to imagine at all, but the idea was described centuries ago by a Greek thinker called Democritus. This idea, or theory, has gradually developed as more evidence has become available.

People who work with science, such as biologists, chemists, physicists, engineers, geologists and materials scientists, give precise names to theories. They call the theory that substances are made up of particles 'the theory of the particulate nature of matter'.

This simple idea by itself can explain a great deal, but it can't explain everything. How can we smell perfume from the other side of a room? The answer is that you have to imagine that these tiny particles are always on the move – that they have **kinetic energy**. (The word kinetic comes from the Greek word for moving.) The particles of perfume must have had enough kinetic energy to move across the room.

> The properties and behaviour of substances can be explained by the idea of tiny particles in constant motion.

This idea is called the 'kinetic theory'. Before we can develop this theory we must have evidence from which to start.

Evidence for the kinetic theory

You cannot see tiny moving particles with an ordinary light microscope. You can see the *effects* caused by these particles in what is called **Brownian motion**.

This was first noticed by the Scots botanist Robert Brown in 1827. He was looking at pollen in water, using a very powerful microscope. Small grains of pollen were moving about in the water. Not just moving in tiny water currents, but apparently jiggling around on the spot. At first, he thought that they were alive – small creatures swimming about like nervous water fleas. The motion continued even after he had boiled the water, so he decided that the particles were not alive. The only explanation was that the particles were being pushed about by something invisible – something smaller.

The smaller, invisible particles were the particles of water jostling around the pollen at high speed. The water itself was knocking the pollen about. You can see Brownian motion for yourself in a 'smoke cell'. There you can see the jittery motion of smoke particles as they are constantly bombarded by particles of air.

Although this is good evidence to support the kinetic theory, it was not until 1905 that a physicist did the mathematics needed to explain Brownian motion fully. The physicist was a young man called Albert Einstein. His predictions were confirmed by experiment in 1908 by the French scientist Jean Perrin.

The kinetic theory also explains how a perfume spreads through a room. The perfume particles are concentrated as a vapour inside the neck of the bottle at first. As they collide with the particles of the gases in the air, they bounce off in all directions. With one collision after another they wander about randomly. This process is known as **diffusion**. With the help of air currents the perfume particles eventually spread throughout the room and reach your nose.

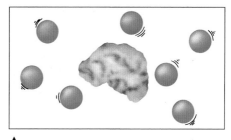

▲
Smoke particles bombarded by moving air molecules.

Questions and Practice

4 Look at the pictures of a jar of air and a jar of bromine gas. Bromine vapour is red-brown in colour and heavier than air. Describe what happens in the two jars. Use the kinetic theory to explain how this happens.

5 Look at the picture of the purple crystal dissolving in water. The purple crystal is called potassium manganate(VII). What is happening? Use the kinetic theory to explain how this happens.

◀
Why does this happen?

◀
There are no water currents, so how can this happen?

▼
A gas race. Which is fastest?

6 Look at the picture of a white gas being made from two colourless gases A and B.

   a Which gas has travelled furthest and fastest?

   b One gas is made up of 'smaller' particles (they have less mass) than the other. Both types of particles have equivalent amounts of kinetic energy. Which gas is made up of the 'smaller' (less massive) particles? Explain your answer.

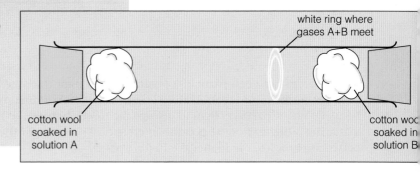

white ring where gases A+B meet

cotton wool soaked in solution A

cotton woo soaked in solution B

Explaining physical changes

R
p208

Physical changes that are easily reversed depend on the forces *between* the particles. As particles move apart, the forces of attraction between them grow weaker. The forces (bonds) *within* the particles are unaffected.

Solids

Solids are made from particles that are closely packed together in a regular arrangement. The particles do not move around but stay in the same position, held to one another by forces of attraction called bonds. At room temperature they shake slightly or vibrate. When energy is transferred to the particles they vibrate more. If they vibrate with enough energy the bonds will break. The particles can then shake loose so that they can slide easily over one another. The solid has become a liquid, which can flow.

The stronger the bonding between the particles of a solid, the more energy is needed to break the structure – to melt the solid. In some strongly bonded solids the melting point can be over 1000 °C.

Liquids

The particles of a liquid are nearly as close together as particles in a solid, but they are no longer neatly arranged. The particles are free to move and slide around each other. This means that the liquid can flow. Liquids take the shape of the container that they are kept in.

When you heat a liquid you are giving the particles more energy – as the temperature increases the particles move more rapidly. As the liquid starts to boil, the fastest particles move apart, widening the gaps between the particles, forming bubbles of gas. At the boiling point these bubbles can rise all the way up to the surface and the particles escape from the liquid.

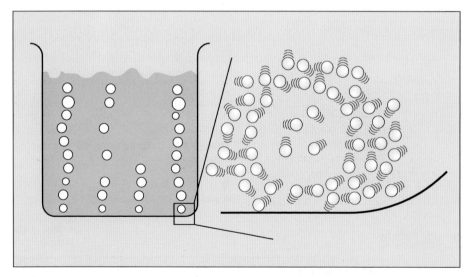

◀
Boiling. The faster molecules form bubbles of vapour inside the liquid.

The forces between particles of water are stronger than the forces between particles of ethanol. More energy is needed to disrupt the forces between water particles than to disrupt the forces between ethanol particles. Water has a higher boiling point than ethanol. The stronger the forces between particles, the higher the boiling point.

Below the boiling point some of the molecules are moving fast enough to break away from the others, but they can only escape at the *surface* of the liquid. This is how liquids evaporate.

Gases

The particles of a gas move very fast. They are widely spaced apart so the forces between them are very weak. The gaps between the particles are very large compared to the size of the particles themselves. Most of the gas is empty space. Through this space the particles of gas hurtle about at speeds of over 300 metres per second – faster than a rifle bullet.

▼
Changing state. The particles stay the same, the way they are arranged and move differs.

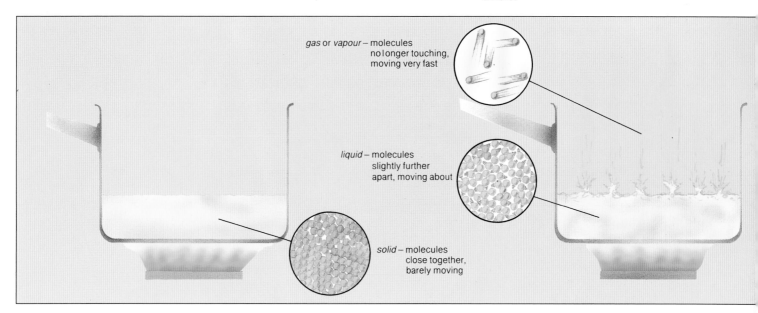

gas or *vapour* – molecules no longer touching, moving very fast

liquid – molecules slightly further apart, moving about

solid – molecules close together, barely moving

▲
A solid has a certain shape because the particles are held together tightly.

▲
A liquid has no fixed shape because the particles are held together less firmly.

▲
A gas has no fixed shape and the particles are a long way apart.

Questions and Practice

7 Describe how the movement of particles is different in solid fat, liquid fat and fat vapour.

8 A friend of yours has decided that there must be air in the gaps between the particles of a gas. Explain why this is wrong.

Solutions

If you put chalk in water it does not dissolve. The water looks cloudy. This is because the small lumps of chalk are surrounded by water particles but the lumps are still big enough to be seen. This is called a **suspension**. The chalk has not broken down to the smallest particles that are possible. The lumps will eventually sink to the bottom of the flask. They will then form a **sediment**.

Sugar and salt are soluble in water. Sugar dissolves, making a clear, colourless solution. You cannot see the particles of sugar. The particles of water surround each particle of sugar. They are so small that you cannot see them, so the solution looks clear. Sugar is the **solute** and water is the **solvent** of this solution.

solute + solvent = solution

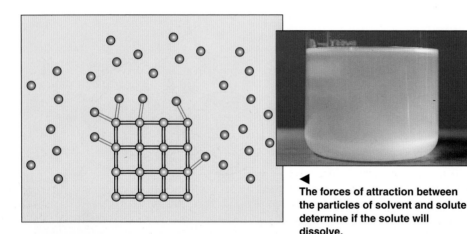

◄
Chalk in water – a suspension. The lumps of particles are still big enough to be seen.

◄
The forces of attraction between the particles of solvent and solute determine if the solute will dissolve.

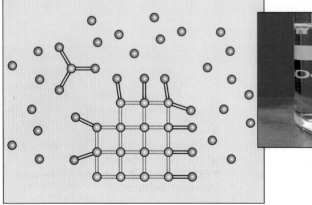

◄
Sugar solution. The separate particles are too small to be seen and are surrounded by water particles. The Latin word for water is aqua. When water is the solvent, the solution is called an aqueous solution. The symbol (aq) in a chemical equation means that the substance is dissolved in water.

Is this change reversible? If you evaporate the water slowly you get the sugar back. No new substances have been made. It is just a physical change.

Why is sugar soluble and chalk insoluble? Sugar particles are held together as a solid by forces of attraction. When the particles of water surround the particles of sugar, there is a very strong force of attraction between the water particles and the sugar particles. The sugar-water forces of attraction are stronger than the sugar-sugar forces of attraction. The particles of water have sufficient force to pull particles out of the solid structure.

This does not happen with chalk. The chalk-chalk forces of attraction are stronger than the chalk-water forces of attraction. So when chalk is put into water, it does not dissolve.

> If the solute-solute particle attractions are weaker than the solute-solvent particles attractions, the solute will dissolve

> If the solute-solute particle attractions are stronger than the solute-solvent particles attractions, the solute will not dissolve

Questions and Practice

9 The forces between particles of candle wax are stronger than the forces between the particles of margarine (both as solids). Is this true or false? Explain your answer.

10 When cooking fat is put into water are the solute–solvent forces stronger or weaker than the solute–solute forces? Explain your answer.

Explaining chemical changes

You have seen that when the fat is in liquid form the particles of the fat are sliding over one another. As the heat source is applied, energy is transferred to the particles and they break away from one another as a gas.

If too much energy is transferred to the particle then the strong bonds inside the particles can be broken too. When these strong bonds are broken the particle changes permanently. This is a chemical change. The fat particles break up to release different, smaller particles of gases - harmful fumes. The changed particles that are left behind form a new liquid. This is no longer cooking fat.

Inside the particles

You may already know that scientists talk about types of particles called **atoms** and **molecules**. A molecule is made from combinations of smaller particles called atoms. There are only one hundred or so different types of atoms, but there are billions of ways of joining them together into molecules.

When a molecule is broken up, what remains is a different molecule - a different substance. If you change how the atoms are linked, or bonded, together you produce a chemical change. These changes often involve energy transfers which affect the temperature of the chemicals involved. If a chemical is getting warmer or colder by itself, this is a good sign that a chemical reaction is happening. There are several different types of chemical reaction. The most common reactions involve gaining or losing atoms of oxygen.

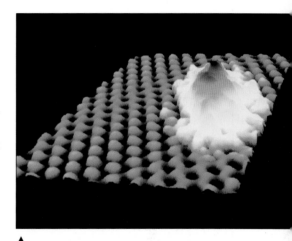

▲
Using powerful electron microscopes, we can detect individual atoms. This picture shows a clump of gold atoms (in yellow and brown) sitting on a graphite sheet – a layer of carbon atoms (in green).

▼
Molecules are particles made of atoms strongly bonded together. A molecule may have only two or three atoms bonded together, such as water, or a large number, like indigo – a molecule used for dyeing jeans.

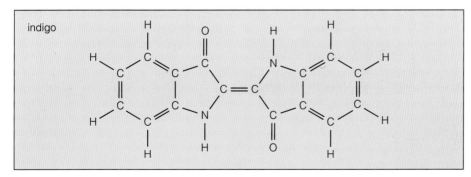

indigo

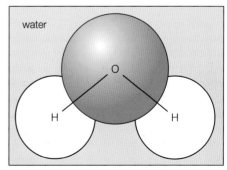

water

Gaining oxygen

There are several different names for the chemical reactions that involve the gaining of oxygen. These are:

- oxidation
- burning
- combustion
- respiration
- rusting

All these reactions are usually grouped together as **oxidation** reactions. Here are some common examples of oxidation reactions:

magnesium + oxygen → magnesium oxide

hydrogen + oxygen → water

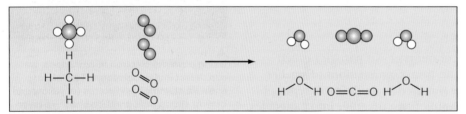

carbon + oxygen → carbon dioxide

methane + oxygen → carbon dioxide + water

glucose + oxygen → carbon dioxide + water

iron + water + oxygen → hydrated iron oxide (rust)

Losing oxygen

Substances that lose oxygen in chemical changes are said to be reduced. The process is called **reduction**.

Aluminium is used for drinks cans, window frames and aeroplane bodies. It is extracted from bauxite (aluminium oxide). The energy needed for this is provided by electricity. During the process aluminium loses oxygen. This is an example of reduction.

$$\text{aluminium oxide} \xrightarrow{\text{energy}} \text{aluminium + oxygen}$$

Decomposition

When some chemicals are heated the molecules break apart and rearrange themselves to make new chemicals. When chemicals break down into simpler substances they decompose. This is called a **decomposition** reaction.

Nitrates decompose on heating. This effect is used in fireworks. Nitrates of sodium or potassium decompose to give off oxygen. This oxygen is then used to help carbon and sulphur to burn to produce the gases that give the explosive power and thrust in firework rockets.

Questions and Practice

11 A distress flare can be made by using the reaction of magnesium burning in air.

   a Which gas in the air is needed to make the magnesium burn?

   b Is burning magnesium a chemical or physical change?

◄ **A bright magnesium flare, but what sort of reaction is this?**

   c From what you see when it is burning, do you think more energy is being transferred to the magnesium or being transferred to the surroundings?

12 A friend of yours describes some paper burning as 'the molecules of paper are burned up and disappear, producing heat and light'. What is wrong with this? How should it really be described? Explain what has really happened to the atoms that make up the paper.

▲ **Potassium nitrate gives a lilac colour to fireworks. Sodium nitrate produces the orange colour. Strontium turns the flames red and magnesium produces the brilliant white sparks.**

Measuring a rate of change

If you want to put out a pan of burning fat you have to stop the oxygen particles from colliding with the fat particles. The best way of doing this is to put a barrier between them, such as a fire blanket or a layer of foam from an extinguisher. Many reactions can not be stopped entirely, but they can be slowed down. We can change the rate of the reaction.

What is a rate? If you react chalk (calcium carbonate) with an acid, a reaction starts straight away:

   calcium carbonate + hydrochloric acid → calcium chloride +
                                                   carbon dioxide + water

A gas (carbon dioxide) is given off. If you choose suitable amounts of chalk and acid (the reactants) you can time how long it takes for this reaction to stop. You can measure the rate of reaction by measuring either how quickly the chalk or acid is used up, or how quickly carbon dioxide is produced.

Measuring the mass

If you mix the chalk and acid together in an open flask, the flask will get lighter as the carbon dioxide bubbles away. If you stand the flask on a mass balance, the reading on the balance will slowly go down. Finally, if you link the balance to a computer, the change in mass can be recorded and plotted on a graph automatically. The graph below is a plot of the results obtained such an experiment.

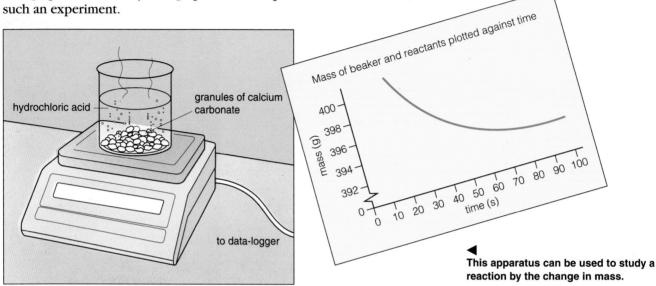

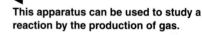

◄

This apparatus can be used to study a reaction by the change in mass.

After 90 seconds the reaction stops. No more gas is produced. This is because either the chalk or the acid has been used up. If there was too much chalk for the acid to react with, some would be left at the end of the experiment. This remaining chalk is called the 'excess'.

Measuring the volume

Alternatively, the change can be measured as the volume of gas produced, in cm^3 per second. The graph below is a plot of the volume of carbon dioxide gas given off every 10 seconds. Again, you can see that after 90 seconds no more carbon dioxide gas is given off.

◄

This apparatus can be used to study a reaction by the production of gas.

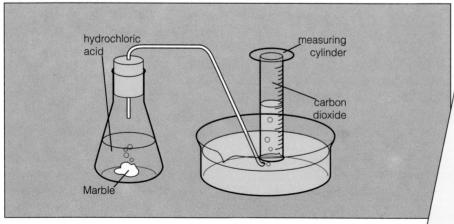

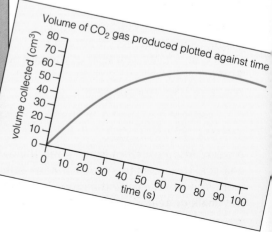

Notice how steep both graphs are at the beginning of the experiment. The rate of the reaction is fastest at the start. This is because there are more chalk and acid particles to react with each other.

Questions and Practice

13 The volume of carbon dioxide produced at 10 second intervals was measured and recorded in a table.

gas (cm³)	0	20	38	52	62	70	76	80	80	80
time (s)	0	10	20	30	40	50	60	70	80	90

   a How much carbon dioxide was given off in the first 10 seconds?

   b How long did it take to produce 62 cm³?

   c How much carbon dioxide was given off by the end of the reaction?

   d After how many seconds was the reaction finished?

14 **a** How much gas was produced between 40 and 50 seconds?

   b Compare your answer with that for the first 10 seconds. During which 10 second interval was most gas evolved?

   c Why was more gas evolved in this interval? Think about the amounts of reactants there are at each stage.

   d What was the average volume of gas evolved per second between 20 and 30 seconds?

Controlling change

Cooking is a chemical reaction. Food changes when it is cooked. Energy is transferred to the food and it changes. It is not easy to reverse the change – try unfrying an egg! How can you speed up the cooking process?

You can cook food at higher temperatures. Potato chips cook more quickly in hot oil at 200 °C than in hot water at 100 °C. You can cut food up into smaller pieces. Slices of carrots cook more quickly than whole carrots. People who make jam boil the sugar solution. The water evaporates and the sugar solution becomes more concentrated. The setting reaction then takes place more quickly.

There are six key factors that can change the rate of a reaction:

- temperature
- concentration (of a solution)
- surface area
- light
- using a **catalyst**
- pressure (of a gas)

▲
Slicing up food means that it will cook quicker.

Temperature

Another way of following the time that a reaction takes, is to follow a reaction that slowly produces a solid. This happens when you mix hydrochloric acid and sodium thiosulphate, a chemical used by photographers to 'fix' photographic prints.

79

Both hydrochloric acid and sodium thiosulphate are colourless solutions. As they react they produce fine particles of solid sulphur, which does not dissolve in water:

sodium thiosulphate + hydrochloric acid $\rightarrow$ sodium chloride + sulphur dioxide + water + sulphur

As the solid is produced it makes the previously clear solution cloudy. The speed of the reaction can be judged by timing how long it takes to obscure the view through the container. For example you could place a flask of the reactants on a piece of paper marked with a cross. You could even use a light sensor and data-logger, so that the rate of the whole reaction can be followed and graphed automatically.

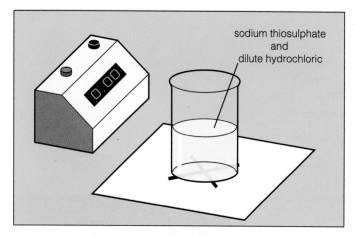

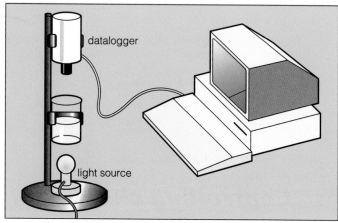

Let us look at the reaction at four different temperatures: 15 °C, 25 °C, 35 °C and 45 °C.

▲
Obscuring the cross and using a data-logger.

temperature (°C)	15	25	35	45
time (s)	600	300	150	75

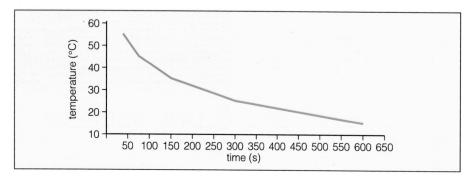

◄
Graph of the time taken to obscure the cross at different temperatures.

Concentration

It is not only the temperature of the fixing solution that photographers have to consider. They also have to take care when they make up the solution with water. They have to adjust the **concentration** of the solution carefully.

Scientists often talk about concentrated and dilute solutions. What do they mean? Some people like a spoonful of sugar in their tea. People with a sweet tooth might like four spoonfuls of sugar in their tea. The solution in this cup

A large can of fizzy drink contains ten spoonfuls of sugar. How many sugars would you put in a mug of tea or coffee to give it the same concentration of sugar?

is more concentrated because it has more spoonfuls per cup. Scientists use mass (in grams) instead of spoonfuls, and volume (in litres) instead of cups. Concentration is measured in grams per litre or more correctly grams per cubic decimetre (g dm^{-3}).

Using the same experiment you can look at the effects of changing the concentration of the sodium thiosulphate. This time the reactions must happen at the same temperature, but with different concentrations of sodium thiosulphate. You can change the concentration by simply making up a volume with water. As an example you could use: 20 cm^3 with no extra water; 15 cm^3 made up with 5 cm^3 of water; and 10 cm^3 diluted with 10 cm^3 water.

▼
Preparing solutions of different concentrations.

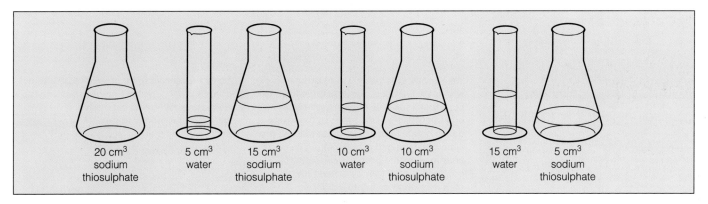

sodium thiosulphate (cm^3)	20	15	10	5
water (cm^3)	0	5	10	15
time (s)	30	60	100	400

▼
Graph of the time taken to obscure the cross using solutions of different concentrations.

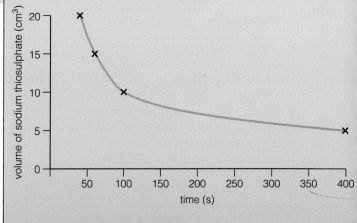

Questions and Practice

15 Look at the graph of the reaction between sodium thiosulphate and hydrochloric acid at four different temperatures (page 80). Predict how long it would take for the reaction to end at 55 °C?

16 Look at the graph of the reaction between sodium thiosulphate and hydrochloric acid at four different concentrations (page 81). Predict how long it would take for the reaction to end using a volume of 12.5 cm³?

17 A photographer wants to develop and fix a film. To get the best results the film must take 2 minutes 20 seconds to fix. He tries the reaction of the fixing solution at different temperatures. Here are his results:

temperature (°C)	20	30	40	50
time (s)	200	100	50	20

Draw a graph and find out which temperature is best for fixing the print.

18 The photographer now wants to develop and fix a film at room temperature. To get the best results the film must take 2 minutes 20 seconds to fix. He tries using the fixing solution but with different volumes of water added. Here are his results.

sodium thiosulphate (cm³)	10	20	30	40
water (cm³)	40	30	20	10
time (s)	250	170	100	20

Draw a graph and find out which concentration is best for fixing the print.

◀ **CAUSE**
We all want electricity and to drive cars whenever we need. To do that we have to burn fossil fuels. Burning fossil fuels creates waste gases. Some of the waste gases create acid rain. Marble statues are severely damaged by acid rain. The solutions to this problem are either to create less acid rain by driving fewer cars less often or to protect the statues.

▼ **EFFECT**
Marble statues can be protected by a thin coat of plastic, called Fomblin, but this is time-consuming and expensive. If there is only enough money to protect some statues each year, how might you go about choosing which to treat first?

Losing your marble

Many public buildings are built with marble fronts. Marble is severely damaged by acid rain because they react together. A scientist asked to investigate the extent of this problem in different areas would start by measuring the concentrations of the acid rain in each area. She could then react a mass of marble with acid of

p193

◄
Over 1500 buildings in Cracow, Poland, have been badly corroded by acid rain. Cracow is considered a World Heritage Site because of its many historic buildings. Only 80 buildings have been restored so far.

▼
Graphs of the loss of mass of marble over time.

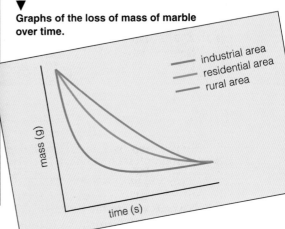

the measured concentrations and monitor the loss of mass. Here are the graphs of some sample results.

The rate that the marble reacts with acid from the industrial area is much faster than the rate with the acid from the other two areas. You can tell this from the slope of the graphs. The first graph is much steeper than the other two. Notice too that the *same mass* is lost by all three samples, but that the more concentrated the acid the *quicker* that mass is lost.

◄
Marble lumps, chips and powder. Which will react quicker?

▼
Graph to show the effect of using marble of different sized pieces.

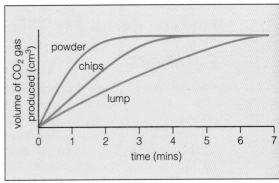

Surface area

The reaction of marble with acid is affected by another factor. The size of the marble lumps used would have to be controlled when testing the acid rain to make it a fair test. The same mass of marble can be measured as one large lump, several small lumps or as lots of powder.

If there is more than enough acid (an excess) to react with the mass of marble we always finish with the same amount of gas given off. However, the rate at which this gas is given off can change.

◄ Light starts a slow chemical reaction on photographic film.

▲ A very important photochemical reaction is photosynthesis. Green plants use light to chemically change water and carbon dioxide into sugars and starch.

Light

Photography uses light to speed up a chemical change. The chemicals that coat photographic film change because of a **photochemical reaction**.

In the upper atmosphere, another important photochemical reaction converts oxygen into a layer of ozone. Most people realise that the formation of this layer is vital to life on Earth as it protects us from the Sun's harmful ultraviolet rays. Unfortunately, manufactured chemicals are obstructing this reaction. Although many of the chemicals are useful, they are often used for unnecessary purposes.

Another chemical reaction that is faster in the presence of light is the break down of a chemical bleach used by hairdressers. Hydrogen peroxide is a colourless solution that decomposes to make water and oxygen:

hydrogen peroxide → water + oxygen

$$2H_2O_2 \rightarrow 2H_2O + O_2$$

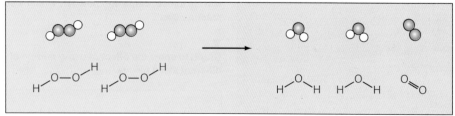

▼ Hydrogen peroxide decomposing with a catalyst.

Catalysts

A catalyst is a chemical that helps a chemical reaction go faster or slower, without being chemically changed when the reaction ends. Only small amounts of catalysts are usually needed.

Hydrogen peroxide decomposes quickly when a small amount of a black powder called manganese(IV) oxide is added. The black powder is a catalyst for this reaction. The same decomposition happens when potatoes or liver are added! This is because both of these things contain catalysts for this reaction too.

When living things change we say that a **biochemical reaction** has taken place. A biochemical catalyst is called an **enzyme.** Both the potato and the blood in the liver contain enzymes that allow the decomposition of hydrogen peroxide to take place. This is very useful as unwanted toxins would build up in our bodies if this biochemical reaction did not take place in our liver!

You may already know about the enzymes in digestive juices that help to break down nutrients in the digestive system, or the enzyme in yeast that is

p222

used in brewing and baking. Catalysts are very important in the chemical and biochemical industry. They speed up reactions so that chemicals can be produced more cheaply. This is why a lot of industrial research is devoted to discovering better catalysts. A particular reaction has a specific catalyst that will not usually work with any other reaction.

Another important use of catalysts is in the conversion of car exhaust gases to nitrogen, carbon dioxide and water. These catalysts are part of the 'catalytic converters' which are now being designed as part of the exhaust system of new cars. These will help to cut down the damage caused by too many cars on the road. The pollutant gases are converted to gases that are normally found in the air.

Catalysts are also important in the process of making ammonia, which is used to make fertilisers. This is called the Haber Process. You will find out more about this process in chapter 5.

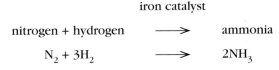

$$\text{nitrogen} + \text{hydrogen} \xrightarrow{\text{iron catalyst}} \text{ammonia}$$

$$N_2 + 3H_2 \longrightarrow 2NH_3$$

Pressure

In the Haber process two different gases are combined to make one gas. This reaction goes backwards as well as forwards – it is an example of a reversible chemical reaction. Both the backward and forward reaction get faster if you increase the pressure – but not by the same amount.

If you increase the pressure, the reaction that will reduce the pressure will speed up the most. In this case the 'forward' reaction producing ammonia speeds up more than the reaction producing nitrogen and hydrogen. This is because the forward reaction converts four volumes of gas into two volumes of gas, which reduces the pressure.

Questions and Practice

19 Examine the graphs of the corrosion of different sized marble chips (page 83). Which type of marble gives off gas at the quickest rate? Look at how steep the curve is at the start.

20 *a* Which photochemical reaction, used by plants, is vital to life on Earth?

    b Which chemical, produced by a photochemical reaction in the upper atmosphere, protects us from the Sun's more harmful rays?

    c Which chemicals are we using that interfere with that natural chemical process?

    d We use these new chemicals in three main ways. Suggest which use of them would do the most harm to the upper atmosphere: (i) as refrigerants in sealed tubes, (ii) as propellants in aerosols, (iii) as anaesthetics during operations. Give a reason for your suggestion.

21 **a** What is the difference between a catalyst and an enzyme?

   b What is the catalyst used in the Haber process?

22 **a** What is a molecule?

   Look back at the equation of the decomposition (breakdown) of hydrogen peroxide on page 84.

   b How many atoms are combined together to make one molecule of oxygen?

   c Which different types of atoms are combined to make hydrogen peroxide?

   d How many atoms are combined to make one molecule of hydrogen peroxide.

   e How many molecules of hydrogen peroxide break down (decompose) to make one molecule of oxygen?

23 The reaction of nitrogen oxide with oxygen to make nitrogen dioxide also depends on the pressure, much like the Haber process.

   $$2NO + O_2 \rightarrow 2NO_2$$

   Would the pressure need to be increased or decreased to make the forward reaction faster? Explain your answer.

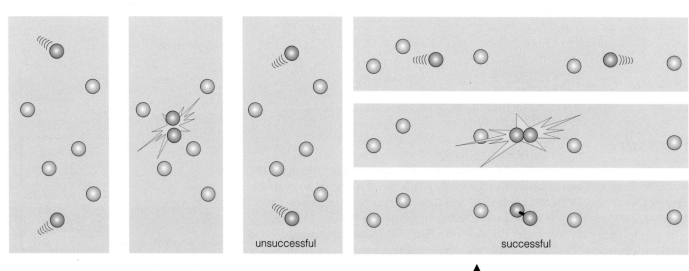

unsuccessful   successful

▲
Particles must collide with sufficient energy to make a successful collision.

Particles colliding

Why do reactions go faster if these key factors are altered? We need to imagine how these factors affect the particles involved.

   For a chemical reaction to happen the particles involved must collide. The collision also has to transfer enough energy for the reaction to be successful. If the energy transfer is not large enough the particles will just bounce off one another without the atoms rearranging into new substances.

Temperature

If you increase the temperature of a chemical you are transferring energy to it. This energy gives kinetic energy to the particles. So heating a chemical results in its particles moving faster. When particles are moving faster they collide more often and because they have more energy, it is more likely that the collision will lead to a reaction.

Concentration

If a dilute solution of acid reacts with marble, the particles of the acid must move through a collection of many particles of water. If the solution is more concentrated, but the volume is the same, then there are more particles of acid moving through fewer particles of water. This means that there is more chance of some acid particles colliding with particles of marble in a concentrated solution.

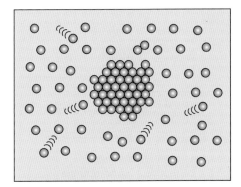 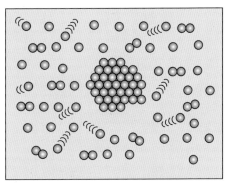

◄
More particles of acid collide with the marble in a concentrated solution than in a dilute solution. The fewer particles of acid must now move past particles of water to get to the marble.

After a while, many of the particles have reacted and changed. The concentration of the original particles has decreased. There is less chance of a successful collision so the rate of the reaction slows down.

Surface area

In this case we have to consider that the particles within a solid can't react until the particles at the surface have reacted and moved away. Think about an acid reacting with a chunk of chalk. If the chalk is in a solid cube, there are six sides for the acid particles to attack. If the cube of chalk is broken up into many smaller cubes, the particles on the surfaces of the small cubes that were inside the large cube are now open to attack. We have increased the area of the exposed surfaces. The bigger surface area is made up of many more particles so there is now more chance of collisions taking place.

Catalysts

Catalysts speed up (or slow down) reactions. If they increase the rate of reaction, time is saved. A catalyst often provides a surface where the particles can meet to react. Reactions on these surfaces need less energy transferred to make a collision successful. They often allow reactions to work at lower temperatures so fuel is saved. There is then less problem of pollution from using fossil fuels.

Both of these savings are very important to industry. Around 90% of all manufactured items use catalysts at some stage in their production. If we wish to continue using the benefits of new materials on a large scale, we need to minimize any problems caused by making them and produce them economically.

Pressure

Increasing the pressure of a gas means that the particles of the gas are closer together in a smaller volume. This is like increasing the concentration in a solution. The particles are closer together, so there is more chance of successful collisions. The rate of the reaction increases.

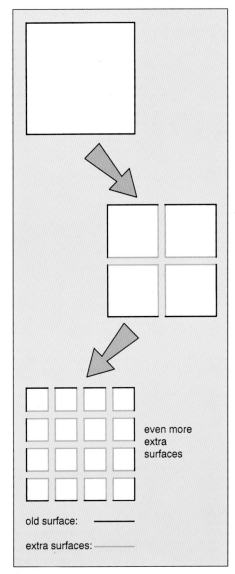

even more
extra
surfaces

old surface: ———

extra surfaces: ———

▲
On a large lump the acid can only attack the outside area. If the lump is broken down the 'inside' surfaces can also be attacked.

Examination Questions

Credit

1 A lump of marble is put into hydrochloric acid. Carbon dioxide is formed. The table shows the total carbon dioxide formed during the first 7 minutes.

carbon dioxide (cm³)							
0	18	34	48	60	66	66	66

time (minutes)							
0	1	2	3	4	5	6	7

a The reaction stops after five minutes. How do you know this? Use the table to help you explain. [1]
b At the end of the reaction most of the lump of marble is still there. Why did the reaction stop? [1]
c You do the experiment again. This time you want the reaction to go faster. What could you do to the lump of marble to make the reaction go faster? [1]

2 **a** Look at the table below. It shows three ways of changing the speed of the reaction between marble and hydrochloric acid. Draw and complete the table. Choose from: goes faster; slows down; no change. [3]

Method	Effect
increasing the temperature	
diluting the acid with water	
adding a catalyst	

b Some chemical reactions need light to start them. Write down one example. [1]

Merit

3 When a lump of marble is put into hydrochloric acid, carbon dioxide is formed. The graph shows the total volume of carbon dioxide formed at different times. Most of the marble is left at the end of the experiment.

a What is the total volume of carbon dioxide formed by the end of the reaction? [1]
b When is it quickest: 0–2 minutes, 2–4 minutes, 4–6 minutes or 6–8 minutes? Explain your answer. [2]

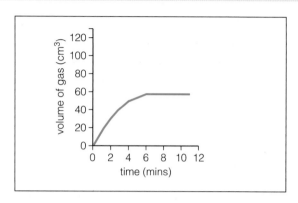

c The experiment is done again at a higher temperature. Sketch the current graph and add the new line you would expect to get. Label the line 'A'. [2]
d The experiment is done a third time. The quantity of marble is the same. The temperature is the same as the first experiment. Double the volume of acid is used. Most of the marble is left at the end of the experiment. On your graph draw the shape of the graph you would expect this time. Label your line 'B'. [2]

Special

4 In question 3, the reaction mixture could be changed to increase the rate of reaction. Explain clearly, in terms of the particles present, why the rate of reaction is increased when: (i) increasing the concentration; (ii) increasing the temperature; (iii) breaking the marble into smaller pieces. [6]

5 **a** Yeast must be added to glucose in order for fermentation to occur. Explain why. [2]
b If the temperature is increased to 70 °C the reaction slows down then stops. Explain why this happens. [2]
c An increase in temperature from 25 °C to 30 °C will increase this rate of reaction. Explain this using the idea of collisions between particles. [2]

[Adapted from the Terminal Examination, 1995.]

Checklist

The facts and ideas that you should understand by studying this topic.

To qualify at Credit level you should:
- know that solids, liquids and gases are made up of particles
- know that particles of a solid are closer together than particles of a gas
- know that particles of a gas move faster than particles of a solid
- know that freezing changes liquids to solids, melting changes solids to liquids, boiling changes liquids to gases, and condensing changes gases to liquids
- know that water dissolves many chemicals
- know that physical changes, such as melting ice, do not make new substances
- understand that chemical changes make new materials and usually involve an energy transfer
- recognise the reactants and products in a chemical word equation
- know that reactions stop when one of the reactants is used up
- know that reactions go faster when using a catalyst, or increasing the temperature, or when increasing the concentration or surface area of the reactants.

To qualify at Merit level you should:
- be able to draw the arrangement of particles in a solid, liquid and gas
- be able to describe the changes of the movement and arrangement of particles during freezing, melting, boiling and condensing
- know that a solution is made up of a solute and a solvent
- know that in a solution, solvent particles surround particles in the solid and remove them from the solid structure
- be able to construct a word equation, knowing the reactants and the products
- know that a collision between particles must take place for a chemical change to happen
- know that an increase in concentration makes particles more crowded
- know that small amounts of catalysts can be used to speed up reactions
- be able to interpret graphs of reaction rates.

To qualify at Special level you should:
- understand changes of state using the idea of forces between particles
- know why some solids will not dissolve because the forces between the particles of the solute are stronger than the forces between the solute and the solvent
- know how to construct symbol equations given the formulae of the reactants and products
- know that increasing the frequency of effective collisions between particles will increase the rate of reaction
- know that higher temperatures result in more effective collisions between particles
- know that increasing the concentration increases the frequency of collisions between particles
- know that a catalyst is specific to a particular reaction.

GCSE FOUNDATION TIER

GCSE HIGHER TIER

Key words from this topic:

particle

solvent

solute

oxidation

reduction

rate

excess

reactants

products

catalyst

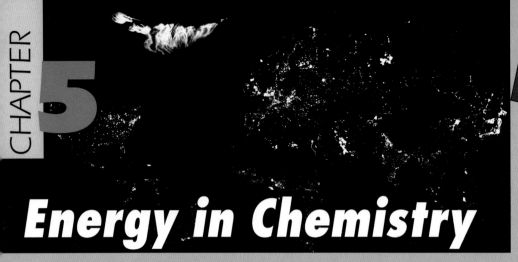

CHAPTER 5

Energy in Chemistry

◀ Highways and railroads spread a network of light pollution across the planet. The aurora provide the only natural light on the night side of Earth. Most of the light you can see here represents wasted energy obtained by burning fossil fuels. You can even see the gas flares burning on oil wells in the Middle East.

Energy is in demand. You use it for cooking, lighting and heating your homes. Travelling for leisure and transporting goods around for business uses a lot of energy. It takes a lot of energy in factories to make the things you use everyday. Some countries use more energy per person than others. Do these people need more energy than the rest? Should we worry about this?

We get most of our energy by burning fossil fuels – fuels that have been buried for millions of years. Even 'clean' electricity is generated mainly in power stations that burn coal, oil and gas. Fossil fuels have the advantage of high energy values per kilogram and, unlike nuclear fuels, are easy to carry around. But they also cause acid rain and produce the 'greenhouse gases' that could cause global warming. There is also the problem that these

fuels can not be replaced as quickly as they are burned.

Fuels have an enormous impact on the quality of all our lives; we have a choice of the type and amount of fuel we want to use. But these are important choices. We must look at wider and more detailed issues, not just our immediate short-term comfort, before we choose.

Energy used by each person in a year (x 10^{11} J)

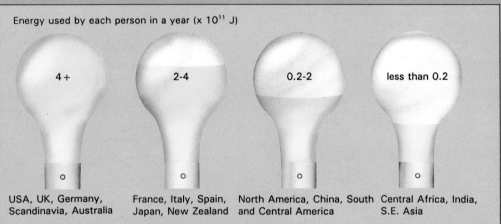

4 +	2-4	0.2-2	less than 0.2
USA, UK, Germany, Scandinavia, Australia	France, Italy, Spain, Japan, New Zealand	North America, China, South and Central America	Central Africa, India, S.E. Asia

▼ The huge amount of fuel needed by this plane can cause unwanted problems.

▲ People in different countries around the world use different amounts of energy.

▶ What makes a good fuel?

▼ Electricity may be clean and convenient in your home, but it still relies on burning fossil fuels.

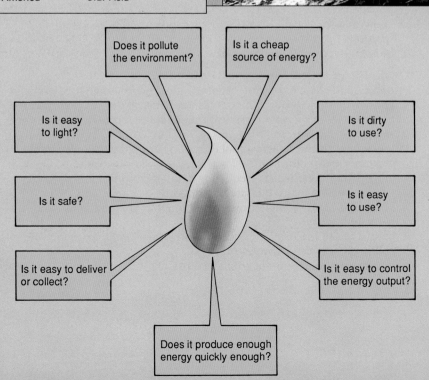

Does it pollute the environment?

Is it a cheap source of energy?

Is it easy to light?

Is it dirty to use?

Is it safe?

Is it easy to use?

Is it easy to deliver or collect?

Is it easy to control the energy output?

Does it produce enough energy quickly enough?

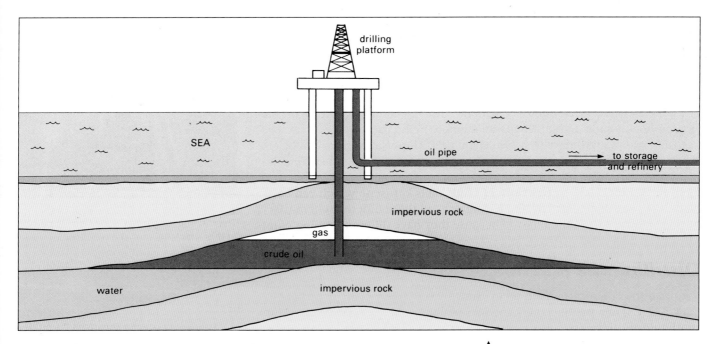

▲
An oil rig has to dig through deep layers of rock.

Getting fossil fuels

Millions of years ago tiny animals died and decayed. Their remains were pressed together under layers of rock and would have become fossils, but instead, became a sticky, dark liquid known as crude oil.

Crude oil is often found buried deep underground. Deep rocks need to be drilled through to get it out. Once it is taken out (extracted) from these areas, it is gone forever. It is a *finite resource*. It would take millions of years to make it again so we must not waste this valuable resource.

Natural gas, called methane, is also a fossil fuel. It often forms in a pocket above the oil deposit, trapped between the oil and a layer of **impervious rock**. Impervious rock does not let water or gas through.

Coal is also a fossil fuel. It is made from the remains of dead plants. These plants used energy from the Sun to make sugars by **photosynthesis**. These plants did not decay but were compressed into coal. The energy 'locked' in as stored energy can be released by burning the coal in the oxygen of the air. Once coal is mined it will take millions of years to replace, so it too is a finite resource.

▲
Drilling for oil on land, in Wytch Farm, Dorset.

Non-renewable fuels

People are often confused about the term 'non-renewable'. It does not mean 'it cannot be used again'. When wood burns, it turns to ash. That piece of wood cannot be used again, but it is still a renewable fuel because you can easily grow another tree.

Trees can be burned as wood and new trees can be planted and grown within a fairly short space of time. But if the trees were to die, fall into a swamp, be compressed and turn into coal it would take millions of years. Coal is a non-renewable fuel.

91

Making the most of fossil fuels

R
p213

Coal is a valuable resource that contains many useful chemicals. These chemicals produce a lot of damaging waste gases when they are burned. This is why coal is often turned into coke, by removing some of the chemicals. The coke is then burned in power stations with less damaging effects on the environment. Crude oil is also separated before being used.

Crude oil is a mixture of over 500 chemicals. These substances can be separated as they are only mixed together and not bonded together. Petrol (gasoline), diesel and butane gas are just some of the ingredients in this mixture. Another part, or **fraction**, of crude oil is kerosene which can be made into aircraft fuel or paraffin. Fortunately, all these different chemicals can be separated from the mixture because they have different boiling points.

▲
The fractionating tower dominates the view of this 'cracking' unit at a refinery.

Distilling the fractions

Nearly all the chemicals mixed up in crude oil boil at temperatures lower than 500 °C. Only the thick tar known as bitumen and a fuel oil used in ships stay liquid at this temperature.

▼
A fractionating column separates the crude oil mixture in to many useful fractions.

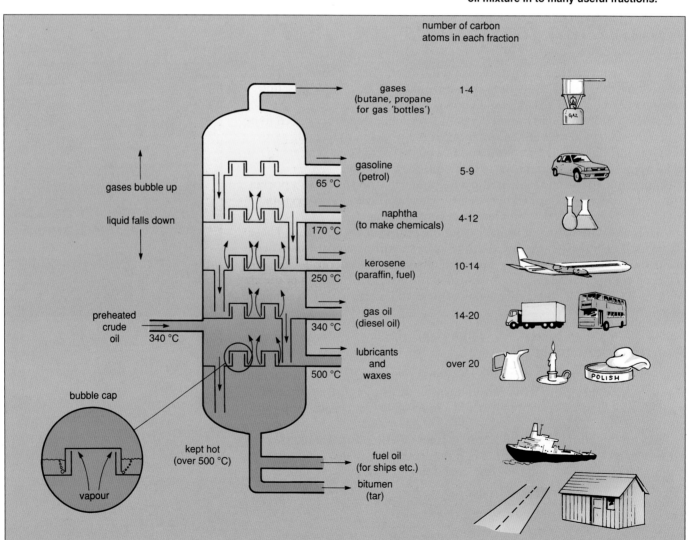

number of carbon atoms in each fraction

gases (butane, propane for gas 'bottles') 1–4

gasoline (petrol) 5–9 65 °C

naphtha (to make chemicals) 4–12 170 °C

kerosene (paraffin, fuel) 10–14 250 °C

gas oil (diesel oil) 14–20 340 °C

lubricants and waxes over 20 500 °C

gases bubble up

liquid falls down

preheated crude oil 340 °C

bubble cap

vapour

kept hot (over 500 °C)

fuel oil (for ships etc.)

bitumen (tar)

To start the separation, crude oil is heated at the bottom of a tall tower. Most of the fractions boil and turn into vapour. The vapour mixture rises up through the tower which is divided up into different stages. Each stage has a set temperature that is cooler than the one below it.

As the vapour rises it is forced at each stage to go through gaps called *bubble caps*. The first set of bubble caps is at a temperature of about 480 °C. Some parts of the vapour condense on these bubble caps and run off as liquids. These liquids have boiling points around 480–500 °C.

The parts of the vapour that did not condense continue to rise up the tower to the next stage. Gasoline is the fraction that boils at the lowest temperature, so it stays as a vapour at lower temperatures. It condenses in the coolest part of the tower near the top.

Temperaure (°C)	Fraction of crude oil
20–65	gasoline (petrol)
65–170	naphtha (to make chemicals)
170–250	kerosene (paraffin, fuel)
250–340	gas oil (diesel oil)

You probably know that the process of evaporation followed by condensation is called distillation. This process of distilling fractions at different heights and temperatures in the tower is called **fractional distillation**. The tower is called a **fractionating column**.

Questions and Practice

1 Describe in your own words how the energy from the Sun was locked into crude oil.

2 Look at the diagram of the fractionating column. What is the boiling point of kerosene?

3 The fraction boiling at 170 °C is not used to make fuel, but is used to make chemicals. What is the main component of this fraction?

Why does fractional distillation work?

Crude oil fractions are easy to separate because they have different boiling points. Why do they have different boiling points? You can see why if you use the theory that matter is made of particles.

You may remember that all matter is made up of small particles called **atoms**. Atoms bonded together make up larger particles called **molecules**. The fractions of crude oil are made of different molecules that have one thing in common: they are made of only carbon and hydrogen atoms. Chemicals like this are called **hydrocarbons**.

Hydrocarbons can have any number of carbon and hydrogen atoms. Fractions from crude oil are mostly a type of hydrocarbon called **alkanes**. The alkanes are a series of molecules made up of long chains of carbon atoms bonded to each other, such as octane (eight carbon atoms) and heptane (seven carbon atoms). Each molecule in the series has one more carbon atom and two more hydrogen atoms (CH_2) than the last one.

93

The **intramolecular** bonds between carbon and hydrogen atoms *within* the molecule are strong. The **intermolecular** forces *between* the separate hydrocarbon molecules are weak. Forces between small hydrocarbon molecules are even weaker than those between larger hydrocarbon molecules. So less energy is needed to separate the smaller hydrocarbon molecules.

A liquid boils when its molecules have so much **kinetic energy** (movement energy) that they can break free of the forces between the separate molecules and spread out as a gas. So a collection of large hydrocarbon molecules will boil at a higher temperature than a collection of small hydrocarbon molecules.

> Large hydrocarbon molecules have large forces between them. The fraction has a high boiling point.

> Small hydrocarbon molecules have small forces between them. The fraction has a low boiling point.

In the fractionating column, the molecules that have sufficient kinetic energy to be part of the vapour move up the tower until they hit the bubble cap surfaces. The bubble caps are only *slightly* colder than the stage below, so only the larger molecules will lose enough kinetic energy to change state. This collection of molecules will then condense to form a liquid that is run off from the tower. The smaller hydrocarbon molecules will still have enough kinetic energy to remain part of the vapour that continues up through the tower. This continues up through the tower, each stage 'catching' molecules of a certain size.

Questions and Practice

4 Look at the diagrams of heptane and octane.

   a How many carbon atoms does heptane have?

   b What is the chemical formula of octane?

5 Molecules of octane have both intermolecular and intramolecular bonds. Which are stronger? (Look in the glossary to remind yourself if you have forgotten what these words mean.)

Burning hydrocarbons

Fuels burn in the air, sometimes out of control, as in a forest fire, sometimes in a controlled way, as in a fuel injection car engine. However, not all the air is used for burning.

Air is a mixture of gases. Nitrogen is the most abundant gas in the air. Oxygen is the gas needed for burning (**combustion**) – it makes up 20% of the air. When chemicals combine with oxygen to make oxides it is called an **oxidation** reaction.

When pure hydrocarbon fuels burn completely in oxygen they make two new chemicals. These are carbon dioxide and water. If carbon on its own burns in oxygen it burns to give carbon dioxide:

$$\text{carbon} + \text{oxygen} \rightarrow \text{carbon dioxide}$$

$$C + O_2 \rightarrow CO_2$$

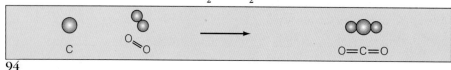

▼
The gases that make up the atmosphere.

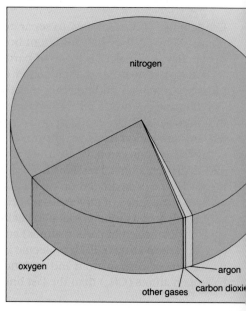

If hydrogen gas burns on its own the product is an oxide of hydrogen: water!

$$\text{hydrogen} + \text{oxygen} \rightarrow \text{water}$$

$$2H_2 + O_2 \rightarrow 2H_2O$$

Hydrocarbons contain only carbon and hydrogen atoms. The carbon and hydrogen atoms are strongly bonded together. When hydrocarbons burn, they react with oxygen. The carbon does not bond to the hydrogen any more but bonds instead with oxygen to make carbon dioxide. The hydrogen does not bond to the carbon any more but bonds instead with oxygen to make water.

The **complete combustion** of hydrocarbon fuel produces carbon dioxide and water as products:

$$\text{hydrocarbon fuel} + \text{oxygen} \rightarrow \text{carbon dioxide} + \text{water}$$

$$CH_4 + 2O_2 \rightarrow CO_2 + 2H_2O$$

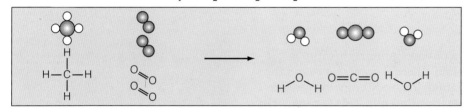

◀ CH_4 is the hydrocarbon called methane (commonly known as natural gas).

$$C_3H_8 + 5O_2 \rightarrow 3CO_2 \rightarrow + 4H_2O$$

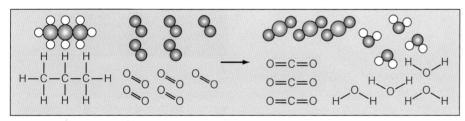

◀ C_3H_8 is the hydrocarbon called propane (used as bottled camping gas).

Questions and Practice

6 a What is the proportion of oxygen in the air ?

b What is the proportion of carbon dioxide in the air?

7 a Use your library to find out how the mixture of air is separated into pure oxygen and pure nitrogen.

b In which ways is this process similar to separating crude oil?

c In which ways is it different?

8 Why are two molecules of oxygen needed to burn one molecule of methane?

Maintaining the atmosphere

When the Earth was formed, about 4.5 billion years ago, it was covered by a sea of molten rock. The atmosphere was a mixture of methane, nitrogen, hydrogen, carbon dioxide and water vapour. As the Earth cooled, liquid water

R p226

R p230

R p226 p227

was formed and the **water cycle** began. At this time there was no oxygen in the atmosphere. Then life began in the oceans, and green plants started to use up carbon dioxide in **photosynthesis**. A waste product of photosynthesis is oxygen. By the time green plants had finished spreading over the land (about 400 million years ago) the atmosphere contained about as much oxygen as it does today – 20 per cent. The rest is mostly nitrogen, which is not chemically very active. Nearly all the carbon dioxide has disappeared – it is now stored in carbonate rocks like chalk and limestone.

At present there is a balance between the production of carbon dioxide by decay processes and respiration and its removal by photosynthesis. This process keeps carbon dioxide and oxygen levels nearly constant. If burning uses up oxygen to make it into carbon dioxide and water where do we get new oxygen from? As oxygen is being used up in one reaction it must be being generated by another reaction. This chemical cycle happens on a global scale. You may already know how many separate parts of this cycle work in the **oxygen cycle** and **carbon cycle**. Scientists are still piecing together the whole story of these cycles. The 'appearance' and 'disappearance' of carbon dioxide in our atmosphere is still not entirely understood.

Oxygen to carbon dioxide

Respiration converts oxygen into carbon dioxide. Animals breathe in oxygen, it passes through to the bloodstream where it is carried round the body to where it is needed. During respiration, the body converts oxygen into carbon dioxide, which the animal then breathes out. This is detailed in chapter 7. Combustion is also a process that uses oxygen in a chemical change to produce carbon dioxide. Plants also need to use oxygen to stay alive, but they also generate oxygen.

Carbon dioxide to oxygen

Photosynthesis is the process that plants use to make oxygen from carbon dioxide. To maintain the atmosphere, there must be enough plants to undergo photosynthesis. This is why, when we cut down large areas of forest, they should be replaced by a managed programme of replanting.

▲ We need plants for food, fuel, materials for building, paper and many other uses, but we must be careful to replant the trees so necessary to maintain the oxygen cycle.

Where has all the carbon gone?

Debora MacKenzie

FORESTS of conifers cover 1·2 billion hectares of Alaska, Canada, Scandinavia and Russia. This is the great boreal belt of northern woodland, which represents a quarter of the world's forests. Boreal forest takes up more land than any other type of biological community, and for the most part it has been little affected by human activity. Now scientists claim that the boreal forest, and the smaller belt of temperate forest below it, is the key to one of the great mysteries of climate research.

When fossil fuels are burnt they release CO_2 into the atmosphere, where it can influence the world's climate. Most of this CO_2 remains in the air or is absorbed by the sea. But fossil fuels produce more CO_2 than can be accounted for in this way, a discrepancy that has puzzled scientists for decades. CO_2 in the atmosphere has

The sea and air store most of the carbon dioxide released by fossil fuels. Now scientists think they know what has happened to the rest

risen from a fairly constant 280 parts per million in the preindustrial period before 1700, to 355 parts per million today. Substantial though this increase is, the amount of CO_2 produced by burning fossil fuels should have resulted in a much more marked increase in atmospheric CO_2, even when increased absorption by the sea is taken into account.

Where has the missing carbon gone? Into the northern forests, says Allan Auclair, a plant ecologist working with the environmental consultancy Science and Policy Associates in Washington DC. F

▲ Scientists are still piecing together the details of the carbon cycle. This article from *New Scientist* magazine (January 1994) described the latest theory.

The problems of burning fuel

Burning fuel in one country can affect people in distant countries. There has been an enormous increase in the use of electricity, petrol, diesel and aviation fuel in the last 70 years. In Great Britain most electricity is generated by burning fossil fuels. The problem is that the products of all this combustion are not just carbon dioxide and water. There are also many impurities in the fuels which can burn to make harmful gases.

Carbon monoxide and soot

When we take oxygen in through the lungs into the blood stream it has to be taken to the brain as well as the muscles. The way it is transported is that it bonds weakly to an iron atom in the middle of a complex molecule called **haemoglobin**. The haemoglobin takes the oxygen to the brain where it is used. Carbon monoxide also fits neatly into this special site and can attach itself four times faster than oxygen can. This means that when the haemoglobin travels to the brain, carbon monoxide, not oxygen, is taken. The brain cells then begin to die.

If carbon monoxide is made during burning instead of carbon dioxide, then the process is called **incomplete combustion**:

$$2CH_4 \quad + \quad 3O_2 \quad \rightarrow \quad 2CO \quad + \quad 4H_2O$$
methane   oxygen   carbon monoxide   water

Soot can also be made during incomplete combustion:

$$CH_4 \quad + \quad O_2 \quad \rightarrow \quad C \quad + \quad 2H_2O$$
methane   oxygen   carbon   water

Soot is mostly carbon and causes buildings to become coated with a dark layer of deposit. Many buildings which became coated have now been cleaned, because there is now a better chance that they will stay clean. This is because the levels of soot, which became a problem at the start of the Industrial Revolution, have now been reduced since the passing of the Clean Air Act in 1957.

Sulphur and acid rain

Buildings made of limestone are still being damaged by sulphur dioxide. Sulphur is an impurity in many fossil fuels that burns in oxygen to make sulphur dioxide. Sulphur dioxide causes acid rain.

Limestone reacts with acid rain and corrodes to a crumbly powder. Acid rain can also damage trees and kill fish. Sulphur dioxide in the air may also be a problem to people with asthma or other breathing difficulties.

Acid rain is a combination of acids, including sulphuric acid. This is made when sulphur dioxide combines with more oxygen and water.

$$2SO_2 \quad + \quad O_2 \quad + \quad 2H_2O \quad \rightarrow \quad 2H_2SO_4$$
sulphur dioxide   oxygen   water   sulphuric acid

Rain is naturally a little acidic. Carbon dioxide in the air dissolves in water to make a weak acid, carbonic acid. Some sulphur dioxide is always present in the atmosphere, produced by natural volcanic action. It is the extra sulphur dioxide that we are producing that is a problem.

Acid rain also includes the solutions of oxides of nitrogen (the so-called

▲
'Peasoup fogs' are a thing of the past. Towns and cities are now cleaner places because of smokeless fuels. We now have fumes from traffic instead.

97

Dumping limestone into an acid lake to neutralise the water.

Fish in some lakes are not affected because the rock that the lake is on is limestone. Acid reacts with limestone to make a neutral environment. So far evidence suggests that fish in lakes on clay soil are damaged because the acid leaches aluminium out of the soil into the lake, which the fish cannot tolerate.

Drax power station in North Yorkshire is the first in Britain to be fitted with a 'Flue Gas Desulphurisation Plant' (FGD). This £650 million project aims to catch 90% of the sulphur dioxide emitted. The process produces a large amounts of calcium sulphate (gypsum), which can be used in the construction industry.

NOx gases). These are produced in the exhaust fumes of cars and aeroplanes. Catalytic converters reduce the nitrogen oxides to nitrogen, which is an unreactive gas, and will not dissolve to cause acid rain.

The production of acid rain caused by the burning of fossil fuels is not just a local problem - it is a global problem. Sulphur dioxide gas may travel hundreds of miles from where it is made, so its effects may be felt far away. Forests may be destroyed in one country by the effects of the sulphur dioxide produced by neighbouring countries. Fish can be killed in a lake by the burning of fossil fuels in electrical power stations in a country far away.

Carbon dioxide

Carbon dioxide in the atmosphere enables energy from the Sun to be trapped as heat instead of reflecting straight back into space - this is the **greenhouse effect**. If there is too much carbon dioxide in the Earth's atmosphere, there will be a greater effect, trapping more heat. The increased temperature could eventually cause the polar ice caps to melt and the sea level may rise.

p216
p217

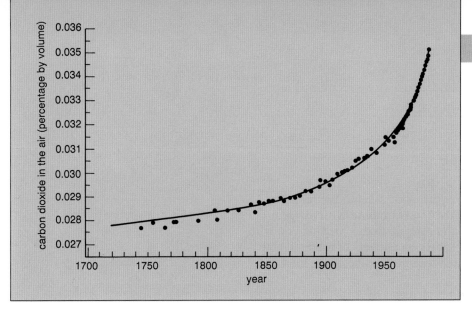

◀
The increase in carbon dioxide in the air since 1700.

▼
A natural chemical reaction in this beetle releases energy in the form of light. The beetle can control the light – flashing it on and off – by controlling the amount of air involved in the reaction. During the mating season, the beetle will use this flashing light to attract mates.

Many people get confused about the various types of pollution of the atmosphere. Burning fossil fuels does not cause the hole in the ozone layer!

Many people think that the only real way to minimize the greenhouse effect is to produce less carbon dioxide. However, there are a number of different 'greenhouse gases' and some scientists are not sure that global warming is happening. Nevertheless, many scientists believe that it is still important to reduce the levels of sulphur dioxide and extra carbon dioxide in the atmosphere by burning less fossil fuel.

Transferring energy in chemical reactions

When fossil fuels burn the surroundings get hot. This is a good example of energy transfer during a chemical reaction. The energy is released when hydrocarbons combine with oxygen during combustion. The temperature increases.

During a chemical reaction energy is always involved. Reactions that transfer energy to the surroundings are called **exothermic** reactions. Sometimes the energy transfer may be noticed as a decrease in temperature. In this case the energy has been taken in from the surroundings. Reactions that transfer energy in from the surroundings are called **endothermic** reactions.

Most chemical reactions transfer energy. The energy released in exothermic reactions can: appear as light, heat the surroundings or drive an electric current.

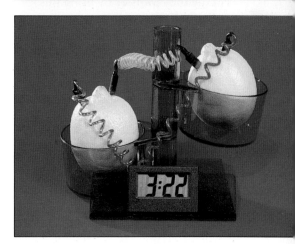

▲
The chemical reaction in the lemons produces a voltage, releasing enough energy to power this clock.

Electricity from chemical reactions

A simple cell can be made by dipping two different metals into a solution which conducts electricity (an **electrolyte**). The size of the voltage produced

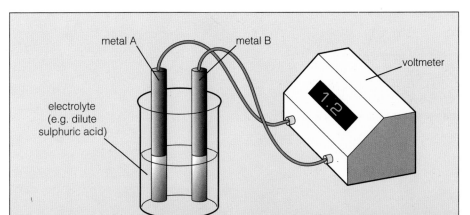

Metal A	Metal B	Voltage (volts)
copper	zinc	1.1
copper	magnesium	2.7
silver	copper	0.4
zinc	magnesium	1.6

◀
A simple electrical cell.

99

depends on the **reactivity** of the metals used. Reactivity is examined more
closely in chapter 6.

Comparing fuels

You get your energy from the food that you eat. Food is a kind of fuel. The
energy is released when the chemicals in the food combine with oxygen
during **respiration** (see chapter 7). Fats and carbohydrates provide you with
more energy than vitamins and minerals. Labels on packets of food tell you
how many **joules** (J) or kilojoules (kJ) each hundred grams of the food will
provide.

What can *one* joule do? If 1 gram of water heats up by 1 °C it has had 4.2 J
of energy transferred to it. If 10 grams of water heats up by 1 °C it has had
42 J of energy transferred it. If 10 grams of water was heated up by 2 °C we
will have transferred 84 J to the water. The energy transferred is calculated
using the formula:

energy transferred to the water = mass of water × 4.2 × temperature change

$$= 10 \times 4.2 \times 2 = 84 \text{ J}$$

If you use two different fuels to heat water you can compare how much
energy they transfer by using this formula. The constant value of 4.2 is the
specific heat capacity of water in joules per gram per degree Celsius.

Questions and Practice

9 Look at the diagrams and the table of results.

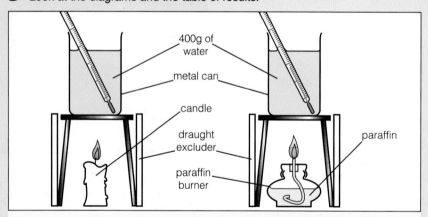

	candle	*paraffin burner*
mass before	25.3 g	80.1 g
mass after	23.8 g	78.0 g
mass burned	1.5 g	2.1 g
water temperature before	20 °C	20 °C
water temperature after	50 °C	70 °C

a What rise in temperature of the water did the candle produce?

b How much energy did the candle transfer to the water?

c What rise in temperature of the water did the paraffin produce?

d How much energy did the paraffin transfer to the water?

e Which fuel transferred more energy per gram of fuel? Explain your answer.

Some fuels transfer more energy than others

You should now be familiar with the theory that everything is made up of small particles called atoms, and that molecules are made up of two or more atoms strongly bonded together. How does this theory explain the differences between fuels?

Remember that fossil fuels are mostly hydrocarbons and that hydrocarbons are molecules made up of only carbon and hydrogen atoms. When hydrocarbon fuels burn they react with oxygen to produce carbon dioxide and water:

propane + oxygen $\rightarrow$ carbon dioxide + water

$$C_3H_8 + 5O_2 \rightarrow 3CO_2 + 4H_2O$$

For this chemical reaction to go ahead the bonds between the carbon and hydrogen atoms in propane must be broken. The bond between the oxygen atoms in the oxygen molecule must also be broken. To do this, energy must be transferred into the molecule.

Breaking bonds needs energy put in.

Making bonds gives energy out.

When the new bonds are made between the carbon and the oxygen atoms in carbon dioxide, energy is transferred out of the molecule. Energy is also transferred out when hydrogen atoms join oxygen atoms to make water molecules.

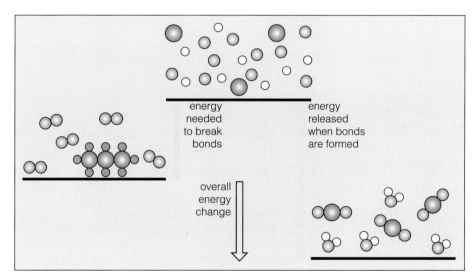

energy needed to break bonds

energy released when bonds are formed

overall energy change

◀
The two stages of a chemical reaction – breaking old bonds and making new bonds.

If energy is transferred in as well as out during the burning of propane, why do the surroundings get hotter? This is because there is more energy transferred out during the bond making process than there is energy transferred in during the bond breaking process. Overall the reaction is exothermic.

A reaction is endothermic if there is more energy transferred in during the bond breaking process than there is energy transferred out during the bond making process.

▲
Some fuels transfer energy in more interesting ways.

101

Examination Questions

Credit

1 For each reaction below, how does the stored chemical energy appear when released. Choose from: heat; light; sound; electricity.

   a Burning natural gas in an oven. [1 mark]
   b Reaction in a car battery. [1]
   c Firing a starting pistol. [1]
   d Burning magnesium. [1]

2 Some cars in Brazil use pure alcohol as a fuel instead of petrol. Petrol is a hydrocarbon made from crude oil. Crude oil is a fossil fuel. Fossil fuels will not last forever. Some fossil fuels contain sulphur. When the fuels burn, sulphur dioxide is made.

   a What does the word *hydrocarbon* mean? [1]
   b Write down the names of two other fossil fuels. [2]
   c Write down the names of two chemicals, other than fuels, that can be made from crude oil. [2]
   d Explain why fossil fuels will run out. [1]
   e Suggest one disadvantage of making sulphur dioxide. [1]

Merit

3 When petrol is burned in oxygen, carbon dioxide and water are formed. This involves a process known as oxidation. Sometimes when petrol burns, there is not enough oxygen. If this happens, carbon monoxide is formed instead of carbon dioxide.

   a Write a word equation for the usual reaction between petrol and oxygen. [2]
   b What does the word *oxidation* mean? [1]
   c Suggest one disadvantage of producing carbon monoxide. [1]
   d Increasing amounts of carbon dioxide may be harmful to the environment. Explain why. [1]

Special

4 When chemical reactions take place, some chemical bonds are broken and others are formed. Energy transfers happen during the making and breaking of chemical bonds. As methane burns energy is transferred to the surroundings as heat.

   a Explain why a flame or spark is needed to start the methane burning. [1]
   b Explain why energy is transferred to heat the surroundings when methane burns. Name this type of reaction. [3]

5 Two fuels, methane and butane, were used to heat some water using a Bunsen burner. The following results were obtained:

	methane	*butane*
mass of water used	100 g	100 g
final temperature of water	86 °C	95 °C
initial temperature of water	20 °C	20 °C
mass of fuel burned	0.5 g	0.25 g

The specific heat capacity of water is 4.2 J/(g °C). For butane the energy transferred when 0.25 g of butane burns is $100 \times 4.2 \times 75 = 31\ 500$ J

   a Calculate the energy transferred when 0.5 g of methane burns. [1]
   b Which of the two fuels transfers more energy per gram? Give a reason for your answer. [2]
   c When methane is burnt carbon dioxide and water vapour are formed. Carbon dioxide may contribute to the Greenhouse Effect. Explain what is meant by the Greenhouse Effect. [2]

[Adapted from the Terminal Examination, 1995.]

Checklist

These are the facts and ideas that you should have learned by studying this topic.

To qualify at Credit level you should:
- know how crude oil forms and that it contains hydrocarbons
- know that fossil fuels give us many useful fuels, e.g. petrol, diesel, coke and paraffin, that can be used for heating, cooking and transport
- understand that hydrocarbons are molecules made up of only carbon and hydrogen atoms
- know that combustion is a reaction with oxygen, and that the complete combustion of fuel produces carbon dioxide and water
- know that a shortage of oxygen during combustion can lead to the formation of carbon monoxide or carbon
- know that carbon dioxide causes a greenhouse effect
- know that air contains nitrogen, oxygen, water vapour and carbon dioxide, and know that carbon dioxide and oxygen levels in the atmosphere are nearly always constant
- know that sulphur impurities in fuels burn to give sulphur dioxide which can cause acid rain
- know that chemical reactions can make light, sound and electricity
- know that a chemical reaction can give out or take in energy
- know a simple method for comparing energy transfers in reactions using a calorimeter.

To qualify at Merit level you should:
- know why crude oil is non-renewable
- be able to describe the process of fractional distillation of crude oil
- know about the series of hydrocarbons called alkanes
- be able to understand simple molecule diagrams
- know that carbon dioxide is not the only greenhouse gas
- know how the oceans and the atmosphere have developed
- know about the conversion of carbon dioxide to oxygen (photosynthesis) and back to carbon dioxide (respiration)
- know the fraction of nitrogen, oxygen and carbon dioxide in the air
- know that oxidation is the reaction with oxygen to form oxides
- know the meaning of the words exothermic and endothermic
- know that two unlike metals in an electrolyte produce electricity
- understand a method to compare the energy transferred in different reactions using a calorimeter.

To qualify at Special level you should:
- be able to explain how fractional distillation works
- be able to write equations using displayed molecular formulae
- understand how the use of fuels has an impact on the quality of life
- understand the role of carbon dioxide in 'trapping' solar radiation in the greenhouse effect
- understand how the atmosphere has evolved and how its composition remains broadly constant
- know that acid rain is a combination of acids, including sulphuric acid
- know that in chemical reactions energy transfers are needed to make and break bonds
- be able to calculate energy changes in kJ using the formula: energy transferred = mass × specific heat capacity × temperature change.

GCSE FOUNDATION TIER

GCSE HIGHER TIER

Key words from this topic:

fossil fuel
non-renewable
fractional distillation
hydrocarbon
alkane
endothermic
exothermic
joule
specific heat capacity

CHAPTER 6

ROCKS AND METALS

▲ This cup was fashioned around 1200 BC. Gold was one of the earliest metals to be used. It is found naturally as an element – not as a compound.

▶ This statue from Nigeria is an early example of the use of an alloy – a mixture of metals. In this case copper has been mixed with a little tin to make it water resistant.

GOLD and silver have always been precious to people. Tin and lead helped ancient empires to flourish. Titanium, aluminium and tungsten are modern metals that helped us to develop the age of technology. All metals are mined out of the ground. So what is so different about modern metals? Why was iron discovered before titanium?

What we find naturally in the ground are ores. Ores are mixtures of rock and minerals. It is the mineral in an ore that gives us metals. Usually the mineral is a compound – it contains the metal bonded to other elements. These elements have to be removed to get the metal out of the ore. Removing these elements from the minerals of modern metals is not easy.

Not all minerals are compounds. Tin, copper and lead are sometimes found as pure elements. Thousands rushed to California in 1848 because a mineral that always occurs as an element was discovered there – gold !

You can easily separate nuggets of gold from the surrounding rock by panning. Gold does not have to be extracted by breaking down a compound, it comes straight out of the rock.

Copper is an early metal that is found in mineral form. The mineral has to go through a simple chemical change to produce pure copper. Copper was often mixed with tin to make bronze, which is harder than either copper or tin. These mixtures are called alloys.

The variety of metals available to modern technologists has produced better and stronger alloys that aid us in our everyday life. Replacement hip-joints, aeroplane hulls even simple coins – all start out as minerals in the ground.

▲ A prospector panning for gold.

▲ Haematite – the mineral that iron is extracted from.

▶ A modern alloy made building the Blackbird aircraft possible. Ordinary metals would either be too heavy or too weak for its aerodynamic design.

Looking inside planet Earth

The Giant's Causeway in Northern Ireland, Hambledon Tor in Dartmoor, Mount Vesuvius in Italy. What do they all have in common? They are all made from hot, molten rock that has cooled down.

Where does this molten rock come from? It comes from beneath the surface of the Earth and is called **magma** before it reaches the surface, and **lava** once it is above the surface. The lava sometimes flows easily and spreads over the land producing low cone shapes. Other kinds of lava flow less easily and so produce steep cones. These are the volcanoes like Mount Vesuvius, Mount Fujiyama in Japan and Mount St Helen's in the USA.

▼
A granite outcrop on Hambledon Tor, Dartmoor.

▼
Giant's Causeway. The result of a basalt lava flow that cooled slowly.

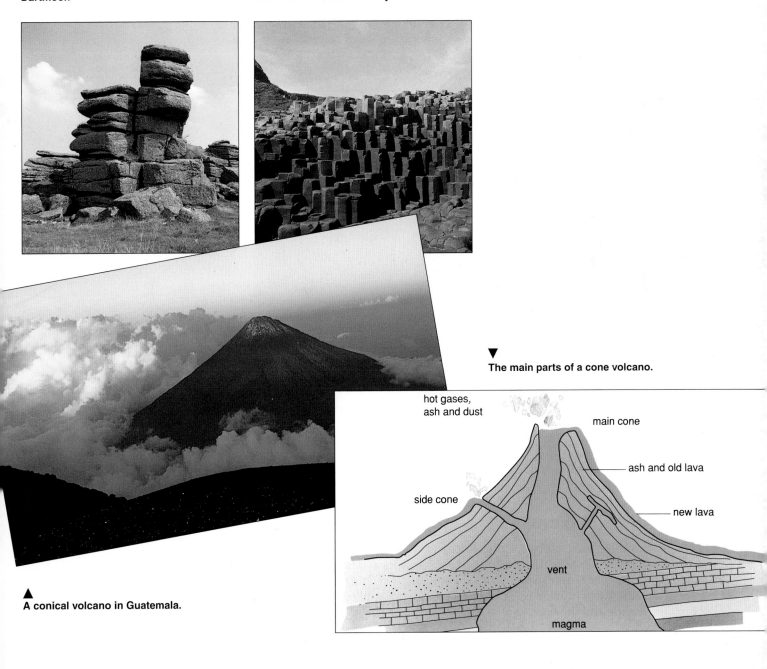

▼
The main parts of a cone volcano.

hot gases, ash and dust

main cone

side cone

ash and old lava

new lava

vent

magma

▲
A conical volcano in Guatemala.

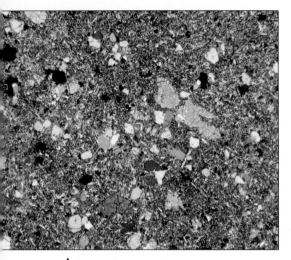

▲ If the molten rock cools quickly, the crystals that form are very small.

▲ If the rock cools slowly the crystals have more time to grow so they can become larger.

Sometimes the magma does not break through the surface. Instead it forms a huge mound of rock that cools slowly underground. The Tor on Dartmoor is the weathered remains of a 'failed volcano' like this.

The areas where volcanoes are found and earthquakes happen form a pattern. The pattern has been known for a long time, but the present theory about why it happens has only been known for about forty years. Perhaps in another forty years we will have a different theory.

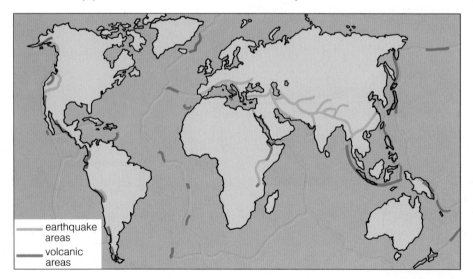

◄ Where to find earthquakes and volcanoes.

earthquake
areas
volcanic
areas

Hard outer layers

The shock waves produced by earthquakes are registered at stations all around the world. These stations are called seismic stations and produce **seismographs**. You can read more about this in chapter 1. The evidence tells us that the Earth is made up of layers. These layers are the thin rocky crust, the mantle and the core.

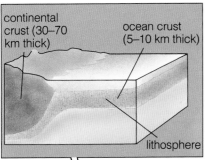

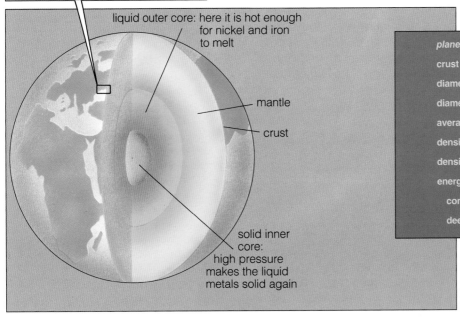

planet data	
crust thickness	50 km (variable)
diameter at the Equator	12 756 km
diameter at the poles	12 714 km
average density	5518 kg/m³
density of continental rock	2670 kg/m³
density of oceanic rock	2850 kg/m³
energy from radioactivity:	
continental rocks	130 J/s per m³
deeper rocks	35 J/s per m³

◄
The Earth is built in layers. The crust is very thin – about as thick as the black outline on the diagram compared to the rest of the Earth.

If magma comes through the surface to form volcanoes and tors it must be very hot inside the Earth. Magma, which comes from the mantle, is much denser than rocks on the surface.

Soft centre

The Earth contains small amounts of radioactive material. When radioactive material decays, it releases energy. The decay of this natural radioactive material is enough to keep the centre of the Earth hot.

As the interior of the Earth is so hot, energy is transferred out through the magma. The energy is transferred by the process of convection (see chapter 2).

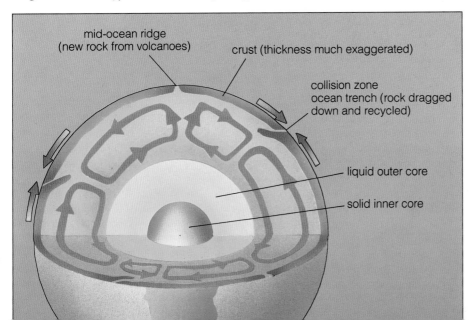

◄
The huge convection currents within the Earth's mantle drive the continental plates across the surface of the Earth.

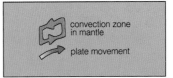

Huge convection currents within the Earth's mantle move the magma around.

Where two currents are moving magma upwards, there is often a weakness or gap in the crust. The magma is sometimes pushed up through these gaps. At these points, the magma can emerge as lava and build up as a volcano. Where two currents are moving magma downwards, rock from the surface is being dragged down and remelted.

The rocky crust is broken up into huge plates that are imperfectly joined together. If magma is carried upwards at one of these imperfect joins, some will escape through the join and the plates will move apart. If magma is carried downwards underneath one of these joins, rock will be dragged downwards through the gap between the plates and the plates will move together.

▼
The formation of a mid-ocean ridge. This is happening in the middle of the Atlantic Ocean.

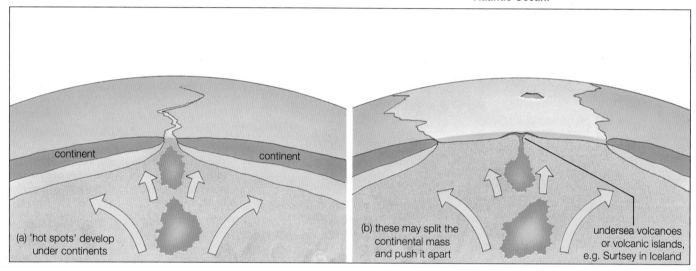

(a) 'hot spots' develop under continents

continent   continent

(b) these may split the continental mass and push it apart

undersea volcanoes or volcanic islands, e.g. Surtsey in Iceland

Tectonic plates

The large plates of crust, called **tectonic plates**, float on top of the denser, churning mantle. Some plates carry continents, others carry oceans. Some plates grind against each other, causing earthquakes, others collide head on.

◄
The main tectonic plates of the Earth.

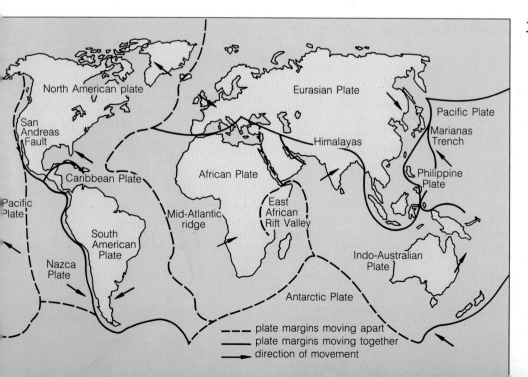

North American plate

Eurasian Plate

Pacific Plate

San Andreas Fault

Marianas Trench

Himalayas

Caribbean Plate

African Plate

Philippine Plate

Pacific Plate

East African Rift Valley

Mid-Atlantic ridge

South American Plate

Nazca Plate

Indo-Australian Plate

Antarctic Plate

- - - plate margins moving apart
——— plate margins moving together
——► direction of movement

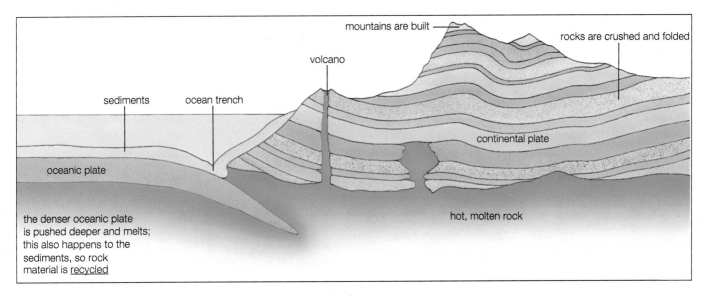

mountains are built — rocks are crushed and folded

volcano

sediments   ocean trench

continental plate

oceanic plate

the denser oceanic plate
is pushed deeper and melts;
this also happens to the
sediments, so rock
material is recycled

hot, molten rock

When two continental plates collide they can form high mountain ranges. They do this by pushing up the rock so that it folds. This process is called **folding**. The Himalayas were formed 26 million years ago when the Indo-Australian plate collided with the Eurasian plate.

If a continental plate collides with an oceanic plate the denser oceanic plate sinks under the continental plate. The rock material of the oceanic plate is remelted. This process is called **subduction**.

North and South America are pushing into the Pacific plate. This collision has produced the great mountain chains of the Rocky Mountains and the Andes. Here we find many volcanoes and earthquakes. This movement has also produced deep oceans, as the American continental plates are dragged downwards, taking some ocean plate with them. The deepest parts of the sea are where continental plates are being dragged down by the returning convection currents. We find these at the edges of the Pacific Ocean.

As the continental plates move apart from one another, they cause the continents to drift. Britain was a tropical country near the equator during the Carboniferous period. This was when our coal deposits formed from the dead remains of tropical rain forests.

The idea that continents moved was first put forward seventy years ago, by Alfred Wegener. The idea has since been tested by measuring from space satellites. The Atlantic Ocean is getting wider at a rate of about 5 cm per year.

▲
What happens when plates collide. This shows the process of subduction – 'drawing under'. This is happening along the west coast of America.

The small plate carrying California is sliding sideways against the main plate that carries North America. At present, it is tearing a huge rip in the Earth's crust, very close to the cities of Los Angeles and San Francisco. This is called the San Andreas fault. This movement resulted in the huge earthquake that destroyed many parts of Los Angeles in 1994.

109

Questions and Practice

1 a What is the name of the Earth's outer layer?

b What is the name of the next inner layer?

c How hot is the liquid outer core?

d Why is the inner core solid?

e Why is the crust thickness not given as a fixed measurement?

2 a What is the name of the plate to the west of South America?

b Is the Pacific Plate moving towards or away from the Eurasian Plate?

c Is a trench or a ridge being formed at the boundary of these two plates?

d What would the convection currents in the mantle be doing at this boundary?

3 Explain how the mid-Atlantic ridge is being formed.

Rock types and formation

Rocks go through a cycle. They are pushed up in the process of mountain building (uplift) and are broken down in the process of **weathering** and **erosion**. The cycle begins again when the eroded material is compressed under great pressure – forming sedimentary rock – or when it melts into magma because of subduction.

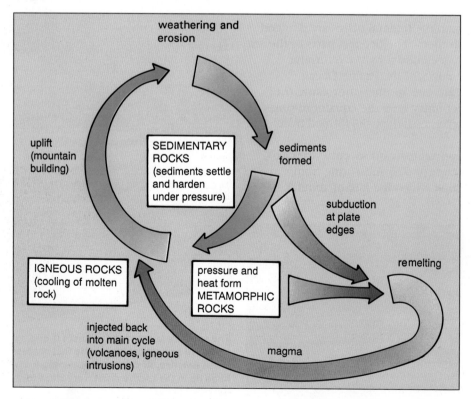

◄
The rock cycle: making, changing and destroying rocks.

When lava or underground magma cools it forms rocks known as **igneous** rocks. When these rocks are on the surface, they are naturally worn down and then *transported* (carried away by wind or rivers) to the sea. They reach there as mud or sand. After a long time, the tiny solid particles suspended in the liquid mud (the sediment) settle and become compressed.

The rocks made when sediments settle under pressure are called **sedimentary** rocks. If a rock is made in this way it may have fossils in it. These fossils will usually be of small shellfish that lived on the sea bottom at the time when the sediments were laid down. The rock is also usually made up of small grains, not crystals. The movement of the continents eventually brings these sedimentary rocks to the surface, where they are likely to be pushed up into mountains.

▼
Weathering and erosion: how rocks are worn down and carried away.

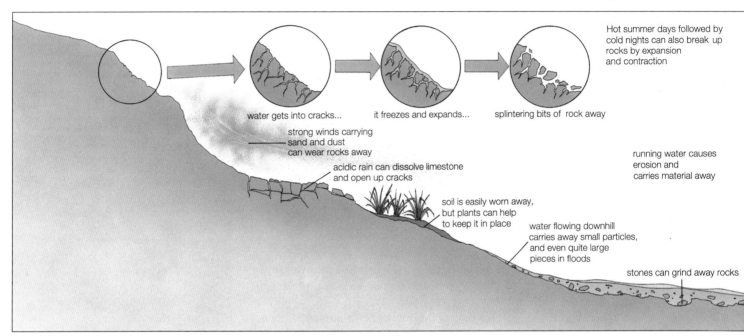

Hot summer days followed by cold nights can also break up rocks by expansion and contraction

water gets into cracks...   it freezes and expands...   splintering bits of rock away

strong winds carrying sand and dust can wear rocks away

acidic rain can dissolve limestone and open up cracks

running water causes erosion and carries material away

soil is easily worn away, but plants can help to keep it in place

water flowing downhill carries away small particles, and even quite large pieces in floods

stones can grind away rocks

◀
Chalk and limestone are made from once living sediments – the shells and bones of sea creatures. These organisms turn calcium hydrogencarbonate from the sea into calcium carbonate in their shells and bones.

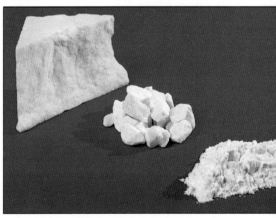

When hot magma flows through the Earth's crust, the high temperature and increased pressure can chemically change the surrounding rocks. The result is **metamorphic** rock. For example, chalk and limestone, both sedimentary, change into marble. Igneous rocks also change. For example, basalt changes into granite.

▲
Marble is a metamorphic rock. This lump of marble was originally chalk.

p214

You can tell if a rock is igneous, sedimentary or metamorphic by examining the evidence of their structure. The evidence from rocks has given us information about how old the Earth is and about the changes taking place over billions of years. The rocks in the Grand Canyon are sedimentary. The ones in the bottom layer must be older than the ones above them. The fossils found in the different layers provide a lot of evidence for the theory of evolution.

	Igneous	*Sedimentary*	*Metamorphic*
Formation	made from hot rock cooling down	made from weathered or eroded particles settling under water and being compressed	made from the other types of rock being changed by heat and pressure
Appearance	glassy appearance made of interlocking crystals	contains fossils, made of grains, occurs as layers	grains and crystals are distorted, fossils are distorted or absent

Minerals and ores

It is not rocks that give us metals, but the **ores** in them. Copper pyrites and malachite are two ores that have copper in them. Haematite is an ore of iron. Bauxite is the ore of aluminium.

p213

To get the useful metal out, you have to mine the ore: mineral *and* waste rock. The mineral and waste rock are a mixture – they are not bonded together. You can crush the mixture, concentrate the mineral and get rid of as much waste as possible. Getting the metal from the mineral is not as easy.

▲ The layers in the Grand Canyon. The canyon walls are a slice through time going down 2000 million years from the present day at the top.

▲ Some important ores. From left to right: malachite (copper), galena (lead), iron pyrites and bauxite (aluminium).

112

Extracting copper

Copper mineral is heated with carbon to extract it from its mineral. Malachite (copper carbonate) first decomposes to copper oxide and gives off carbon dioxide gas:

copper carbonate $\rightarrow$ copper oxide + carbon dioxide

$$CuCO_3 \rightarrow CuO + CO_2$$

The problem is getting the remaining oxygen away from the copper. This is where the carbon is needed. The carbon makes bonds with the oxygen forcing the copper to break its bonds with the oxygen:

copper oxide + carbon $\rightarrow$ copper + carbon dioxide

$$2CuO + C \rightarrow 2Cu + CO_2$$

This process of using carbon to remove oxygen from metal compounds is called **reduction**. The impure copper is run off at the bottom of the furnace. The waste material that floats on top is also run off to be used for road building. The copper still needs purifying before it can be used.

Extracting iron

Iron is extracted from its ore by reduction using carbon monoxide. This happens in a 'blast' furnace, so called because high temperatures are needed, so hot air is blasted in at the bottom.

The ore haematite, which contains the mineral iron(III) oxide (Fe_2O_3), is fed into the top of the furnace with coke and limestone. Coke is mainly carbon and is used for the reduction process. The limestone is there to remove the impurities. The coke oxidises (burns) to make carbon dioxide:

carbon + oxygen $\rightarrow$ carbon dioxide

$$C + O_2 \rightarrow CO_2$$

The carbon dioxide travels up the furnace and is reduced by more coke to carbon monoxide:

carbon dioxide + carbon $\rightarrow$ carbon monoxide

$$CO_2 + C \rightarrow 2CO$$

The carbon monoxide then reacts with the iron(III) oxide. The bonds between the iron and the oxygen are broken and the iron(III) oxide is reduced to iron. Bonds are made between the carbon monoxide and the oxygen. The carbon monoxide is oxidised to carbon dioxide.

iron oxide + carbon monoxide $\rightarrow$ iron + carbon dioxide

$$Fe_2O_3 + 3CO \rightarrow 2Fe + 3CO_2$$

Only metals such as copper, lead, zinc and iron can be extracted in this way. Metals like aluminium, magnesium, calcium, sodium and potassium form bonds with oxygen that are too strong to be broken just by heating with carbon or carbon monoxide. They are too **reactive**.

Potassium reacts violently with water – it melts into a ball and burns with a lilac flame.

Metal reactivity

Some metals are more reactive than others. You can see this in the typical reactions with air, water and acid.

Perhaps you have seen the spectacular effect of putting potassium in water. But when copper metal is put in water, all it does is sink. It does not even react with steam.

Perhaps you have also seen the remarkable reaction of heating magnesium in air. If you heat copper in air, a black powder, copper oxide, slowly forms. Magnesium is much more reactive than copper. Magnesium will not react with cold water though, but it does react with steam.

▲
Magnesium burns so brightly in air that it can damage the retina when the reaction is seen close up. This reaction is used in distress flares.

▼
The reactivity series.

Questions and Practice

4 Write down the order of reactivity of copper, potassium and magnesium.

5 Look at the diagrams of different metals in dilute acid. Write down an order of reactivity based on this evidence.

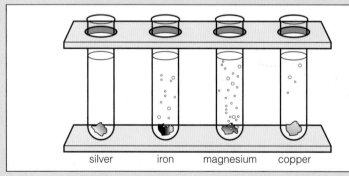

silver   iron   magnesium   copper

6 Zinc is between iron and magnesium in order of reactivity. Predict how it reacts with acid and air.

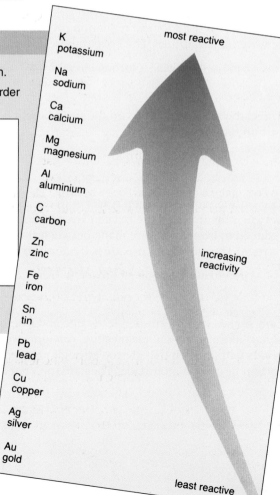

most reactive

K	potassium
Na	sodium
Ca	calcium
Mg	magnesium
Al	aluminium
C	carbon
Zn	zinc
Fe	iron
Sn	tin
Pb	lead
Cu	copper
Ag	silver
Au	gold

increasing reactivity

least reactive

Why some metals are more reactive than others

Metals are elements. Elements cannot be broken down into simpler substances. Elements are made up of only one kind of the same small particle. These small particles are called **atoms**. The atoms of an element are all identical. What is the difference between atoms of different elements?

Atoms have a **nucleus**. This nucleus carries a positive electrical charge – the size of this charge is always the same for a particular element. The nucleus is surrounded by negatively charged **electrons** – enough to balance the positive charge in the nucleus. Some electrons can leave and join another atom. If an electron leaves an atom, the atom has fewer electrons than usual. This is no longer an atom, it is now a positive **ion**. It has lost some of its negative charge that was balancing the positive charge in the nucleus. If spare electrons join an atom it will have more electrons than usual. It is now a negative ion.

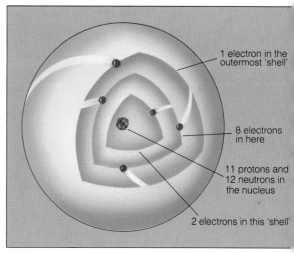

1 electron in the outermost 'shell'

8 electrons in here

11 protons and 12 neutrons in the nucleus

2 electrons in this 'shell'

▲
The structure of a sodium atom.

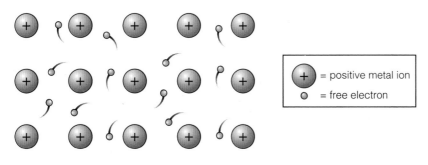

+ = positive metal ion
○ = free electron

◀
The flow of electrons through a collection of metal atoms is an electric current.

When metals react with other elements, they lose electrons. Reactive metals lose electrons more readily than less reactive metals. Sodium and potassium are very reactive metals and lose a single electron when they react. Magnesium is less reactive because it needs to lose two electrons and it takes more energy to do this. Copper also needs to lose two electrons, and they are held more tightly by the nucleus. Copper is therefore even less reactive than magnesium.

The easier it is for a metal to lose electrons, the more reactive it is.

The electron from sodium is so easily lost that the electron will soon find another atom to accept it. Sodium is always reacting with something. It will always make a **compound** with another element. This is why the metal must be stored under oil, otherwise it would react straight away with oxygen in the air.

Extracting reactive metals

The only way to separate sodium out of the compounds that it makes is to pass an electric current through it. If you try to do this when the compound is a solid, the ions are locked in place and so they are unable to move as an electric current.

If you melt the sodium compound, the ions are free to move. They can then move as an electric current. The positively charged sodium ions will travel towards a negatively charged electrode – a **cathode** – because opposite charges attract. In the same way, the negatively charged ions will travel towards a positively charged electrode – an **anode**.

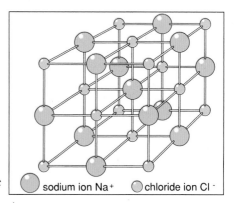

sodium ion Na+   ○ chloride ion Cl⁻

▲
Solid sodium chloride. The ions are held firmly in place – they are not free to move.

115

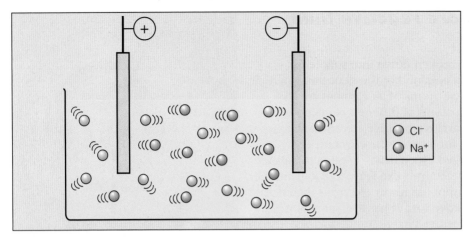

◄ **Molten sodium chloride. The ions are now free to move – in this case the ions are attracted to the charged electrodes.**

When the positive sodium ion reaches the cathode it takes up an electron and becomes a sodium atom again:

sodium ion + electron → sodium atom

$$Na^+ + e^- \rightarrow Na$$

Using electrolysis to extract aluminium

Aluminium is a very reactive metal. This is surprising, as we make many things from it: saucepans, aeroplane bodies, kitchen foil and drinks cans. The secret is that the aluminium has already reacted with the oxygen in the air and made a very thin layer of oxide on the surface so that it can no longer react.

You can only get aluminium from its mineral by electrolysis. The energy needed is relatively high, which is why we are encouraged to recycle aluminium. It is cheaper to get impure aluminium by remelting and reusing it than it is to start from the ore.

The ore, which is called bauxite, contains the mineral aluminium oxide. This is purified and heated so that it melts. A substance called cryolite (sodium aluminium fluoride) is added to help it melt at a lower temperature and so save on energy costs. The liquid mixture is held in a large carbon-lined steel case. Carbon rods hang down into the liquid. The case (cathode) and the rods (anode) are the electrodes where the ions collect.

The aluminium ions move to the carbon case and the oxygen ions move to the rods. The oxygen ions become oxygen gas. The rods burn in this oxygen to make carbon dioxide and the rods are lowered further into the liquid. The

▼ **Aluminium is useful for a large variety of purposes. Aluminium is used widely in a lot of throw-away packaging despite its cost in terms of energy.**

◄ **The extraction of aluminium.**

carbon anodes

pure aluminium oxide is added continually

carbon lining of the cell is the cathode

the electrolyte is molten cryolite and aluminium oxide

molten aluminium tapped off

molten aluminium

aluminium ions become molten aluminium metal which is tapped off from the bottom of the tank.

Aluminium atoms lose *three* electrons to become an ion – which is why it takes a lot of energy to get them back again. At the cathode, the aluminium ions accept three electrons and become aluminium atoms again:

aluminium ion + electrons → aluminium atom

$$Al^{3+} + 3e^- \rightarrow Al$$

At the anode, each oxide ion gives up *two* electrons and becomes an oxygen atom. A pair of the atoms join together to become an oxygen molecule:

oxide ion → oxygen atom + electrons

$$O^{2-} \rightarrow O + 2e^-$$

pair of oxygen atoms → oxygen molecule

$$2O \rightarrow O_2$$

We normally write these equations together as:

$$2O^{2-} \rightarrow O_2 + 4e^-$$

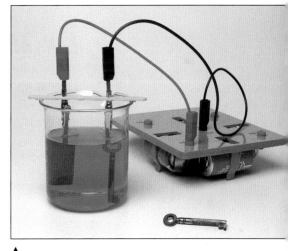
▲ **Electroplating an ordinary key with copper.**

Questions and Practice

7 Write equations in words, symbols and in pictures of model atoms to show the reaction between the carbon anode and the oxygen that makes it burn to carbon dioxide.

8 A copper atom loses two electrons to form a copper ion. Which electrode will a copper ion move towards during electrolysis?

9 Write an equation, using the symbol e⁻ for an electron, to show how a copper ion becomes a copper atom.

Using electrolysis to purify copper

As copper is an unreactive metal it is extracted from its ore by reduction with carbon. This produces impure copper which must be purified before it can be used to make water pipes and electrical wire. You can do this with electrolysis.

Perhaps you have already coated a metal object with copper using electrolysis. To do this in a laboratory you need a solution of copper ions. The copper ions are free to move about in the solution amongst the water particles. Electrodes placed in the solution will attract ions – a negative electrode will attract the positive copper ions. The copper ions accept two electrons from the electrode and become copper atoms. The electrode slowly becomes coated with copper. This is called **electroplating**.

This process is the basis for the large scale purification of copper. This time the cathode is a small sample of pure copper. The impure copper (the 'boulder') is the anode. The copper atoms from the anode lose two electrons to become ions. These ions move through the solution of copper(II) sulphate towards the cathode. Here they accept two electrons and deposit as atoms on the cathode. The atoms build up, forming pure copper metal.

The copper in the pipes that carry your water have come a long way. From the centre of the Earth, round the rock cycle, drifting with continents, chemically reduced with coke and finally electrolysed.

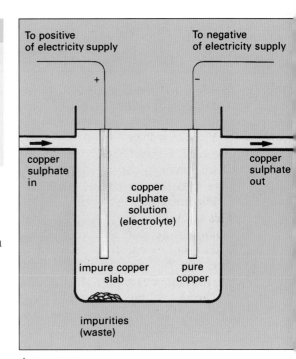

To positive of electricity supply To negative of electricity supply

copper sulphate in copper sulphate out

copper sulphate solution (electrolyte)

impure copper slab pure copper

impurities (waste)

▲ **Purifying copper.**

▼ **The secrets of a modern house – copper pipes under the floor.**

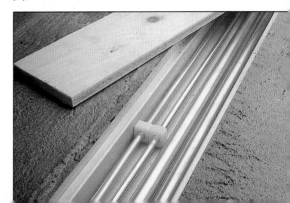

Examination Questions

Credit

1 The diagram shows how aluminium is extracted from its ore in a factory. The aluminium ore contains aluminium oxide. Electrodes are placed in the molten aluminium oxide. Aluminium is formed at the cathode. Oxygen gas is formed at the anode.

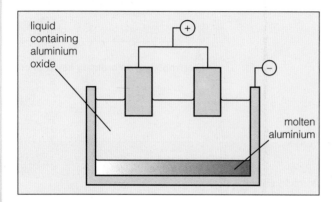

a Where does the energy come from to make the ions move? [1 mark]
b Aluminium is one of the substances made during the process. Write down the other one. [1]
c Write down two uses of aluminium. [2]

2 This question is about rocks. Finish the sentences by choosing words from the list. Do not use a word more than once.

crust, earthquake, erosion, igneous, metamorphic, sedimentary, volcano, weathering

a One type of rock is made when molten rock from a _____ turns solid. This type is called _____ rock. [2]
b Small bits of rock are broken off larger rocks by _____ and _____ . [2]
c High temperature and pressure underground change sedimentary rocks into _____ rocks. [1]

Merit

3 Describe the processes involved when:

a Sedimentary rocks change into metamorphic rocks; [2]
b Igneous rocks change into sedimentary rocks; [3]
c Magma changes into igneous rocks. [1]

4 This question is about the electrolysis of copper(II) sulphate using copper electrodes. The solution contains copper ions (Cu^{2+}) and sulphate ions (SO_4^{2-}). After 5 minutes the negative electrode has increased in mass, and the positive electrode has decreased in mass.

a What is the name given to the positive electrode? [1]
b Explain how copper(II) sulphate solution conducts electricity. [2]
c Explain why the negative electrode increases in mass. [1]
d Explain why the positive electrode decreases in mass. [1]

Special

5 Electrodes are placed in a solution of copper(II) chloride. Copper(II) chloride solution contains copper ions (Cu^{2+}) and chloride ions (Cl^-).

a What is the name given to the negatively charged electrode? [1]
b What is the name given to the positively charged electrode? [1]
c Explain how copper(II) chloride solution conducts electricity. [2]
d Chlorine is formed at one electrode. Which ion is discharged to form chlorine? [1]
e Copper is deposited on the other electrode. Write an equation to show the reaction which forms copper at the electrode. Use the symbol e^- to represent an electron. [2]

6 The Earth's crust is made up of sections of rock called tectonic plates. These tectonic plates float on top of the molten mantle. The tectonic plates are able to move slowly. There are two types of plates, called oceanic and continental plates. Oceanic plates are more dense than continental plates. When two continental plates slowly collide, the plates buckle up and form mountains. Describe what will happen when an oceanic plate slowly collides with a continental plate. Explain how this can help in the recycling of rocks. You may wish to draw a labelled diagram to help give your answer. [5]

[Adapted from Terminal Examination 1995, and Periodic Examinations 1994 and 1995]

Checklist

These are the facts and ideas that you should have learned by studying this topic.

To succeed at Credit level you should:
- know how igneous, sedimentary and metamorphic rocks are made
- know that the Earth is made up of a thin crust, mantle and core
- know that molten rock comes out of volcanoes
- know that metals are extracted from ores, and that ores are mixtures of a mineral and surrounding rock
- know that mixtures consist of two or more separate components
- know that you can physically separate an ore to get a mineral
- know that you can get copper from its mineral by heating it with carbon
- know that metals have different reactivities
- know that you can only get aluminium from its mineral by using electricity
- know how to copper plate things by electrolysis
- know that atoms have a positively charged nucleus surrounded by negatively charged electrons
- know that an ion is a charged atom or group of atoms
- know that liquids containing ions conduct electricity.

To succeed at Merit level you should:
- understand the scientific processes involved in the formation of igneous, sedimentary and metamorphic rocks
- know that the Earth's crust is made up of large interlocking plates and that their movement causes volcanic activity and earthquakes
- know that rocks and minerals can be used to make a variety of useful substances, e.g. pottery (from clay)
- know that an ore is a mixture, found in the Earth, containing a metal or metal compound
- recognise variation in the properties and reactions of metals
- know that reactive metals are usually extracted by electrolysis
- know that the extraction of less reactive metals often involves reduction with carbon or carbon monoxide
- know that reduction is the loss of oxygen from an oxide
- understand the key features of the electrolytic decomposition involved in the production of aluminium
- understand the purification of copper by electrolysis
- know that the conduction in a solution is due to moving ions
- know that positive ions move to the negative electrode (cathode) and that negative ions move to the positive electrode (anode).

To succeed at Special level you should:
- be able to interpret evidence of rock formation
- understand the theory of plate tectonics and the contribution this process makes to the recycling of rocks
- be able to identify chemical equations as oxidation or reduction
- be able to make predictions based on the reactivity series
- be able to write equations that show the formation of an ion from an atom and the formation of an atom from an ion
- know that in electrolysis, positive ions gain electrons at the cathode.

GCSE FOUNDATION TIER

GCSE HIGHER TIER

Key words from this topic:

igneous
sedimentary
metamorphic
tectonic plate
ore
reactivity
ion
electrolysis
anode
cathode

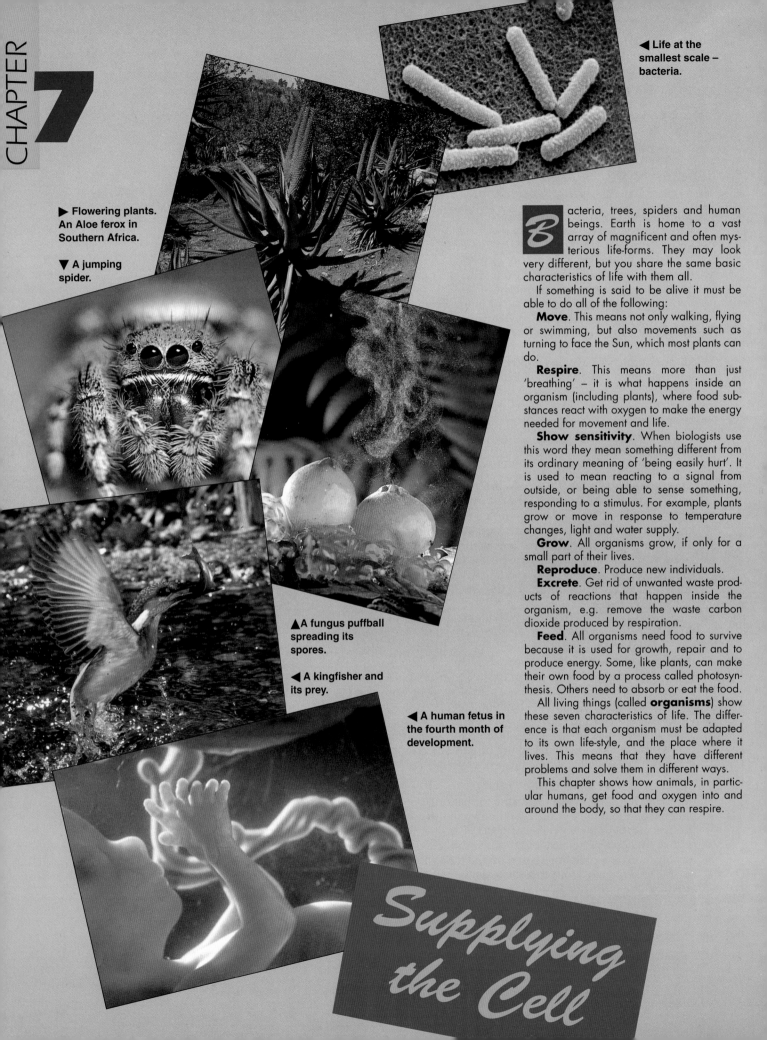

◀ Life at the smallest scale – bacteria.

▶ Flowering plants. An Aloe ferox in Southern Africa.

▼ A jumping spider.

▲ A fungus puffball spreading its spores.

◀ A kingfisher and its prey.

◀ A human fetus in the fourth month of development.

B acteria, trees, spiders and human beings. Earth is home to a vast array of magnificent and often mysterious life-forms. They may look very different, but you share the same basic characteristics of life with them all.

If something is said to be alive it must be able to do all of the following:

Move. This means not only walking, flying or swimming, but also movements such as turning to face the Sun, which most plants can do.

Respire. This means more than just 'breathing' – it is what happens inside an organism (including plants), where food substances react with oxygen to make the energy needed for movement and life.

Show sensitivity. When biologists use this word they mean something different from its ordinary meaning of 'being easily hurt'. It is used to mean reacting to a signal from outside, or being able to sense something, responding to a stimulus. For example, plants grow or move in response to temperature changes, light and water supply.

Grow. All organisms grow, if only for a small part of their lives.

Reproduce. Produce new individuals.

Excrete. Get rid of unwanted waste products of reactions that happen inside the organism, e.g. remove the waste carbon dioxide produced by respiration.

Feed. All organisms need food to survive because it is used for growth, repair and to produce energy. Some, like plants, can make their own food by a process called photosynthesis. Others need to absorb or eat the food.

All living things (called **organisms**) show these seven characteristics of life. The difference is that each organism must be adapted to its own life-style, and the place where it lives. This means that they have different problems and solve them in different ways.

This chapter shows how animals, in particular humans, get food and oxygen into and around the body, so that they can respire.

Supplying the Cell

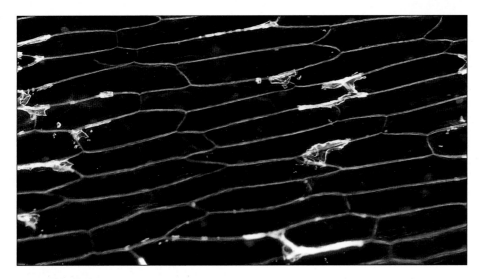

This 'wall' of cells is from a thin onion skin. It is easy to see with just a simple microscope.

The building brick of life: the cell

The wall of a house is obviously a large and solid structure but if you look closely at the walls you can see that it is made of much smaller units – bricks – joined together to make the whole. Living things are made up in the same way. The basic units of life are microscopic living **cells**. Some organisms are made of only a single cell, but they can still do everything necessary to stay alive.

Plant and animal cells

The cells of plants and animals have the same basic *structure* (features), but there are some differences. These differences reflect their different needs for movement, growth and feeding.

In order to survive a cell must take in certain materials and release others. How each of these materials is dealt with often depends upon the size of the organism. If it is a single-celled organism the single cell will have the job of dealing with all of them.

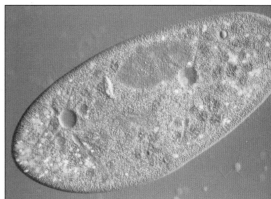

Inside this single-celled protozoa you can see a lot of detail. The cell has many organelles (a bit like our organs) that work to keep it alive.

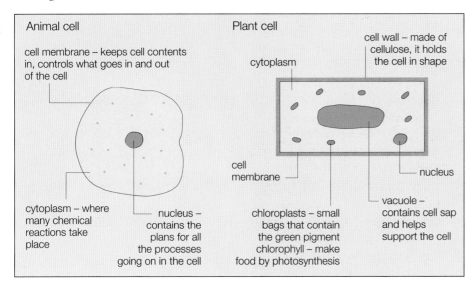

Animal cell

cell membrane – keeps cell contents in, controls what goes in and out of the cell

cytoplasm – where many chemical reactions take place

nucleus – contains the plans for all the processes going on in the cell

Plant cell

cytoplasm

cell wall – made of cellulose, it holds the cell in shape

cell membrane

nucleus

chloroplasts – small bags that contain the green pigment chlorophyll – make food by photosynthesis

vacuole – contains cell sap and helps support the cell

The structure of animal and plant cells.

121

In many-celled organisms, cells often become specialised in structure so that they can do a particular job as well as possible. This allows the organism to work in a very efficient way. The cells do not have to do all the jobs a single-celled organism would have to do. This is often called *division of labour*. This means that some cells may be responsible for getting food into the body, some for getting oxygen into it and some for removing wastes.

Questions and Practice

1 Look at the drawings of the cells. There are some structures found in both animal and plant cells. Make a list of these similarities. Write a sentence on each, outlining where it is found in the animal and plant cells.

2 Look at the drawings of the cells. There are some structures only found in plants cells. Make a list of these differences. Write a sentence on each, suggesting why plant cells need these structures but animal cells do not.

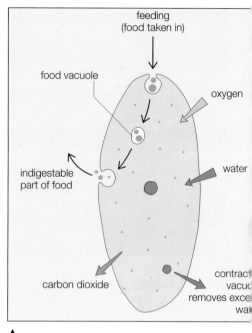

What a healthy cell needs.

The multicellular way of life

Large organisms are made up of millions of cells. They are **multicellular**. The cells are all carefully organised so that they can work together:

● similar cells are grouped together to make **tissues**,

● different tissues are grouped together to make **organs**,

● different organs work or function together as body **systems**.

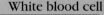

p219

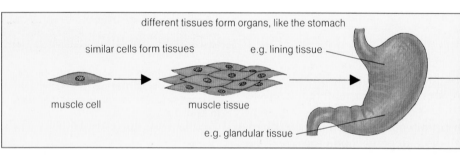

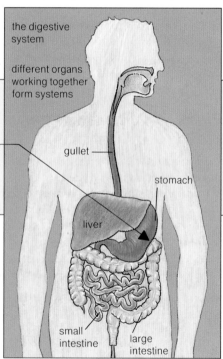

Cell type	How structure is linked to function
Red blood cell 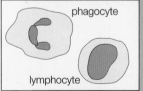	Has no nucleus so plenty of room for the red pigment **haemoglobin**. This allows it to pick up a lot of oxygen in the lungs and carry it in the bloodstream to all parts of the body.
White blood cell 	There are two types of white blood cell. Both types help the body to fight disease. **Phagocytes** can eat harmful bacteria. They can change shape and even squeeze out of blood vessels to attack bacteria in surrounding tissues. **Lymphocytes** are adapted to produce antibodies which are chemicals designed to help destroy bacteria.
Palisade cell	Palisade cells are found near the upper surface of leaves. They contain a lot of chloroplasts needed for the plant to absorb sunlight and make food by photosynthesis.

Systems of the human body

Cells form part of every system in a multicellular organism. The human body, like many other animal bodies, has seven main systems:

- **Digestive** system: brings food into the body. The food can then chemically react with oxygen to release energy.

- **Respiratory** system: the lungs take oxygen into the body from the air we breathe and remove carbon dioxide (and water) from the body.

- **Circulatory** system: the heart pumps blood through a system of vessels, transporting food, oxygen and substances that help to fight disease around the body.

- **Excretory** system: the kidneys filter the blood to remove harmful wastes, spare water and salts. The lungs, liver and skin are also excretory organs.

- **Nervous** system: the brain, spinal cord and nerves help to co-ordinate the workings of all the other systems.

- **Endocrine** or hormone system: produces chemicals that also help to control other body systems.

- **Reproductive** systems: in males responsible for producing sperm, in females responsible for producing eggs and allowing the development of the fetus.

Each of these body systems can be linked with one or more of the seven characteristics of life. The first three of these systems will be explained in greater depth in the remainder of this chapter.

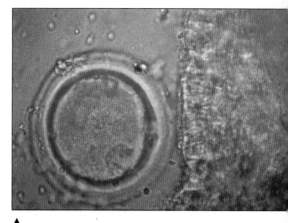

▲
This is the biggest human cell: the ovum (egg cell). It is almost 0.1 mm in diameter. The longest cells are 1.3 m in length and stretch from the spinal cord down to the big toe. The smallest cells in the body are found in the brain and measure 0.005 mm in diameter.

Questions and Practice

3 Copy out and complete the following table on supplying a cell.

Materials taken in	Materials released

4 Photosynthesis is the name of the process used by plants to make their food.

a In which cells of a plant does photosynthesis mainly occur?

b Explain how these cells are well designed for photosynthesis.

5 Copy out the following table, but match the body system with the correct function.

Body system	Function
reproductive	to get food into the body
excretory	to transport materials around the body
digestive	to remove waste products from the body
circulatory	to produce new individuals

123

Getting food into the body

What is digestion?

Most of the food you eat contains molecules that are too large to pass into your bloodstream. The aim of **digestion** is to break these large molecules, which may not dissolve in water, into smaller ones that do. There are two main stages of digestion:

- **Mechanical digestion**. This is usually the first stage of digestion. The teeth, tongue and muscles of the digestive system help to break big pieces of food into smaller chunks. The food is not being changed chemically, this is a physical change.

- **Chemical digestion**. This involves the chemical breakdown of the large food molecules into smaller ones. Chemicals made by the digestive system, called enzymes, cause this change by helping the food to react with water. This reaction is called **hydrolysis**.

p221

All of the chemical reactions inside our bodies are controlled by proteins called **enzymes**. They are only needed in small amounts because they are **catalysts**, speeding up reactions without being changed themselves. Each enzyme has its own special reaction that it is involved in. Different enzymes are involved in the breakdown of each of the main food groups.

p221

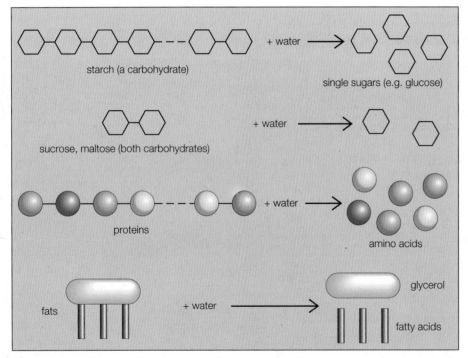

◄
Breaking down food.

Most enzymes work best in certain conditions. These ideal conditions may be slightly different depending upon the enzyme.

Temperature

A rise in temperature speeds up most chemical reactions and a fall in temperature slows them down. Usually, a rise of 10 °C will double the rate of reaction, but above 50 °C enzymes change shape and this means that they can no longer work. When this happens they are said to have been **denatured**. Do not make the mistake of thinking they have been killed. Enzymes are not alive in the first place.

pH

Acidic or alkaline conditions can also alter the shape of an enzyme and so affect the rate at which it works. Inside the cells, most enzymes work best in neutral conditions – pH 7. In the digestive system, the enzymes of the stomach work best at an acidity of pH 2.

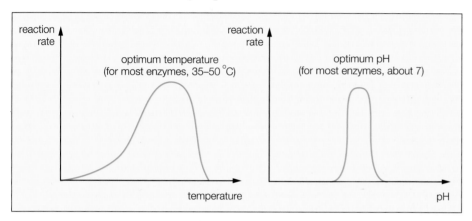

◀ **The effect of temperature and pH.**

The path food takes

The human **alimentary canal** or digestive system is a tube, passing through our bodies from **mouth** to **anus**. It is about nine metres long.

- Food enters at the mouth (it is **ingested**) and is mixed with **saliva** which softens and lubricates the food for swallowing.
- Saliva contains an enzyme called salivary **amylase** which begins the *chemical* digestion of any starch in the food.
- The teeth, tongue and mouth form the food into a small ball called a **bolus** ready for swallowing. This is part of the *mechanical* digestion of food.
- The bolus is swallowed and moves down the gullet to the stomach.
- The stomach churns and mashes the food and adds an enzyme that begins the digestion of protein foods. Acid is also added to kill many of the bacteria taken in with food.
- Small amounts of partly digested, semi-liquid food pass into the small intestine.
- The small intestine is narrow, seven metres long and coiled up inside the lower part of the body. The food is digested mainly in the **duodenum** – the first thirty centimetres. The food continues along the intestine, where digestion is completed, and is absorbed in the **ileum**.
- The **pancreas gland** releases digestive juices into the duodenum to mix with the food. The juice neutralises the stomach acid and contains more enzymes. These enzymes help continue the digestion of starch and proteins and begin the digestion of fat.

▼ **The journey through the digestive system.**

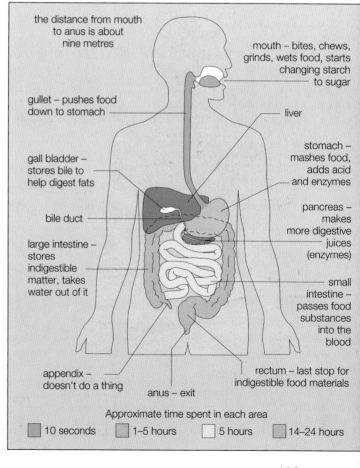

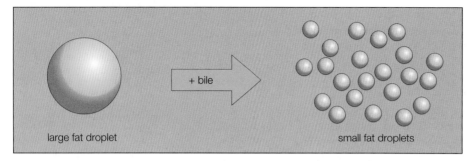

large fat droplet   + bile   small fat droplets

◄ Bile lowers the surface tension of large fat droplets so that they break up. This part of the digestive process is called emulsification. No chemical change is involved.

● The **gall bladder** in the liver releases bile into the duodenum. Bile acts rather like washing-up liquid (detergent), reducing fat to small droplets which are easier for enzymes to work on.

● By the time the food has reached the ileum, most of it has been broken down into small soluble molecules. These molecules are small enough to be absorbed across the wall of this part of the small intestine into the blood.

● The indigestible parts of the food (fibre) move into the first part of the large intestine (the **colon**).

● In the colon, water is absorbed into the blood from the still liquid food so that drier and harder pellets – faeces – are formed. Faeces consist of indigestible fibre, minute pieces broken off from the wall of the gut as the food moves along, and the millions of dead bacteria from the intestines.

● The faeces are stored in the second part of the large intestine, the **rectum**, until they can be removed from the body through the **anus**. This removal is called **egestion**.

Why is the small intestine good at absorbing food?

A lot of soluble food has to be absorbed into the bloodstream from the small intestine. To do this effectively it has the following features:

● It is long (seven metres). This gives time for absorption.

● It has a very large surface area. This gives more chance of absorption.

● The internal surface of the small intestine is folded and covered by millimetre long, finger-like projections called villi. Each villus has its own

▼ The structure of the small intestine.

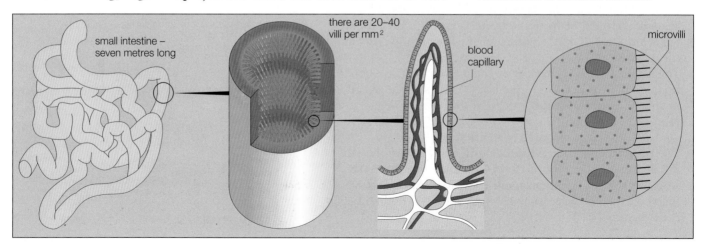

small intestine – seven metres long

there are 20–40 villi per mm^2

blood capillary

microvilli

projections (microvilli). The result is a surface like a fluffy towel. The surface has a good blood supply and it can let small molecules pass through it by a process called **diffusion**. This means that the food particles will eventually be absorbed into the bloodstream.

Diffusion is the net movement of a substance from an area where there is more of it (high concentration) to an area where there is less of it (lower concentration). In living organisms this often takes place across a membrane.

How does food move along the digestive system?

Food and drink does not move through the digestive system by relying on gravity. You can even eat and drink while standing on your head. Muscles in the walls of the gullet, stomach and intestines squeeze the food along by a process called **peristalsis**.

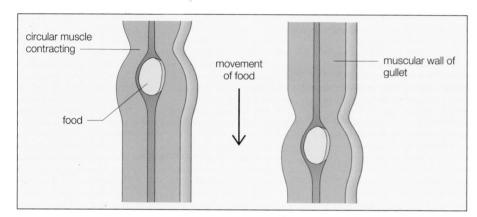

▲
Because of peristalsis, this is possible, but not too clever.

◄
Peristalsis at work.

Questions and Practice

6 Name three different substances that are released into the duodenum.

7 Read the section on enzymes.

   a Why does the body need enzymes?

   b Why can enzymes only work on specific reactions?

8 Copy out the following table

Mechanical digestion	Chemical digestion

Complete it by putting the following points in the correct column.

teeth chew and grind food; salivary amylase works on starch; tongue helps roll food into a ball; muscles squeeze food along digestive system; proteins converted into amino acids; bile emulsifies fats; fats converted to fatty acids and glycerol.

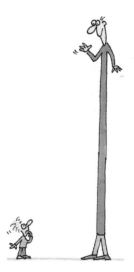

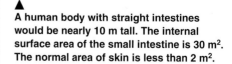

▲
A human body with straight intestines would be nearly 10 m tall. The internal surface area of the small intestine is 30 m². The normal area of skin is less than 2 m².

127

Getting air into the body

The lungs of a mammal, together with the heart and major blood vessels, are found in the chest (**thorax**). When you breathe in, your lungs bring air into your body. Oxygen in the air passes into your blood to be carried off to the cells where it is used in respiration. Waste carbon dioxide in your blood passes out of your body when you breathe out.

The pathway of air

● Usually air is breathed in through the nose. The nose moistens, smells and warms the air as well as using its hairs to filter it (trapping dust and particles of dirt).

● The air then passes down the **trachea** (windpipe). The tiny hairs (cilia) that line the trachea continue to clean the air.

● The air now enters each of the lungs by a large tube called the **bronchus**. Inside the lungs the tube divides into smaller and smaller tubes known as **bronchioles**.

● The bronchioles end in tiny clusters of air sacs called **alveoli**. It is here that **gaseous exchange** takes place. Each alveolus is surrounded by blood vessels bringing blood to the lungs and taking it away again. These minute blood vessels are called **capillaries**. Oxygen in the air passes into the blood in these capillaries. The blood carries off the oxygen to the living cells which will use it in respiration.

▼
The respiratory system.

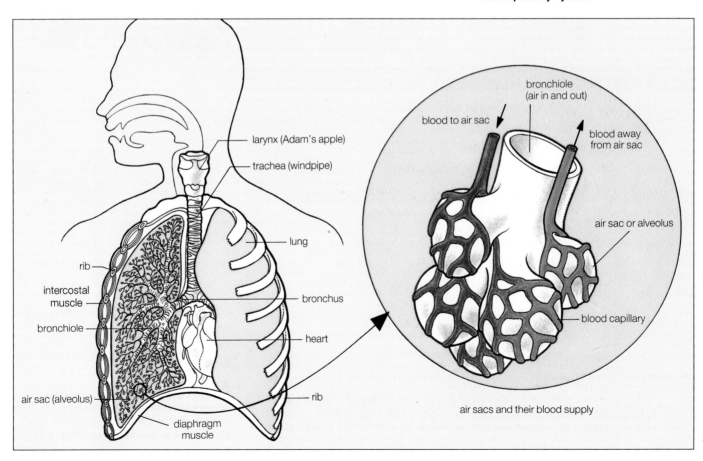

air sacs and their blood supply

- Carbon dioxide, released by respiration in these body cells, passes in the opposite direction – out of the blood capillaries and into the alveoli. It is then removed from the lungs by being breathed out.

How is air breathed in and out?

Air cannot just pass into and out of our lungs on its own. It needs to be actively breathed in (**inhalation**) and breathed out (**exhalation**). This process is called **ventilation** and involves movements of the rib cage and diaphragm muscle.

Inhalation

Muscles between the ribs (intercostal muscles) help to pull the rib cage up and out. The **diaphragm** muscle contracts and becomes flatter in shape. Both of these changes make the space in the thorax bigger. This makes more room for the lungs and causes them to expand. This results in a reduced air pressure in the lungs so that air is now pushed into them by the larger pressure in the atmosphere. Rings of cartilage in the trachea, bronchi and bronchioles stop them from collapsing while air is drawn into the lungs.

Exhalation

The intercostal muscles help to pull the rib cage down and in. The diaphragm muscle relaxes and becomes more dome shaped. Both of these changes make the space in the thorax smaller. They squeeze the lungs, which are elastic and shrink back to their relaxed state. This causes an increase in air pressure and forces air out.

What is gaseous exchange?

Gaseous exchange is based on the process of diffusion. We have already seen that food is absorbed in the small intestine by diffusion. Food in the small intestine is at a high concentration and diffuses into the bloodstream of the intestine wall because it is at a lower concentration there. Gaseous exchange involves the diffusion of oxygen and carbon dioxide.

Why are lungs a good surface for gaseous exchange?

The body needs to get oxygen into the bloodstream and on to every cell as quickly as possible. The waste carbon dioxide, made by the cells, needs to be removed just as quickly. To make sure this can happen the lungs have the following features:

- Large surface. The millions of alveoli in the lungs give a large surface for oxygen to get into and carbon dioxide to get out of the blood.

- Thin. There is only a two-cell layer between the alveolar space and the blood, this includes the alveolar and capillary walls. This short distance (about 0.0002 mm) allows the gases to diffuse quickly.

- Moist. Oxygen has to dissolve in the thin film of moisture in the alveoli before it can diffuse across the permeable cell layers and into the blood.

▲ This device is measuring the patient's lung capacity. Even after a deep breath out, the lungs still contain about $1\frac{1}{2}$ litres of air. In a lifetime, we breathe in enough air to fill 50 000 000 party balloons (about 400 000 m^3) In each human lung there are about 350 000 000 alveoli. If the alveoli of both lungs were laid flat they would have a surface area of 90 m^2. That would more than cover a badminton court.

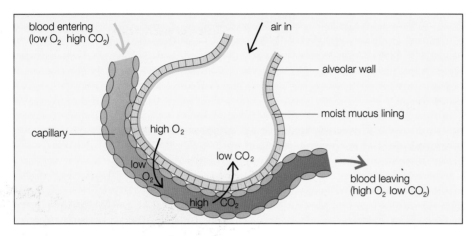

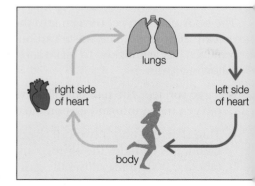

◄
Gaseous exchange when alveoli are filled with air.

● Air and blood supply. For gases to diffuse quickly a high *concentration gradient* must be maintained – in this case lots of the gas on one side of the cells and not much on the other.

The oxygen concentration is kept low in the surrounding blood vessels because it is continually taken away to the body. This results in oxygen diffusing rapidly from the alveoli into the blood. The story for carbon dioxide is similar. The continued supply of blood from the body keeps the carbon dioxide concentration high. The carbon dioxide concentration in the alveoli is kept low by air being exhaled. The result is that carbon dioxide diffuses rapidly from the blood into the alveoli.

Questions and Practice

9 Look at the drawing of the respiratory system (page 128). Draw a flowchart tracing the passage of oxygen from the air into the bloodstream.

10 Study the diagram of gaseous exchange (above).

   a Write about the movement of oxygen. Include the following words: alveolar space; bloodstream; high concentration; low concentration; diffusion.

   b Use the same words to write about the movement of carbon dioxide.

Getting around the body

The digestive system gets food into your body, the respiratory system gets oxygen into your body. Now it is important that these materials are transported around your body to the cells that need them. It is also important that any waste products that the cells produce, like carbon dioxide, are carried away for disposal. In humans, as in many other animals, this need for transport is solved by having a circulatory system composed of a heart, blood vessels and blood.

p224

The heart

The heart is a muscular double pump, about the size of a clenched fist. Its job is to push blood around the body. Each side acts as a separate pump, the right side pumping blood to the lungs, the left to the rest of the body.

▼
The heart's double-pump action.

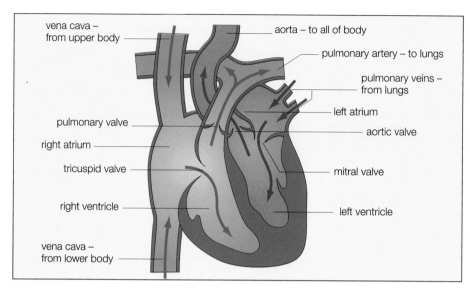

vena cava –
from upper body

aorta – to all of body

pulmonary artery – to lungs

pulmonary veins –
from lungs

left atrium

aortic valve

pulmonary valve

right atrium

tricuspid valve

mitral valve

right ventricle

left ventricle

vena cava –
from lower body

◄
The flow of blood through the heart.

The double pump runs a double circulation system – one circulation involves the heart and lungs, the other the heart and body.

Questions and Practice

11 Look at the diagram of the heart. Starting at the label 'vena cava' draw a flowchart showing the pathway blood takes through the body, lungs and heart.

12 Which side of the heart will contain blood with the most oxygen? Explain your answer.

13 The heart is made of four chambers. The thickness of the walls is linked to how much force they can exert.

a Why do the atria (top chambers) have such thin walls?

b The left ventricle (bottom chamber) has a thicker wall than the right ventricle. Use the double circulation diagram to explain why.

Arteries, veins and capillaries

The blood pumped around the body is carried in three types of blood vessels.

▼
How the blood vessels are adapted to their function.

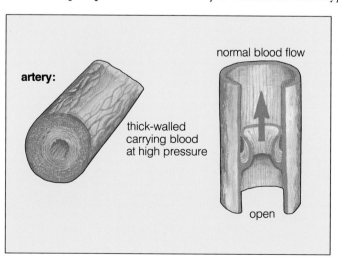

artery:

normal blood flow

thick-walled carrying blood at high pressure

open

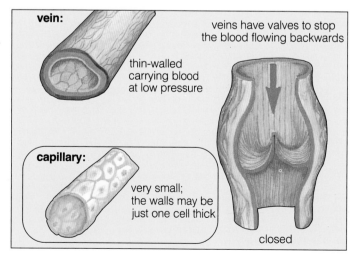

vein:

veins have valves to stop the blood flowing backwards

thin-walled carrying blood at low pressure

capillary:

very small; the walls may be just one cell thick

closed

Arteries carry the blood away from the heart and **veins** carry the blood back to the heart. You can remember this by: 'artery goes **away** from the heart, ve**in** goes **in** to the heart'. The arteries are connected to the veins by a system of tiny **capillaries**. This is where materials leave and enter the blood, to or from the cells surrounding them.

Questions and Practice

14 Look at the diagram of arteries, veins and capillaries. Use these, together with the text, to complete the following table.

	Artery	Vein
wall thickness		
size of middle space		
valves		
direction of blood flow		
blood pressure		

15 Why can material like oxygen and food diffuse out of capillaries so quickly?

16 Capillaries slow the blood down and cause a drop in blood pressure. Use this fact to explain why blood that has been through the capillaries in the lungs needs to go back to the heart, rather than straight on to the body.

A recipe for blood

On average a human adult has about five litres of blood inside them. About 40% of blood is made up of blood cells. There are three kinds of blood cell.

Red blood cells

There are 25 million million of these in an adult's body. They contain the red pigment haemoglobin and their main function is to carry oxygen from the lungs to the cells of the body. These cells live for about four months and are continually replaced.

White blood cells

These are the cells of defence and are fewer in number than red blood cells. There are two types; the phagocytes which eat disease organisms (microbes) and lymphocytes which produce antibodies that act like chemical missiles against disease.

Platelets

These are tiny bodies in the blood that help to clot the blood. If the skin is damaged or cut this can let microbes in, so an emergency repair system quickly comes into action. Once a blood vessel is damaged the blood starts to leak out. When platelets comes into contact with the air they break open. This causes a chain of reactions involving other chemicals in the blood (blood proteins) that leads to a clot forming in the damaged area.

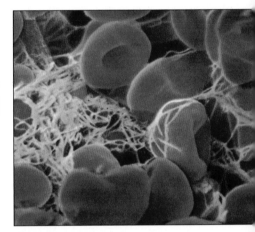

▲
Red blood cells in a blood clot. The white material is strands of fibrin – the basis of the clot.

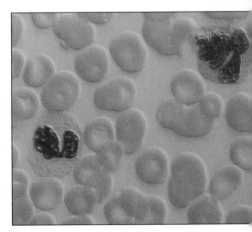

▲
Two white blood cells in a sea of red blood cells. The nuclei have been stained so that you can see their structure.

Plasma

The other 60% of blood is a fluid called **plasma**. This is an almost colourless liquid (slightly yellow) that contains an enormous amount of substances such as:

- water

- dissolved food (glucose, amino acids, fats)

- waste products (carbon dioxide, urea)

- minerals

- antibodies

- blood clotting proteins

- hormones

The bone marrow produces about 200 000 million red blood cells each day. Before a red blood cell dies it will have made about 172 000 journeys around the body. The blood vessels of the average adult would stretch almost $2^{1}/_{2}$ times around the Earth (about 95 000 km) if they were unravelled.

Questions and Practice

17 a Which two materials must diffuse out of the blood into the surrounding cells for respiration to occur?

b Which waste material produced by respiration needs to diffuse out of cells into the blood?

Examination Questions

Credit

1 This is a diagram of the human digestive system.

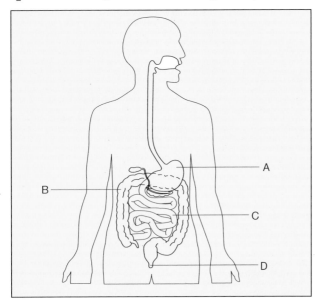

a Label the diagram. Choose the right words from: lung, stomach, liver, heart, large intestine, anus, kidney, small intestine. [4 marks]
b Write down one job that the stomach does. [1]
c Write down one job that the small intestine does. [1]
d Write down one job that the large intestine does. [1]

Merit

2 This question is about the digestive system. Look at these three types of food molecules found in the small intestine.

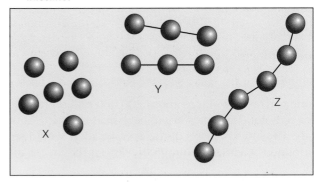

a Which type of molecule will most easily get into the blood? [1]
b How do food molecules get into the blood? Write down the name of the process. [1]
c Why do food molecules need to get into the blood? [1]

Special

3 This question is about blood vessels.

a Arteries are adapted to carry blood at a high pressure. Write down one way they are adapted for this. [1]
b Veins are adapted to carry blood at a lower pressure. Write down one way they are adapted for this. [1]
c Capillaries are adapted to allow substances to pass between the blood and body tissues. Write down one way they are adapted for this. [1]
d The small intestine is adapted so food can easily enter the blood. Write down two ways the small intestine is adapted so food can easily enter the blood. [2]

[Adapted from the Terminal Examination, 1994, and the Periodic Examination specimen paper.]

Checklist

These are the facts and ideas that you should have learned by studying this topic.

To succeed at Credit level you should:

- know the seven characteristics of living things
- know that livings things are made of cells and what cells are like
- know where the liver, intestines and stomach are located
- know what the main parts of the digestive system do
- know where the trachea, diaphragm, rib cage and lungs are located
- know what the main parts of the breathing system do
- know that the heart pumps blood around the body in arteries, veins and capillaries
- understand that blood carries food and oxygen to cells and removes waste products
- know that blood is made of red and white cells, platelets and plasma
- know what the different parts of blood do.

To succeed at Merit level you should:

- be able to identify the seven life processes in typical organisms
- know the similarities and differences between plant and animal cells
- be able to link the structure of a cell to its function
- know where the gall bladder, bile duct and pancreas are located
- understand how the digestive system works as a whole to bring about digestion, including knowledge of peristalsis and digestive juices
- know that digestive enzymes break down large food molecules into smaller ones
- know that stomach enzymes work better in stomach acid
- know that small molecules, in the small intestine, are absorbed into the blood by diffusion
- know where the bronchi, bronchioles and alveoli are located
- understand how the respiratory system works as a whole to bring about gaseous exchange
- know the changes in the position of the ribs and diaphragm that cause ventilation
- know that arteries take blood away from the heart, veins take blood to the heart, and capillaries exchange materials with tissues
- know the basic structure of the heart
- know that plasma transports food, hormones, water and waste products around the body
- know where oxygen and carbon dioxide enter and leave the blood.

To succeed at Special level you should:

- know how the small intestine is adapted for the absorption of food
- know how enzyme activity is affected by pH and temperature
- know that bile improves fat digestion by emulsification
- know how the alveoli are adapted for efficient gaseous exchange
- understand the function of cartilage in bronchi and bronchioles
- understand that pressure changes cause inhalation and exhalation
- understand the advantage of the double circulatory system in mammals
- know how arteries, veins and capillaries are adapted to their function
- know the role of haemoglobin in red blood cells in carrying oxygen
- understand that diffusion occurs due to differences in concentration.

GCSE FOUNDATION TIER

GCSE HIGHER TIER

Key words from this topic:

absorption
chemical digestion
mechanical digestion
diffusion
emulsification
enzyme
exhalation
gaseous exchange
inhalation

▲ HEARING – The shape of the bat-eared fox's ears makes the most of their sense of hearing, keeping the foxes alert to nearby danger.

▲ SIGHT – Owls, like humans, can judge distances effectively, because their eyes are on the front of their heads. This is called binocular vision. Animals with eyes on the side of their heads, like rabbits, can see all around, but do not have binocular vision.

▲ SMELL AND TOUCH – Animals rely on smell a great deal. A parent will rarely take care of any offspring that do not smell right. A mother's touch reassures her offspring.

CONTROL IN ANIMALS AND PLANTS

From the day that we are born we try to make sense of the world around us. As we grow and change, our minds and bodies respond to the environment. We make decisions based on what our senses tell us. Our bodies develop in distinct stages, taking us from the embryo, through childhood and adolescence to maturity.

These abilities to grow and change, to sense and respond, are features of *all* types of living things. Plants too must grow from smaller seeds or shoots. Plants too need to respond to the world around them – growing away from hazards, towards sources of nutrition and energy – if the species is to continue. It's a matter of survival.

This chapter details how plants and animals – including you – receive and use information about their surroundings in order to survive as well as possible.

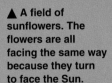

▲ A field of sunflowers. The flowers are all facing the same way because they turn to face the Sun.

▶ Fight or flight? Senses provide the raw information, but a decision has to be made. The body is prepared for fast action.

▲ This fly is on dangerous ground. The plant (a venus fly-trap) is sensitive to touch and will snap shut on any unsuspecting prey that it senses.

Stimulus and response

Humans have five main organs that act as **receptors** for information. We know these as the sense organs. Each responds to a different type of **stimulus**.

Stimulus	Sense organ (receptor)	Sense
light	eyes	sight
sound	ears	hearing
pressure, temperature hot/cold, pain	skin	touch
chemicals in the air	nose	smell
chemicals in food	tongue	taste

There are other receptors that are stimulated by changes that go on inside our bodies. Your balance is monitored by a part of the ears not responsible for hearing.

More important than getting information is using it. The way we react to information is called the **response**. If a tiger rushes towards you, you do not decide to stand still! The response to the danger (the tiger) is to run away.

The information from your senses is usually passed through nerve cells to the brain. The brain co-ordinates this data and decides the best way to deal with it. The brain acts together with the spinal cord as a control centre called the **central nervous system** (CNS). The decisions made by the CNS are passed through more nerve cells to muscles or glands (**effectors**), which give the desired response. Biologists sometimes call this basic system the *stimulus-response* model of behaviour.

An important receptor – the eye

Light reflects off objects, including people, in all directions. If any of this reflected light enters your eye, you can tell a lot about that object. How far away it is, if it is moving, its size and colour. In short you can *see* it.

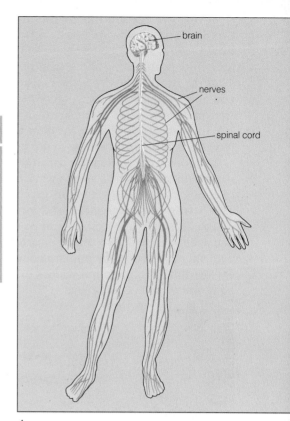

▲
The central nervous system.

▼

This cross-section of a human brain shows the main parts of the brain. From the age of 20 we lose 50 000 brain cells a day.

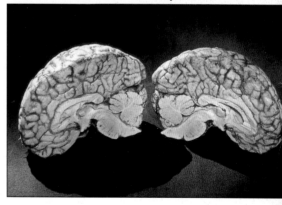

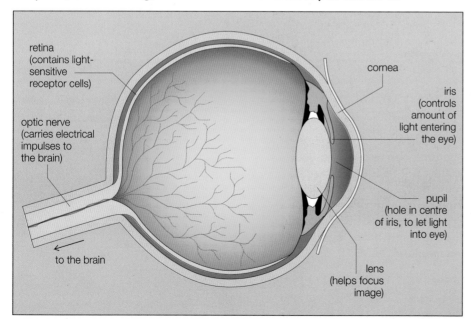

retina (contains light-sensitive receptor cells)

optic nerve (carries electrical impulses to the brain)

to the brain

cornea

iris (controls amount of light entering the eye)

pupil (hole in centre of iris, to let light into eye)

lens (helps focus image)

◀
The structure of the eye. Each part of the eye has its own job to do.

137

In your eye is a lens that focuses the light into an image on the back of the eye. This image is always upside down. The light entering the eye is refracted by the lens to focus it (see chapter 1). The lens can change shape so that the light from both nearby and distant objects can be focused.

At the back of the eye is the **retina**. The retina, only 0.4 mm thick, contains a top layer of transparent nerve cells and a layer of light-sensitive 'rod' and 'cone' cells. There are over a 100 million rods and 6 million cones. It is these cells that change the light image into electrical impulses which travel along the **optic nerve** to the brain.

The rods work best in the dark and help us see shades of grey. The cones need higher light levels and so work better in daylight. There are three types of cones, each sensitive to blue, green or red light, providing colour vision. This is why we see colours best during the day.

Too little light and nothing can be seen, but high-intensity light can damage the retina. Two sets of muscles in the **iris** (the coloured part of the eye) alter the size of the pupil to control the amount of light getting in the eye. In dim light, the pupil widens to let more light enter the eye. In bright light, the pupil becomes smaller. This is an example of the body being controlled by a **reflex**.

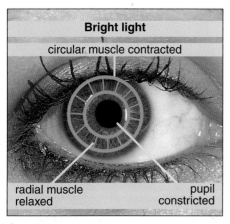

Bright light
circular muscle contracted
radial muscle relaxed
pupil constricted

▲ **In bright light the pupil constricts (narrows).**

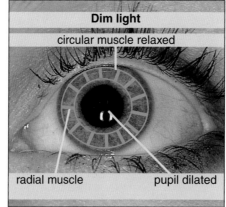

Dim light
circular muscle relaxed
radial muscle
pupil dilated

▲ **In dim light the pupil dilates (widens).**

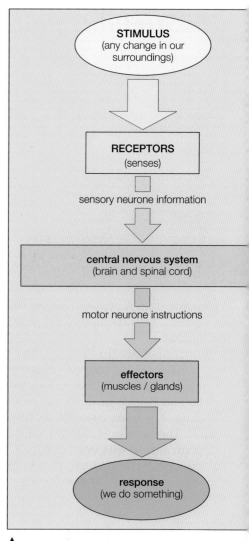

STIMULUS
(any change in our surroundings)

RECEPTORS
(senses)

sensory neurone information

central nervous system
(brain and spinal cord)

motor neurone instructions

effectors
(muscles / glands)

response
(we do something)

▲ **The stimulus–response model of behaviour.**

Questions and Practice

1 Write down what is now stimulating each of your five sense organs.

2 Suggest a reason why some people have problems telling the difference between various colours (i.e. they are colour blind).

Reflexes

Some stimuli need a rapid response. If something comes too near your eyes, you blink. If you place your hand on something hot, you pull it way without even thinking. If you swallow bad food, you vomit.

All these actions are called reflexes. You have many reflexes to protect your body from harm. Eyelids come down to cover your eyes. You remove your hand from the hot object before the skin is badly burnt. Food that could make you ill passes out of your body by the quickest route.

One of the first things that happens to a newborn baby is that the doctor or nurse will tickle the soles of its feet. If its toes curl up the doctor knows that one of the important reflexes is working. These reflex actions are automatic – you do not think before you respond. Thinking wastes valuable time during which you could be hurt.

Of course, human beings *can* think. The brain can over-ride some reflexes. If you are stupid enough you can keep your hand on a hot object for as long as you can bear the pain. You can even train yourself not to blink when something moves near your eyes.

The reflex paths

There are two different types of reflex. The type of reflex depends on the route that is taken. Reflexes that link to the spinal cord are called *spinal reflexes*. Some reflexes, like blinking, do not pass through the spine – they link directly to the brain. The brain passes back the signal for an immediate response without any thinking. This type of reflex is called a *cranial reflex*.

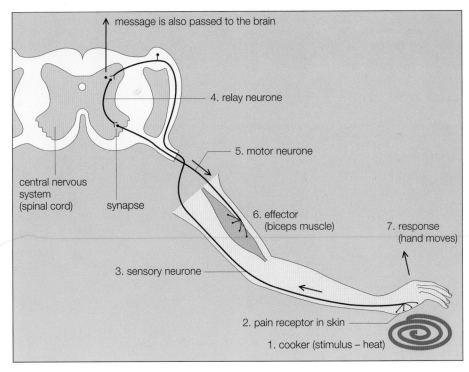

message is also passed to the brain

4. relay neurone

5. motor neurone

central nervous system (spinal cord)

synapse

6. effector (biceps muscle)

7. response (hand moves)

3. sensory neurone

2. pain receptor in skin

1. cooker (stimulus – heat)

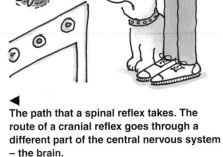

◄ The path that a spinal reflex takes. The route of a cranial reflex goes through a different part of the central nervous system – the brain.

When a receptor is stimulated, it sends impulses along a **sensory neurone** (sensory nerve) to the CNS. A relay neurone passes the information straight on to a **motor neurone**. Signals pass from neurone to neurone via tiny gaps called *synapses*. The signal is carried across the gap by a tiny amount of a chemical. The motor neurone sends its message to an effector (a muscle or gland) to produce the required response.

Pathways like this are often called reflex *arcs* because of their curved shape. The original impulse is not only passed on to the motor neurone but also to the part of the brain which will make you aware of what is happening.

Nerve cells

The central nervous system is an incredibly complex system made from

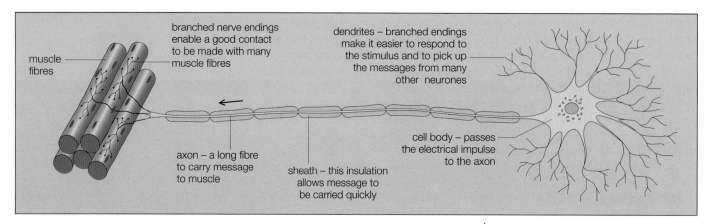

muscle fibres

branched nerve endings enable a good contact to be made with many muscle fibres

dendrites – branched endings make it easier to respond to the stimulus and to pick up the messages from many other neurones

cell body – passes the electrical impulse to the axon

axon – a long fibre to carry message to muscle

sheath – this insulation allows message to be carried quickly

thousands of millions of simple neurones (nerve cells). For *any* system to work efficiently its cells have to be adapted to their functions. Neurones are no exception.

▲ Nerve structure. The average adult has 75 km of nerves throughout the body. The poison *curare* can paralyse by blocking the synapses that link nerves with muscles.

Questions and Practice

3 Look at the diagram of the hand withdrawal reflex (page 139). When someone puts their hand on a hot object they remove it, before they scream out in pain.

   a Outline the nervous pathways involved in removing the hand and in screaming out.

   b Why is it important to remove the hand before the brain knows what is going on?

4 Copy out the following table:

Spinal reflex	Cranial reflex

Complete the table by putting each reflex into its appropriate column:

iris reflex to bright light; knee jerk reflex to being hit below the knee; salivation reflex when smelling food; swallowing reflex to food at the back of the mouth; withdrawal reflex to bare foot on a pin

Controlling inside the body

The nervous system gives us a quick and exact response to the information the sense receptors pick up. This information usually comes from changes that are happening in the outside world. However, inside the body a different system is needed.

   If the living cells of our tissues and organs are to work properly they must have the conditions they need to stay alive. Most of our cells are deep inside our bodies so the environment inside the body around the living cells must be strictly controlled. The cells need water, chemicals and the right temperature. Ensuring that conditions within the body are kept constant is called **homeostasis**. These conditions are controlled by chemicals called **hormones**.

   Hormones can reach every cell in the body, because they are transported around in the blood. Hormones can also help control long-term changes in the body. The nervous system has neither of these advantages. It is not connected to every cell of the body. To control long-term changes, the nervous system would have to be continually stimulated over a long period of time.

Where are hormones made?

Hormones are made in **glands**. Glands are organs or parts of the body designed to produce these special chemicals. There are two main types of gland found in the body. The first type, the **exocrine glands**, have ducts (tubes) that deliver the chemicals they make into the surrounding area. Examples include the sweat glands and tear glands. The second type, the **endocrine glands**, make hormones and do not have ducts. They rely on the blood that passes through them to pick up the hormone and transport it through the body. These second type of glands form part of the **endocrine system**.

Controlling growth

Human growth hormone is made by the **pituitary gland** which is at the base of the brain, just behind the eyes. Growth hormone affects our body in different ways according to our age. It has a great effect on young people, ensuring that they grow quickly. These hormones are still produced in the adult body, but adult tissues and organs no longer respond to them.

When children are injected with extra human growth hormone, their bones grow bigger. In adults, the growth regions at the tips of the bones are no longer active and the bone cells cannot respond to the hormone.

Some people go on growing for longer than they should, others grow unusually fast. This is because their pituitary glands produce too much growth hormone or their cells don't stop responding to it. Such people can become 'giants'. If a person cannot produce enough growth hormone they do not grow to full height. This condition is called *achondroplasia*, more commonly known as dwarfism. It affects about one in 5000 people.

Controlling blood sugar

When you eat a starchy meal, your digestive system breaks down the starch into small units of a sugar called glucose. The glucose is absorbed across the wall of the small intestine into the bloodstream. The amount of glucose in the bloodstream – your blood sugar level – is crucial.

If your blood sugar level gets too high, the brain can be affected, with the possibility of a coma. If untreated this condition can cause death. If your blood sugar level gets too low, you could faint and, in serious cases, might even die from the lack of sugar in the blood.

Normally, if you skip the occasional meal or eat a plateful of very starchy food, you do not suddenly faint! This is because our bodies have an automatic system to control the level of glucose in our blood at all times.

Too much sugar

After a meal, the glucose from starch digestion is carried to the liver by a large blood vessel called the *hepatic portal vein*. The liver stores the glucose by changing it into another type of carbohydrate called *glycogen*. The liver is a very important organ that does many other jobs as well.

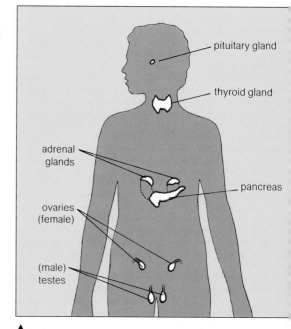

▲
The positions of the main endocrine glands in the body.

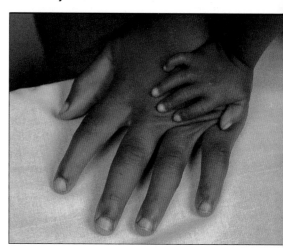

▲
These hands belong to three-year-old children. One of the children has a hormone imbalance and has grown to giant size. By law the pituitary gland is the only part of the body that can be collected and kept after a post-mortem examination. Growth hormone is extracted from it for use with children who cannot produce enough of it themselves.

141

The meal will cause the blood sugar level to rise. If it gets too high, the hormone insulin is released from special cells in the pancreas.

Insulin travels to the liver in the blood and makes the liver change more glucose to glycogen, which is then stored. The higher the blood sugar levels rises the more insulin is produced and the more glucose is taken out of the blood stream and stored. This causes the blood sugar level to fall back to normal levels.

Too little sugar

If the blood sugar level falls below normal levels, for example when we are exercising, the amount of insulin released from the pancreas is reduced. Another hormone, called *glucagon,* is released instead. Glucagon stimulates the liver to convert glycogen back into glucose and to pass glucose into the bloodstream. The blood sugar level then rises back towards normal levels.

Insulin and glucagon work together to keep the amount of glucose in the blood at an almost constant level. Insulin helps lower the level if it gets too high and glucagon helps raise the level if it gets too low.

Not enough insulin

In some people, the pancreas gland cannot produce enough insulin to regulate their blood sugar level. This disease is called *diabetes mellitus* or sugar diabetes. The symptoms are:

● almost constant thirst;

● general weakness;

● loss of weight;

● too much sugar in the blood, and so glucose is present in urine;

● possible coma followed by death.

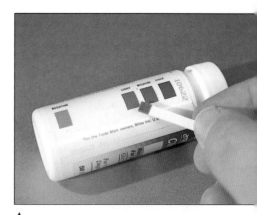

▲
Test strips are used to test for glucose in urine.

There was a time when doctors used to test for this disease by tasting the patient's urine! If it tasted sweet, sugar must be present and the doctor would know that the person was suffering from diabetes. No one would recommend testing urine that way these days!

People with diabetes are now able to live relatively ordinary lives. They must regulate their diet very carefully, and may also require daily injections of insulin hormone. The balance between sugar taken in as food and the amount of insulin needed to control it must be exactly right. This balance is something that the rest of us take for granted.

Controlling emergencies

When you are frightened, excited or angry the body gets itself ready for action. Glands located just above the kidneys release the hormone **adrenalin** into the bloodstream. These glands are called the *adrenal glands.* The changes that adrenalin causes are designed to help you stay alive. In animals this usually means a *fight* against an enemy or running away – *flight.* In both cases the changes that need to happen in the body are the same. Adrenalin ensures that these changes are fast.

If the body is to respond quickly to a stressful situation, it is very important that the muscles are supplied with lots of glucose and oxygen. These are then used to make the energy either to face up to the stress (fight – you perform

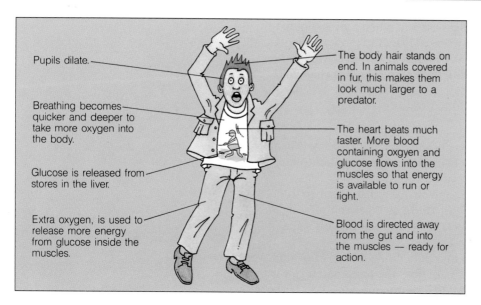

◄
This is what adrenalin does to the body.

Pupils dilate.

Breathing becomes quicker and deeper to take more oxygen into the body.

Glucose is released from stores in the liver.

Extra oxygen, is used to release more energy from glucose inside the muscles.

The body hair stands on end. In animals covered in fur, this makes them look much larger to a predator.

The heart beats much faster. More blood containing oxgyen and glucose flows into the muscles so that energy is available to run or fight.

Blood is directed away from the gut and into the muscles — ready for action.

better in a sporting activity, or even in an exam) or to run away from the stress (flight – it is sometimes safer to run away rather than stay and get hurt).

Controlling the changes into adulthood

Adult animals are capable of reproduction. They can make more of their own kind from sex cells (**gametes**). These cells are brought together in sexual reproduction.

At birth, a human baby is classed as being either a boy or a girl. This decision is mainly based upon whether the baby has a penis (a boy) or a vagina (a girl). These are known as *primary sexual characteristics*.

At puberty, children start the change into adults. The changes do not happen overnight and they happen at different times in different people, so there is no

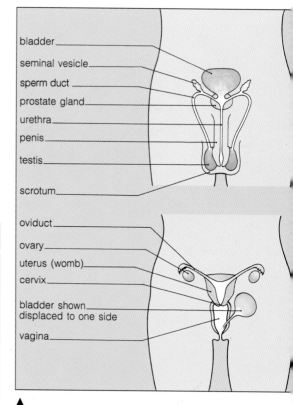

bladder
seminal vesicle
sperm duct
prostate gland
urethra
penis
testis
scrotum

oviduct
ovary
uterus (womb)
cervix
bladder shown displaced to one side
vagina

▲
The human male and female reproductive systems.

In the male	In the female
Body size increases dramatically	Body size increases dramatically
Body hair starts to grow – armpit and pubic hair	Body hair starts to grow – armpit and pubic hair
Sexual 'drive' develops	Sexual 'drive' develops
Body becomes more muscular, chest broadens, body becomes 'squarer'	Hips get wider, body becomes 'rounder'
Beard starts to grow	Breasts develop (humans are the only species where this happens before pregnancy)
The voice breaks	
Penis, testes and scrotum get larger and start to produce sperm and semen	Vagina, uterus and oviducts grow and develop
	Menstrual cycle begins

◄

How the body changes during puberty.

'normal', only an average of what the changes are and when they happen. Puberty is triggered by hormones that are released from the pituitary gland. These cause other hormones to be released, from the **testes** in boys and the **ovaries** in girls. These sex hormones control the way our bodies change.

Leaving childhood

Girls usually begin puberty when they are 11–13 years old. Puberty is usually two or three years later for boys. Puberty takes several years to complete. During this time, young people are called adolescents.

The sex hormones cause the size and shape changes that occur to the adolescent body (see the table on page 143). These changes to the body are called the *secondary sexual characteristics*. They are the outward signs of adulthood.

During puberty changes also take place inside the body. The sex hormones literally 'switch on' the reproductive systems. In boys the penis and testes get larger and the testes start to produce sperm. In girls, the menstrual cycle starts.

The menstrual cycle

Girls start to have periods as their menstrual cycle starts. This is a series of events that takes about 28 days in most women. It is controlled by two hormones, *oestrogen* and *progesterone*, which are produced by the ovaries. At birth the ovaries contain about 400 000 cells capable of becoming eggs.

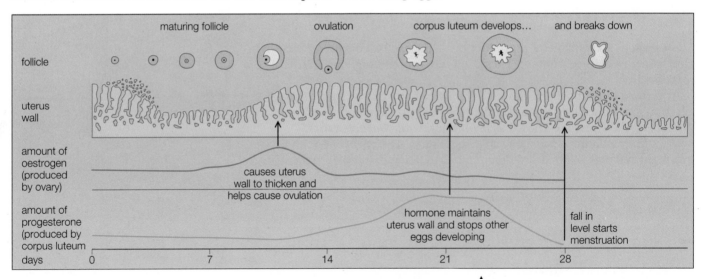

The menstrual cycle.

First the pituitary gland produces a hormone which causes part of the ovary to become a follicle. The follicle is a ball of cells containing a single developing egg (**ovum**). It grows and carries the egg to the edge of the ovary. When the egg is ready the follicle bursts open and the egg is released into the oviduct. This is called **ovulation**. The egg now travels down the oviduct to the uterus. The wall of the uterus has been repaired since the previous cycle by the presence of oestrogen produced by the ovary. A high level of oestrogen also helps ovulation to happen.

After ovulation the part of the follicle that is left does another job. It develops into a kind of temporary gland called the *corpus luteum* which produces **progesterone**. The progesterone completes the development of the uterus wall, which is now ready to receive a fertilized egg that would grow into a baby. If this happens the corpus luteum continues to make progesterone which keeps the uterus lining growing. It also stops the pituitary from releasing the hormone that causes a new egg to develop.

If the egg is not fertilized the corpus luteum starts to disappear and stops making progesterone. The thickened uterus wall breaks down and is shed through the woman's vagina. This is called **menstruation** or a *period*. In addition the pituitary can now release the hormone to start the whole cycle again.

And in boys ...

The male sex hormone, **testosterone**, as you might guess from the name, is made in the testes. Testosterone causes a boy's testes to mature and produce sperm. Sperm are produced in a continuous cycle. The human female produces a single egg every 28 days, but sperm cells are made continuously by the million. Sperm production is very sensitive to temperature. This is why the testes lie outside a boy's body where the temperature is lower.

Using sex hormones

One of the strongest behavioural urges in animals is to produce offspring – to reproduce. Humans are no exception. But some people are unable to have children.

One of the many causes of the inability of would-be parents to have children is that the woman's ovary is unable to produce the egg follicle. Fertility drugs act like sex hormones in stimulating the production of follicles. Sometimes fertility drugs can start several follicles working at the same time, leading to several eggs and multiple births.

Sometimes it is the man who is infertile. His testes may not produce enough sperm, or the sperm may be too weak to reach and fertilize the egg cell.

The best known use of artificial hormones is the birth pill or oral contraceptive. When taken regularly at the correct time of the female menstrual cycle it can stop the ovaries from releasing an egg. It does this by introducing artificial progesterone into the body, so that the ovaries behave as though the body is already pregnant.

▲
Fertility drugs can give even better results than you expected.

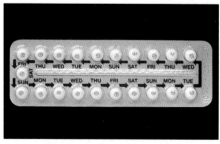

▲
An oral contraceptive. It is designed to work with the natural menstrual cycle.

Questions and Practice

5 How are hormones carried around the body?

6 Name a gland that makes both digestive enzymes and hormones.

7 Explain what endocrine means.

8 Copy and complete the following table:

Hormone	Endocrine gland	Effects on body
growth hormone		
insulin		
oestrogen		
progesterone		
testosterone		
adrenalin		

9 Name two hormones that can cause glycogen, which is stored in the liver, to be converted into glucose.

Controlling plant development

Growth and development in plants is controlled by chemicals that are very much like the hormones found in animals. These chemical substances are called **auxins** or plant hormones.

Plant hormones control every aspect of the plant's life:

● shoot growth 'upwards' and towards the light

● root growth 'downwards'

● seed germination

● growth of fruits and flowers

● opening and growth of buds

● healing of wounds

● ripening of fruits

● dormancy in the winter (the plant's leaves fall and it becomes inactive).

▲
Plants have been bred to be exactly what we want them to be. These carrots are very different from their wild counterparts – and shops want fruit and vegetables that fit the packaging. Does this affect the taste?

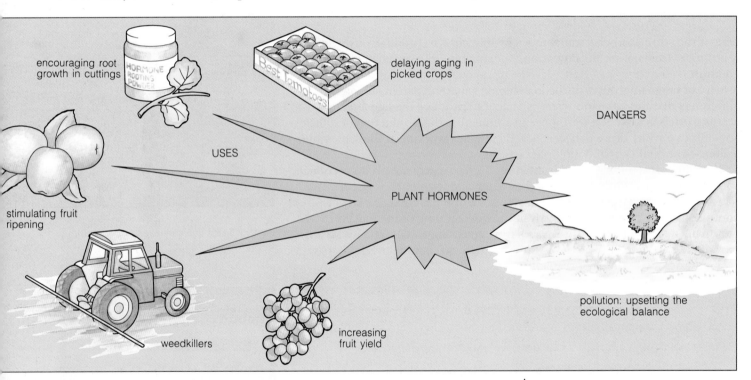

▲
The dangers and uses of plant hormones.

Can we make use of plant hormones?

When plant hormones were first discovered it was thought that they might solve all of the world's food problems by allowing us to grow enormous vegetables and other plants in huge amounts. This didn't work out. The hormones simply made giant plants that were weak-stemmed and did not live for very long. However, our knowledge of different types of plant hormones has been useful in some ways:

● Preventing spoiling of cereal foods and potatoes to enable them to be stored for longer periods of time. This is done by keeping them dormant or inactive.

- Making sure that barley seeds all germinate at the same time. This is used in the malting industry.

- Making selective weed-killers such as 2,4–D. These do not affect grasses, but make weeds outgrow themselves and die.

- Fruit ripening can be accelerated or delayed by using plant hormones. This is especially important where machines harvest the fruit crop, for example with grapes. Unripe fruit is tougher and easier to pick without bruising. It can be transported with less damage, and then ripened before being sold in shops.

- Rooting hormones help in the propagation of plants through taking cuttings. When a cutting is dipped in a rooting preparation it is stimulated to make roots and grow.

Plants have an essential positive tropism for light.

Plant growth responses

Plants react to light, gravity, temperature, chemical substances, water and touch. There are two types of responses: *nastic* and *tropic*.

Nastic responses do not have a direction. Examples are when flowers close their petals at night, or when a venus flytrap snaps shut on an insect.

Tropic responses, or **tropisms**, have a definite direction of movement that is determined by the direction of the stimulus causing the response. The plant may move or grow towards the stimulus, a positive tropism; or it may move or grow away, a negative tropism. Tropisms are controlled by auxins.

Auxins and phototropism

Experiments have shown that plant shoots grow towards the light (positive phototropism) due to the production of auxin at their tips. The auxin moves away from the tip by diffusion. It can do this because it can dissolve in the water found inside plants. When it reaches the area just behind the tip it causes the cells to grow longer (cell elongation). Shoot and root growth is also affected by gravity.

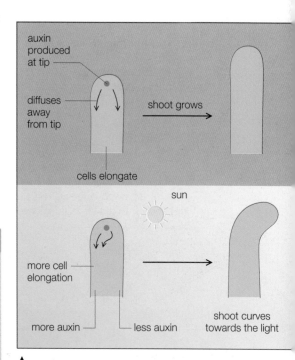

If light shines on the plant from one side it will grow towards the light because more of the auxin will diffuse to the darker side.

Questions and Practice

10 Explain the economic advantages of the use of plant hormones to:

  a stop potatoes sprouting;

  b kill weeds;

  c encourage the growth of roots when taking cuttings.

11 A gardener experiments with auxins. He paints some near to the tip of the shoot on the right-hand side. Explain how the growth of the shoot will be affected.

12 Explain why the growth of a seed is not affected by which way up it is planted.

13 What is different about where plant hormones (auxins) are produced compared to animal hormones?

Examination Questions

Credit

1 Here is a list of endocrine glands: pancreas, testes, adrenal glands, thyroid, pituitary. The diagram shows some of the endocrine glands in the body of a man.

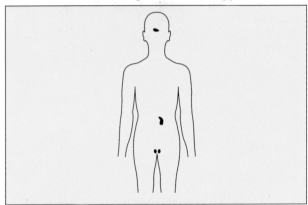

a Write the name of the glands from top to bottom. [3 marks]
b Ovaries are also glands found in humans. The person in the diagram does not have ovaries. Explain why. [1]

Merit

2 As part of an experiment, Jake had to press a buzzer with his left hand whenever his partner touched Jake's right hand. Jake was blind-folded.

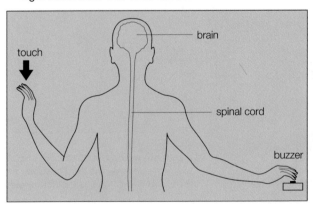

a The steps below describe what happens in Jake's body. Place the steps in the correct order.
message leaves spinal cord; message passes along sensory nerve; message leaves brain; message passes along motor nerve; message enters brain; message enters spinal cord. [3]
b Sketch the diagram and draw on the route taken by the nerve message from Jake's right hand to the muscle that moves the finger of his left hand. Use arrows to show the direction the message takes. [2]
c Write down two ways in which a reflex like the knee jerk is different from the reaction to touch in Jake's experiment. [2]

3 Hormones are chemicals that pass round the bodies of animals and plants. Hormones cause changes in their bodies. Insulin and adrenalin are hormones.

a Write down two effects that male sex hormones have on boys' bodies during puberty. [2]
b What is the function (job) of insulin? [1]
c Write down two effects of adrenalin. [2]

Special

4 A cat suddenly sees a nearby dog. A large amount of adrenalin is released into the cat's bloodstream. Adrenalin affects the level of glucose in the blood.

a Which organ releases the adrenalin? [1]
b What happens to the level of glucose when adrenalin is released? [1]
c Explain why this is important. [2]

5 This is a drawing of a young growing plant. The tip of the plant (labelled X) was removed.

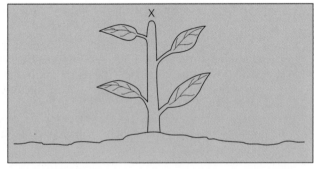

a How will the growth of the plant be affected? [2]
b Explain your answer. [1]

[Adapted from the Periodic Examination, July 1993 and July 1994.]

Checklist

These are the facts and ideas that you should have learned by studying this topic.

To succeed at Credit level you should:

- ■ know the areas of the body that gather sense information
- ■ know that reflexes are fast, automatic responses to a stimulus
- ■ be able to name and locate the main parts of the nervous system
- ● know that reflexes are fast and automatic responses to a stimulus
- ● be able to name and locate the main parts of the eye and endocrine system
- ● know the names of the glands that produce growth hormone, insulin, adrenalin and the sex hormones
- ● know that hormones travel in the blood
- ● know that diabetes is caused by the failure of the pancreas to make insulin
- ● know that insulin can be used to treat diabetes, growth hormone to treat poor growth and sex hormones to treat infertility
- ● know that plant hormones are chemicals that control growth, flowering and ripening
- ● know that shoots grow towards light
- ● know that plant hormones can be used to speed up or slow down plant growth.

To succeed at Merit level you should:

- ■ know the path taken by nerve impulses
- ■ know the structure of a motor neurone
- ■ know the path taken by a spinal reflex
- ● know the functions of the lens, retina, iris and optic nerve
- ● know the functions of male and female sex hormones
- ● know what insulin and adrenalin control
- ● understand that people with diabetes have large fluctuations of blood sugar level, and that insulin injections can treat the condition
- ● know that plant hormones move in solution and are involved in the response to light and gravity
- ● be able to link the action of plant hormones to their commercial uses.

To succeed at Special level you should:

- ■ understand how neurones are well adapted to their function
- ● understand the pathways that make the brain aware of reflexes
- ● understand how muscles in the iris control pupil size
- ● know that oestrogen causes the repair of the uterus wall, progesterone maintains the uterus wall and the two control ovulation
- ● understand how insulin controls blood sugar levels
- ● understand how the effects of adrenalin prepare the body for 'fight or flight'
- ● know that fertility and infertility can be affected by the use of female sex hormones
- ● understand that contraceptive hormones stop ovulation by mimicking pregnancy
- ● be able to interpret phototropism in terms of auxin action
- ● be able to explain how auxin brings about shoot curvature by affecting cell elongation
- ● be able to evaluate the benefits of hormone use in agriculture.

GCSE FOUNDATION TIER

GCSE HIGHER TIER

Key words from this topic:

| stimulus |
| central nervous system |
| receptor |
| neurone |
| effectors |
| response |
| reflex |
| auxin |
| endocrine system |
| hormones |

CHAPTER 9

◀ Woodland.

▼ Rocky coast – unique forms of life have adapted to the influence of the tides on this ecosystem.

▲ Of all the ecosystems, rainforests contain the widest variety of plants and animals. One biologist discovered 600 new species of beetle in just one type of tree in the rainforests of Costa Rica.

▲ Meadow land.

▲ Icelandic tundra – mosses and wetland wildlife.

▲ Canadian mountains.

ECOLOGY

Living things depend upon each other. Animals depend on plants for their nutrients. In turn, plants depend on dead animals, the body wastes they produce and even the carbon dioxide they breathe out. Human beings are a unique sort of organism, but they are part of this dependency too. We depend on the other organisms around us in a variety of ways that are not always obvious.

All the organisms in an area are called the *community*. The community and the physical features of the area are referred to as an *ecosystem*.

The dependency of organisms on all the other organisms in an ecosystem means that the study of ecosystems, *ecology*, can become very complicated. Fortunately it all starts with some very simple ideas. Investigating an ecosystem is the first step. What is it like and what organisms are there?

▼ Coral reefs – a rich and diverse underwater ecosystem.

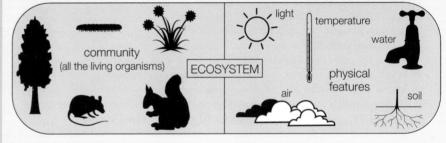

community (all the living organisms)

ECOSYSTEM

light
temperature
water
physical features
air
soil

Living organisms (community)

To study an ecosystem in depth, it is often necessary to collect the organisms in it. If you are doing this it is important to remember the following rules:

- Obtain permission from the land-owner before starting to study a particular area.
- Never take organisms away or needlessly destroy them.
- Replace stones, logs, etc. that you have moved.
- If you have to take specimens away take as few as possible and try to return them when you have finished.
- Keep your animals in separate pots or you could end up with one eating the rest!

R The equipment used to collect insects and sample plants are detailed in the reference section.

p189

Physical features

These features depend upon the particular ecosystem or habitat that is being investigated, but may include:

- The type of rock, soil, stream bed, etc.
- If the ground slopes, the way it faces (e.g. south facing).
- Drainage – does water run off easily or soak into the ground?
- Temperature and pH of soil, water or air.
- Cloud cover – whether it is raining or not.
- Light level (open or shaded, or a reading from a light meter).
- Humidity of the air (amount of moisture).
- Wind speed and directions, or water speed in a river.
- Time of day and date.

Factors such as light, pH and temperature can be measured by using special environmental probes. These probes often allow readings to be recorded over a period of time.

◄
The polar bear is well adapted to its environment:

- **Eyes on front of head for good judgement of size and distance.**
- **Sharp teeth for killing prey and tearing through flesh.**
- **White fur is good camouflage – less likely to be seen by prey.**
- **Thick fur to trap heat to keep warm.**
- **Lots of fat to act as a food store and to keep warm.**
- **Strong legs for walking and swimming long distances.**
- **Sharp claws to grip ice.**

Adapted for survival

When investigating any particular habitat it becomes clear that each organism is adapted (suited) to where it lives. The adaptations may be physical (camouflage, special teeth, deep roots, etc.) or behavioural (living in groups, running for cover, etc.). These adaptations have developed over millions of years. For example, different animals have adapted to life in running water in different ways.

- The trout. These fish are **predators**, which have to catch their food (**prey**). They are good at this because they are strong swimmers, with streamlined bodies.

- Caddis fly larvae. The larvae of the caddis fly hatch and live in water. They have soft bodies, and some build protective shelters of small stones around themselves. They can also attach themselves to rocks to prevent themselves from being washed away.

- Limpets. The limpet is found in tidal zones and has a strong muscular 'foot' that it uses to hold on to rocks. The strongest tides wash over the limpet, unable to remove it from its foothold.

Out of the thousands of young trout produced, the ones that are better camouflaged against predators, the ones that swim quicker and react faster, are the ones that are likely to survive and produce children of their own. How the abilities of parents are passed on to their children is dealt with in Book 2.

◄
Plant adaptations to life in water.

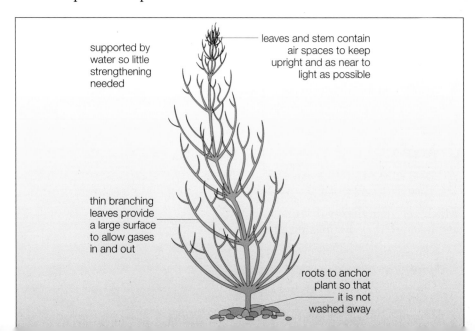

supported by water so little strengthening needed

leaves and stem contain air spaces to keep upright and as near to light as possible

thin branching leaves provide a large surface to allow gases in and out

roots to anchor plant so that it is not washed away

Questions and Practice

1 Use the photographs on the first two pages of the chapter to list six ecosystems.

2 What does the word *community* mean? How is a community different from an ecosystem?

3 For each of the following animals, list the ways that they are adapted for survival: zebra, tiger, rabbit, fish.

Food chains and food webs

The relationships between organisms are usually very ordered. For example, the nutrients in grass are passed to a rabbit when the rabbit eats the grass. When a fox eats the rabbit, it gains the nutrients it needs. This linkage is known as a **food chain**. The diagram below shows a number of different food chains. The direction of the arrows show the way in which the materials are moving. They also show the direction of energy flow in the food chain.

◄
Sample food chains.

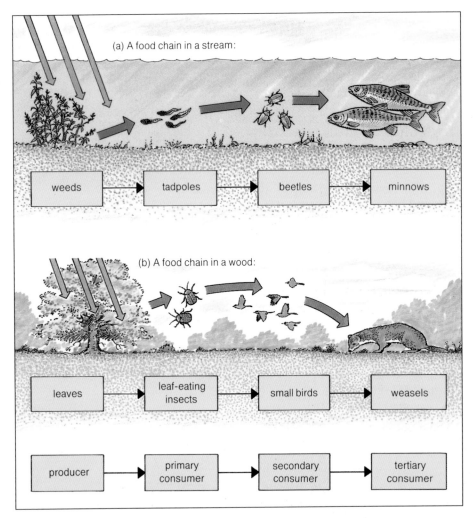

(a) A food chain in a stream:

| weeds | → | tadpoles | → | beetles | → | minnows |

(b) A food chain in a wood:

| leaves | → | leaf-eating insects | → | small birds | → | weasels |

| producer | → | primary consumer | → | secondary consumer | → | tertiary consumer |

Food chains always begin with plants, which get their energy from sunlight. This is why plants are so important, because they are making all of the food that the rest of the food chain and ultimately all life on Earth depends on. All the energy that we get from our food originally comes from plants.

The feeding relationships in an ecosystem are a lot more complicated than the simple food chains shown above. Most plants are eaten by more than one type of animal and in general most of these animals are then eaten by more than one type of other animal. If all the feeding links between the various organisms of an ecosystem are drawn out a **food web** is obtained.

▼
Food web for an English oak wood. The decomposers have been omitted.

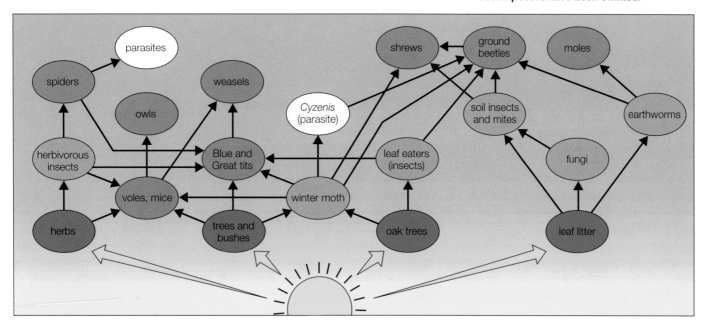

Within a food web, each living thing has a role to play. The key roles are:

● **producers**: the green plants that can use the energy of sunlight to make food from water and carbon dioxide gas (this reaction is called **photosynthesis**);

● **consumers**: animals that either eat plants or eat other animals (some animals do both – like us);

● **decomposers**: bacteria and fungi that live off the dead remains of plants and animals, turning these into soil nutrients, especially the nitrates essential for plant growth.

Pyramids of number

When looking at a food web, it is useful to know the number of animals and plants involved at each stage.

For example, a single rabbit needs to feed on a large number of grass plants, and it takes several rabbits to satisfy the feeding requirements of a fox. This can be shown in a diagram. The number of individuals at each stage in a food chain can be shown by using different-sized boxes. The organisms in the higher boxes feed on the lower ones. The result is a kind of pyramid. Plants always provide the energy and materials for animals and so they form the base of the pyramid. The rabbit is a primary consumer – it feeds on the plants directly. The fox is a secondary consumer.

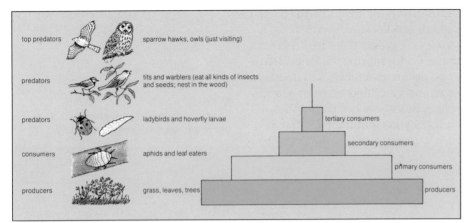

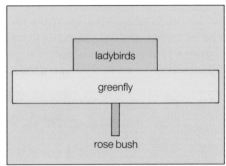

▲
A pyramid of numbers for a rose bush food chain.

The idea of the pyramid of numbers is useful when an unknown area is sampled. It is a reasonable guess that the most common animals that we find are the primary consumers or herbivores (plant eaters). There will be a smaller number of secondary consumers. (For example, when you walk in the countryside you are more likely to see a rabbit than a fox.)

However, this idea does not always work. A large number of greenfly can live on one rose bush. So a pyramid of numbers for this food chain would look more like an upside-down pyramid.

Questions and Practice

4 Look at the diagram of the food web for an English oak wood (page 153). Use it to answer the following questions.

  a Name two producer organisms.

  b Name two primary consumers (herbivores).

  c Name two secondary consumers (carnivores).

  d Draw a simple food chain including three of the organisms.

5 In a pond, mayfly larvae feed on plant algae. Trout feed on stonefly larvae that in turn feed on the mayfly larvae.

  a Draw a food chain for these organisms.

  b Sketch a pyramid of numbers.

  c What would happen to the population of mayfly and trout if something was added to the water that killed stonefly larvae?

Building pyramids of biomass

Instead of counting the greenfly, we could weigh all the greenfly on a rose bush, and weigh the rose bush. Then we can compare the total mass of the greenfly with the mass of the rose bush. This gives us a better idea of how the greenfly depend on the rose bush. Such a pyramid is called a pyramid of **biomass**. Biomass is the total mass of all the organisms of one species in the area being studied. Ideally, it should be dry mass (the mass with the water removed).

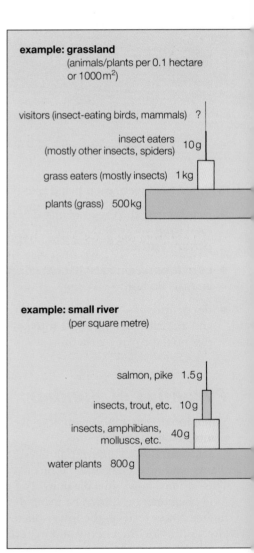

▲
Pyramids of biomass.

Energy pyramids

Energy is vital for life. Perhaps the best way to look at feeding relationships is to consider the movement of energy. All the energy to support life on Earth comes from the Sun. But of all the energy that falls on the Earth, only one part in every hundred is actually used by plants to make food, by the process known as photosynthesis. Most of the Earth's surface is sea, with hardly any plants. Also, plants cannot absorb all the light they get and photosynthesis is not perfect. Only 1% of all the light falling on a meadow is actually transferred to the grass. Energy transfers are never perfect. So when rabbits eat the grass, they do not get all of the energy in the grass. They do not eat the roots, for example. Also, some of the energy is used by the grass to produce seeds and to grow. Of all the energy taken in by the grass, less than one-tenth is passed on to the rabbit. And only about one-tenth passes from the rabbit to the fox. Again we can show this by a pyramid, a pyramid of energy. The energy flow in a typical habitat is shown in this diagram.

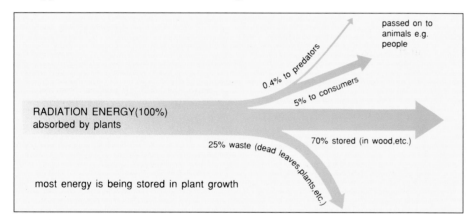

◀
Energy flow in a young woodland.

What would you do with a field? A field can be farmed – used to grow plant food like wheat – or the farmer can keep animals such as cows or sheep on it. When we eat meat, we do not get as much energy from it as the cow or sheep got from the grass. This is because animals can only get one-tenth of the available energy from the grass. And if we then eat the meat we only get one-tenth of that energy. This means that we only receive 1% of the energy originally in the grass.

Questions and Practice

6 What is meant by the *biomass* of an animal?

7 Look at this simple food web, described in the passage on energy pyramids.

Explain why it is more energy efficient for humans to eat wheat directly, rather than to feed it to cows, and then eat the cows.

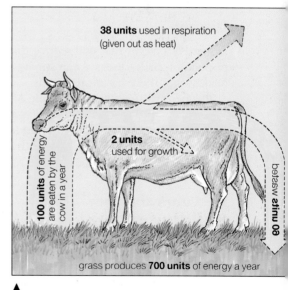

▲
The energy flow through a young cow.

155

Populations

In any ecosystem, the number of individuals of a particular species is called its **population**. This number depends on several different factors. Some of these help the population to grow, others tend to reduce it. The more important factors are:

● the number of offspring per female per year;

● the suitability of places to live;

● the availability of food and water;

● the climate or weather;

● the occurrence of diseases;

● the number of predators;

● competition from other populations.

Weather

Insect numbers are often affected by the weather. We often find a lot of greenfly after a mild winter. Then, with all the greenfly to feed on during the summer, the population of ladybirds increases. They eat more greenfly so the population of these pests is kept down.

   Most plants need a good amount of sunlight to grow well, but if this is accompanied by a lack of rain, they may not do so well. To make sure that they get enough light, many plants will grow very tall, to avoid being shaded by others. To get enough water, plants may have roots that either grow very deep into the soil, or spread out very wide.

Disease

Disease is a factor that will reduce the size of a population. Usually, as a population rises, diseases can spread more easily. So big populations are less healthy and there are more deaths.

   Plagues are an extreme example of the effect of disease on a population. The rabbit population of Britain was almost wiped out by the terrible disease myxomatosis. The disease is carried from rabbit to rabbit by fleas. Some farmers even helped to spread the disease by taking fleas from infected rabbits and putting them down the rabbit holes.

Predators and prey

Apart from natural disasters or plagues, like myxomatosis in the rabbits, animal populations stay more or less constant. The average number of wild animals such as rabbits, deer or mountain sheep tends to stay fairly constant. Most die from old age or are killed by predators. But the numbers can change very quickly in the short term. Suppose that the weather has been very good and that there is plenty of plant food. The number of wild sheep would start to increase. This means that the wolves that feed on the sheep now have lots of food as well. This means that more wolf cubs tend to survive to become adult wolves. These eat more sheep and breed more successfully. There are more wolves, so the sheep numbers drop. This makes life hard for the extra wolves – so the wolf population falls.

▲
Cacti are adapted to avoid some of the problems of a dry existence by storing lots of water in their fleshy stems.

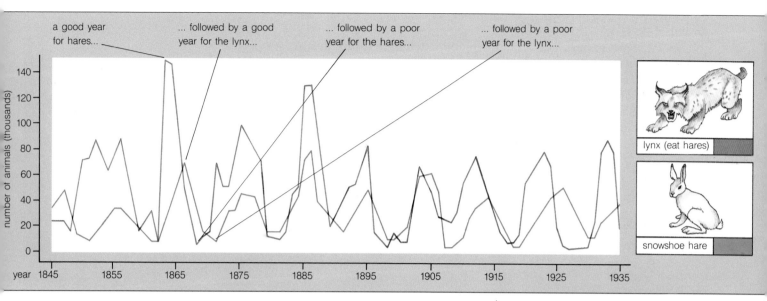

a good year for hares...

... followed by a good year for the lynx...

... followed by a poor year for the hares...

... followed by a poor year for the lynx...

The graph above shows this effect with the number of hares and lynx in the Arctic.

Competition

Another important factor that affects population is competition. If a particular species has enough food, water and space it will reproduce and increase in number, if on the other hand it does not, it will not. For example, when there were plenty of hares, the number of lynx could increase. However, when there were fewer hares, there was not enough food for the lynx so they had to compete for the remaining ones, with only some lynx surviving.

Plants also compete with each other. They compete for growing space, the water and minerals in the soil and for sunlight.

▲ The graph show the number of animal skins bought from fur trappers by the Hudson Bay Company between 1845 and 1935. The lynx is a large wild cat that catches hares for its food. More hares mean more lynx, but more lynx mean fewer hares ...

▲ Bluebells are adapted to overcome the problem of competing with trees for sunlight, by growing and flowering before the trees start to grow in the spring.

Questions and Practice

8 Look at this food chain:

Lettuce → Slug → Frog

a Which is the prey organism?

b Which is the predator organism?

9 Lots of frogs are produced each year but, because of competition, not all of them survive.

a Explain what competition is?

b Why might one individual frog have a better chance of surviving than another?

Human populations

Humans are very successful animals. Before 1600 it had taken about 2000 years to double the world's population. By 1850 it had doubled again. It took just 80 years to double again, and then only 50 years to complete the next doubling. This rapid increase in population is an example of exponential growth.

   Improvements in health care and food production have meant that more children survive to become adults, and adults live longer. This growth in population can cause problems too. This was first considered by an economist, called Malthus, as long ago as 1798. He said that the population would always outrun the food supply. He predicted that there would be widespread famine, disease or war. He said that this would be the natural way of keeping the human population steady.

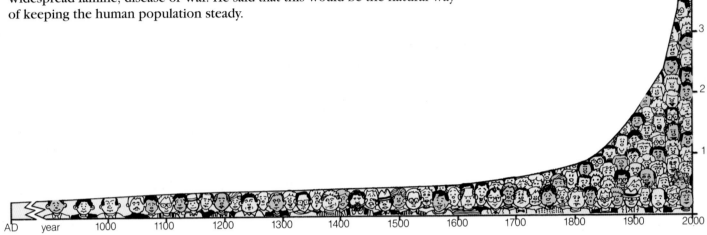

▲ **The increase in the population of the world.**

This has not happened as quickly as Malthus thought. He was not able to predict the massive increase in food production brought about by artificial fertilisers, new strains of plants and animals, and better farming methods.

   However, we are running out of essential resource materials such as oil, aluminium and other metals. Fertilisers and other chemicals may help to increase food production, but they often have harmful affects on the environment. The fact that there are more humans means that there is more air and water pollution. Will all of these factors mean that Malthus's predictions will be proved right in the end?

How has food production been increased?

As stated before, plants start every food chain. If we can increase the amount of food plants that are grown, we can have more to eat - either by eating the plants themselves, or the animals that they are used to feed.

   There are four key ways in which the amount of plants grown can be increased:

● by using more land for planting - either by clearing land of trees and hedges and growing crops instead, or by growing more on the existing land;

● by improving the quality of the soil, i.e. by using fertilisers to increase the growth of plants;

● by cutting down on the competition to the crops from other plants (weeds) by the use of herbicides;

● by reducing damage to crops from pests and disease, by the use of insecticides, fungicides or biological control (introducing natural predators of the pests).

In one way or another each of these methods improves the efficiency of energy transfer, either increasing the amount of sunlight hitting crops, or reducing the amount of energy that is lost to weeds, insects or fungi. Three of the methods involve the use of *agrochemicals*.

Agrochemicals

Fertilisers

These consist of extra minerals that plants need for healthy growth.

Nitrates which contain nitrogen are needed to make proteins for growth, especially of leaves. *Phosphates* help to make roots grow and function properly. *Magnesium* is important for making chlorophyll, the green pigment vital for photosynthesis.

Fertilisers are either natural (sewage, manure, compost) or artificial (made from phosphate rocks and the nitrogen in the air).

The crops on the left have been grown in nitrate-deficient conditions. In the 1930s sixty thousand tonnes of nitrogen fertiliser were used each year. Today 1.6 million tonnes are used worldwide.

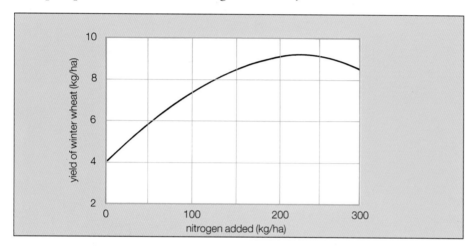

◀
The effect of nitrogen on the yield of wheat crops.

Herbicides

These are used for killing weeds. The weeds would otherwise compete with the food crops for light, water, and mineral salts from the soil. The yield of crop plants would be smaller. Herbicides can be applied by spraying.

Insecticides

Insects that damage crops and stored food are usually killed with insecticides. Insecticide is usually sprayed onto crops from tractors or aircraft.

Biological control

This is sometimes used as an alternative to insecticides, but involves the use of living organisms to kill the pest, instead of a chemical. For example, a small wasp can be bought by gardeners, to use against the greenhouse whitefly. The wasp lays its eggs inside immature whiteflies. When the eggs hatch they feed on the insides of the larvae and eventually kill them.

Fungicides

These are used to stop diseases on crop plants caused by fungi. Common types of fungal diseases are mildews, blights and rusts. They spread quickly and can wipe out an entire crop. Seeds are often treated by fungicides before they are planted to stop them rotting in the soil.

Insecticides and fungicides are sometimes grouped together as pesticides, because they are used to kill the pest organisms that decrease crop yields.

Problems with the use of agrochemicals

Agrochemicals can be clearly seen to increase the crop yields of farmers. Unfortunately, many of them can cause harm to the environment.

Too much fertiliser

Artificial fertilisers, spread onto the land, can cause serious problems of pollution. The minerals may be washed out of the soil, into lower layers of the ground, by rainwater. This is called leaching.

The mineral-rich water then drains underground into nearby rivers and lakes. This results in **eutrophication**, which simply means 'enrichment in nutrients'. Unfortunately, it often leads to the problem outlined below:

● The nitrates and phosphates help the growth of water plants, especially green algae, which reproduce in vast numbers. This algal 'blooming' clogs up the waterways.

● A thick layer of algae forms on the surface of the water. It stops sunlight reaching the bottom of the waterways and as a result plants growing there will die.

● In addition, some of the algae will die and colonies of bacteria will develop to feed on them. These bacteria will use up oxygen in the water.

● The fish and other forms of animal life which need the oxygen to breathe, will also die and decay, leaving putrid, poisonous ponds and streams.

Organic fertilisers such as manure can cause similar problems, but they are not so easily leached through the soil. If, however, they are washed by rain from the surface of the soil, into a waterway they can be harmful. Bacteria will feed on the manure and as a result will use up the oxygen in the water. This will again cause the death of other organisms.

Unfortunately, because minerals are so important for plant growth, some farmers add too much fertiliser to the soil, to make up for any lost due to leaching. Obviously, the surrounding waterways will suffer as a result.

The problem with herbicides

Using herbicides to kill off all of the weeds that affect a crop often leads to fields that are used to grow a single crop. This is known as *monoculture*. Farms that specialise in monoculture may gain large yields of the crops grown in this way, but in the long run may have the following problems:

● the crop provides an unlimited amount of food for certain organisms, which can expand to pest levels;

● large amounts of pesticides are needed to control the possible problem of these pests;

● the soil loses its nutrients due to the large amounts removed by the crops each year, so lots of artificial fertiliser needs to be used;

▼
A fenland dyke clogged with algae and weeds.

▲
Specialised machines are needed to clear the overgrown algae and weeds.

● the soil is left bare between crops, so may be easily washed or blown away (eroded).

Too much insecticide

When gardeners see that their rose trees are being attacked by greenfly, they may spray them with insecticides. Most insecticides kill all insects, and not just pests. So the helpful insects, like ladybirds, are also killed. Unfortunately, the greenfly are able to reproduce very quickly, and so their numbers are soon back to their original level. Ladybirds take longer to recover. Within a few weeks the gardener can have as many greenfly on the rose bushes as before, but the helpful ladybirds that keep the numbers in check are gone. A similar situation is often the case for farmers, but the numbers of useful organisms killed is usually much larger.

Some insecticides do not break down very easily and stay in the environment for a long time. These persistent pesticides, like the organochlorine-based insecticides, for example DDT, cyclodienes and dieldrin, can seriously affect the food chain.

DDT was a widely used insecticide during the Second World War, when it played an important role in controlling lice, fleas and other carriers of disease. After the war it was used to kill mosquitoes and so helped control the disease malaria, but it was also used to kill farm and garden pests. However, it does have long-term effects. For example:

● if roses were sprayed to kill greenfly, most of the flies would die, but some do survive, despite absorbing the DDT;

● the DDT is not broken down, so when any of these flies are eaten by birds, such as tits, the level of DDT in their bodies, especially in the fat tissues, will build up;

● if a number of these tits are now eaten by a predator such as a sparrowhawk, the level of DDT can build up to a level high enough to kill them, affect their behaviour, or lead to eggs being laid that have thin shells and are unlikely to hatch;

● during the 1950s and 1960s the populations of birds such as the sparrowhawk fell. This was one of the factors that led to the ban on the use of DDT in Britain.

▲
The 'Dust Bowl' laid waste vast areas of farm land in the United States. The problem was accelerated by the monoculture of cereal crops.

◄
DDT affected many food chains. In this one, the figures give the relative concentration of DDT at each stage.

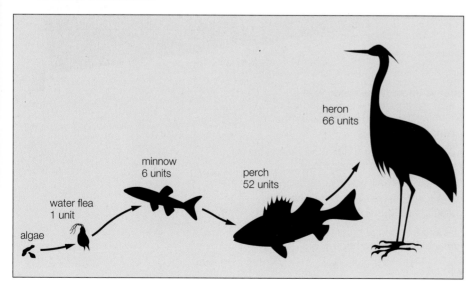

heron
66 units

minnow
6 units

perch
52 units

water flea
1 unit

algae

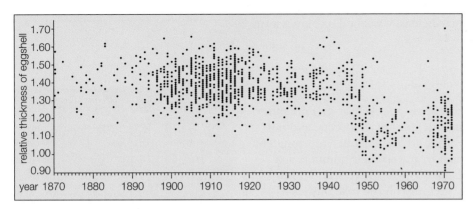

▲ This graph shows the relative thickness of sparrowhawk eggshells over a period of 100 years.

Increasing animal production

It is also possible to increase the amount of food we get from animals, by reducing their energy 'losses'. For example, hens may be kept in cages in artificial light. These battery hens are fed a controlled diet by the farmer. Because they do not need to use energy to move around and find their food, they tend to produce more eggs compared to hens that are free-range.

◄ Free range chickens.

▼ Battery hens are more efficient at transferring energy along the food chain.

Questions and Practice

10 Sewage from towns and cities was not always treated by sewage works. Sewage was often pumped directly into rivers. It contains a large amount of nitrogen compounds. Write down how you think this would affect the living organisms in the river. Give reasons for your answer.

11 Insecticides may kill useful insects such as ladybirds. Name one other useful insect that they may kill, that most plants need if they are to reproduce successfully.

12 Look at the graph of thickness of sparrowhawk eggs (above). Explain what this graph shows and how it may have been used to help ban the use of DDT.

13 Compare the photographs of battery hens and free-range hens. Draw a table to compare the advantages and disadvantages of keeping hens in battery-farms.

Biological recycling

As stated earlier, when looking at energy pyramids, the energy transfers that occur in a food chain are never perfect. Some energy is always 'lost'. This is why the Sun is so important, because it always continues to transfer more energy to the earth and its organisms.

Unlike energy though, there are no additional supplies of minerals. The basic minerals are only found in certain amounts. For this reason we are encouraged to recycle valuable materials such as aluminium, steel, glass and even paper. This means using them again and again. This helps save what are often limited supplies, and usually saves energy: recycling aluminium cans is much cheaper than making aluminium from its ore (see page 116). Nature also recycles materials, and for much the same reasons.

◀
In Britain about 78 million tonnes of material is dumped into the dustbin every year. Most of it could be recycled or used as fuel. This could save the equivalent of 12–14 million tonnes of coal.

Recycling carbon

Carbon is an element needed by all living creatures. Charcoal is mostly carbon, and the 'lead' in pencils is really a form of carbon called graphite. But most carbon is found in compounds, like the gas carbon dioxide used in fizzy drinks. Coal and oil are mixtures of more complicated compounds called **hydrocarbons** that also contain carbon. 'Energy foods' like starch and sugar are similar carbon-based compounds called carbohydrates. In fact, all life on Earth is carbon-based.

In studying the recycling of carbon, in the **carbon cycle**, it is helpful to start with the carbon dioxide found in the air. Plants use this in the process of photosynthesis, using the energy from the Sun, to make sugars.

The sugars may then be converted into starch, fats or proteins. The carbon can then be transferred through the food chain when herbivores eat the plants and when carnivores eat the herbivores. To complete the cycle, carbon needs to get back into the air in the form of carbon dioxide. This can happen in one of three ways:

- **Respiration**. When plants and animals need to make use of the energy 'trapped' inside compounds such as carbohydrates, they break them down. This process is known as respiration and involves the release of carbon dioxide.

- **Decomposition**. When any organism dies, it begins to rot, usually due to the action of microbes such as bacteria and fungi. These microbes are actually using the dead organisms for food and will eventually get energy from them, due to respiration. This also releases carbon dioxide into the air. The process of decomposition happens most efficiently when it is warm and damp and air (oxygen) is available.

- **Combustion**. When organisms die, they are not always broken down by microbe action, but over the space of millions of years may get converted into fossil fuels such as coal, oil and gas. When fossil fuels are burnt, the trapped carbon is released as carbon dioxide. In fact, even the organisms themselves, such as trees, if burnt will release carbon dioxide.

Recycling nitrogen

Nitrogen is another important element for life. All proteins contain it. Proteins are the compounds that the 'bodies' of living things are made of.

Nitrogen is found in the air as an element. The air is four-fifths nitrogen. But plants and animals can't use it directly. Plants must take it in as the nitrate ion. Animals can only take nitrogen in the form of 'ready-made' protein. The **nitrogen cycle** is shown in the Reference Section.

R
p227

How does nitrogen get into the soil?

Nitrogen-fixing bacteria can absorb nitrogen from the atmosphere and build up nitrogen compounds such as ammonia. Some of these bacteria live freely in the soil, but certain strains live in the roots of a particular group of plants called the leguminous plants. By growing these plants, farmers and gardeners improve the amount of nitrate in the soil. Peas, beans and clover are all leguminous plants. The plants produce special lumps on their roots for the bacteria.

Farmers and gardeners can also add nitrates to the soil by using artificial fertilisers. Lightning can cause the nitrogen in the air to react with oxygen to form oxides. These nitrogen oxides dissolve in rain and end up as nitrates in the soil. But neither lightning nor artificial fertiliser produce much useful nitrate. Nitrates have to be recycled. Most of the nitrates in the soil come from decaying animal or plant tissue, or from animal droppings or urine. These waste products are broken down by bacteria in the soil and the nitrogen appears in ammonia (NH_3). Then some bacteria in the soil, known as *nitrifying bacteria*, use the ammonia as food. In the same way as we convert glucose to carbon dioxide and water in respiration, the bacteria convert the ammonia into nitrates. They get energy by doing this.

▲
The nitrogen-fixing bacteria are held in the roots of plants like this runner bean.

How nitrogen is removed from the soil

Plants take in nitrates through their roots and combine them with carbon compounds to form proteins. This protein can then be transferred through the food chain to herbivores and carnivores.

Because nitrates dissolve easily, as mentioned earlier in the chapter, they can be washed out of the soil by rain, in the process known as *leaching*.

There is yet another group of bacteria which use nitrates as food. These unhelpful bacteria get their energy by breaking down the nitrates, so releasing nitrogen gas back into the air. These bacteria are known as *denitrifying bacteria*.

Questions and Practice

14 *a* Give three examples of carbon-containing compounds that are found in living organisms.

** *b*** Where do (i) plants, (ii) animals get their carbon from.

** *c*** Describe how the carbon inside an organism may be released back into the air.

15 Name the three main types of bacteria involved in the nitrogen cycle. Write down what each one does.

Examination Questions

Credit

1 A gardener wants to make compost for her garden. She collects grass cuttings and other waste material.

Look at this list: milk bottle; apple core; bread; plastic cup; newspaper; nylon shirt; wood shavings; potato peelings.

a Which of these things will *not* rot to make compost? [3 marks]
b To help decay you need _____ and _____ conditions.
Choose from the following words: dry; damp; warm; cold. [2]
c The gardener's compost maker has holes in the sides. Explain why the holes are important. [1]

2 Here is a food chain found in a wood.

oak trees → greenfly → blue tits → owls

After a very cold winter there are fewer blue tits than usual.

a What would probably happen to the number of greenfly? Explain your answer. [2]

b What would probably happen to the owls? Suggest two answers. [2]

Merit

3 The drawing shows how a river can become polluted by fertiliser causing too much growth of green algae in a river.

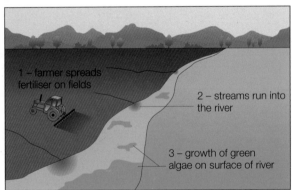

1 – farmer spreads fertiliser on fields
2 – streams run into the river
3 – growth of green algae on surface of river

a Explain how the fertiliser gets from the fields to the river. [2]

The layer of green algae on the surface of the river grows thicker. Many plants that grow on the river bed start to die.

b Explain why these river bed plants die. [2]
c What would happen to the amount of oxygen in this part of the river? [1]

The River Authority looks after rivers.

d Write down one thing they could do to put the river back to normal. [1]
e Explain fully why this would work. [2]
f What is meant by an *organic* fertiliser? [1]
g Name one type of organic fertiliser. [1]
h Why is organic fertiliser less likely to cause river pollution? [1]

Special

4 Stoats are predators on rabbits. Drawn below are four possible pyramids of biomass.

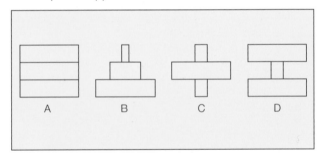

A   B   C   D

a Which one of the four pyramids of biomass correctly shows the relationship between plants, rabbits and stoats? [1]
b What two measurements are used to estimate the biomass of the population of rabbits? [2]
c Rabbits can be a major pest by feeding on farmers' crops. One farmer tries to control the number of rabbits by regularly shooting them. Another farmer tries to encourage natural predators, such as stoats and hawks, by leaving rough corners of fields to act as wildlife habitats.
Write down one advantage and one disadvantage of each control method. [4]

[Adapted from the Terminal Examination, June 1994, and the Periodic Examination, June 1994 and June 1995.]

Checklist

These are the facts and ideas that you should have learned by studying this topic.

To succeed at Credit level you should:
- ■ be able to describe how to use pooters, pitfall traps and quadrats
- ■ know that animals and plants are adapted to their environment
- ■ be able to recognise how organisms are adapted for survival
- ■ know that population size of animals and plants can be affected by competition for food, water, shelter, light and minerals
- ■ understand that food chains are a way of showing the feeding relationships in an ecosystem
- ■ know that energy enters food chains when plants absorb sunlight
- ● know that farmers can produce more food if intensive practices are used, but that the environment and health may also be affected
- ● understand why farmers use nitrogen fertilisers and understand the harm they can do to rivers and lakes
- ● know about the key factors that cause decay.

To succeed at Merit level you should:
- ■ understand how collecting and counting methods allow quantitative estimates of population size and distribution to be made
- ■ be able to explain how adaptations improve survival chances
- ■ be able to explain how competition for food, water, shelter, light and minerals may influence the population size of animals or plants
- ■ understand that the size of a predator population will affect the numbers of prey and vice versa
- ■ be able to construct food chains from given information
- ■ understand the terms producer and consumer
- ■ understand and be able to construct pyramids of numbers
- ● understand how intensive farming produces more food and know that herbicides and insecticides may cause problems
- ● know why using large amounts of fertiliser damages the environment
- ● be able to predict how changes in temperature, oxygen and moisture affect the rate of decay
- ● know that natural materials are recycled biologically
- ● know that the resources we use are finite (fossil fuels, minerals).

To succeed at Special level you should:
- ■ understand the limitations of counting and collecting methods
- ■ be able to describe how populations of predators and prey regulate one another
- ■ be able to construct and interpret food webs
- ■ understand and be able to construct pyramids of biomass
- ■ understand energy flow by photosynthesis and feeding
- ■ understand how some energy is transferred to less useful forms at each stage in the food chain (heat, solid waste)
- ■ understand how the efficiency of energy transfers explains the shape of pyramids of biomass
- ● understand how intensive food production improves the efficiency of energy transfer
- ● understand the problems linked to eutrophication
- ● be able to describe the involvement of microbes and other living things in the cycling of carbon and nitrogen.

GCSE FOUNDATION TIER

GCSE HIGHER TIER

Key words from this topic:

biomass

consumer

decomposer

ecosystem

eutrophication

herbicide

insecticide

population

predator

prey

Revision

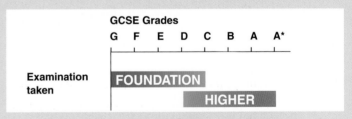

Checklist

**These are the facts and ideas that yo[u]
learned by studying this topic.**

To succeed at Credit level you should:
- know the areas of the body which gather sense in[...]
- know that reflexes are fast, automatic protective r[...]
stimulus
- be able to name and locate the main parts of the e[...]
and endocrine system
- know the names of the glands that produce growt[...]
adrenalin and the sex hormone
- know that diabetes is caused by the failure of the [...]
insulin
- know that insulin can be used to treat diabetes, gr[...]
treat poor growth and sex hormone to treat infert[...]

When you follow this course you can either enter for a single award GCSE, which will give you one GCSE grade in science, or a double award GCSE, which will give you two identical GCSE science grades. Both awards allocate marks as follows:

25% Coursework

This is for the experimental and investigative work you do throughout your course.

25% Periodic Examination

This tests the content of the chapters in this book. If you are taking the single award you will not be tested on 'Rocks and Metals' and 'Moving Around'.

50% Terminal Examination

This tests the content of the chapters in GCSE Book 2 and some of the 'key ideas' covered in this book. These key ideas are shown in the checklists alongside a ■ symbol.

The reason for including a Periodic Examination is to take some of the pressure off the revision needed for the Terminal Examination at the end of the course. It means that the work done in the first year of the course can be tested while it is still fresh in your memory. If you miss the Periodic Examination through illness or some other good reason there is no need to worry – you can still take it at the end of the course.

In the Periodic and Terminal Examinations you will be entered for either the Foundation examination or the Higher examination. The Foundation examination allows you to obtain grades from C to G. The Higher examination allows you to obtain grades from A* to D. Obviously it is important that you are entered for the right examination. Your teachers will give you a lot of help and advice when it comes to making that decision.

GCSE Grades

G	F	E	D	C	B	A	A*

Examination taken: **FOUNDATION** / **HIGHER**

The Foundation examinations will test the ideas covered in the Credit and Merit checklists given at the end of each chapter. The Higher examinations will test ideas covered in the Merit and Special checklists. As you will see, the Merit section acts as an overlap between the two examinations. Therefore some of the questions will be the same in both examinations.

In all examinations, equal numbers of marks are given to biology, chemistry and physics units.

How to prepare for written examinations

This section is intended to help you revise for your science examinations. Most of the suggestions will also help you to revise for end-of-unit tests that you may be given throughout the course. First some general points:

1 Start early – it is better to take some time off if things go well than to be in a rush to get through everything.

2 Decide the best length of time to spend on one subject at any one time – if the time is too short you will have made little progress by the time you finish; if it is too long you will lose interest and concentration. For many students one hour sessions are about right.

3 Draw up a revision timetable – this will help you identify how much time you have and how it can be shared between science and other subjects. It is better to revise a subject on several separate occasions rather than all in one go. So use shorter lengths of time more regularly. In this way you can revisit the work a number of times.

4 Allow for rest periods – it is important to take breaks. These don't need to be very long (the longer they are the harder it is to get back to work!) but long enough to walk around and have a drink. About five minutes should be enough.

5 Divide your science revision into manageable 'chunks' – this may be whole units or chapters of work or you might to decide to split these into smaller sections.

6 Don't always start from the same place – it is easy to always start at the beginning. The problem is that the more difficult ideas often come at the end of a chapter. So make sure you cover *all* the important parts.

7 Be active! For many students just reading a chapter will not be a successful way of learning. Try writing notes or produce summaries of each section. Try testing yourself on small sections. Try to answer the questions in the chapter.

8 Make a note of any difficulties you have and ask for help – there is nothing worse than opening the examination paper and seeing a question just like one you came across in revision and left out. Ask your friends or teacher for help.

Using this book when starting your revision

1 Read through the chapter, matching sections with those in your own lesson notes and homework – remember, be active!

2 Try the questions that are given at the end of each section in the chapter – do this even if you've done them before. Check your answers with those in your lesson notes.

3 Refer to the Reference Section – the **R** icon appears in the left margin to show you when to do this. This is important as there may be some basic information in the Reference Section which you will need to know.

4 When you have worked through the chapter look at the list of key words –

you should have come across all these words in the chapter. Do you know what they mean or refer to? Can you use them when describing or explaining something?

5   Look at the checklists – these summarise exactly what you need to know, understand and be able to do. Can you match them to ideas in the chapter?

Using this book when nearing the end of your revision

1   Start with the checklists – can you remember the information they refer to? Try talking yourself through it or sketching out the main points.

2   Try the examination questions at the end of the chapter – these will be grouped under the headings of credit, merit and special. Try the ones that match the examination you will be taking.

3   Check the Reference Section – remember that there is important information in this section that you will need to know.

4   Get someone to test you – a member of the family or a friend should be able to ask you questions from the checklists.

5   Ask for help if needed – it's still not too late to get that last piece of help or advice.

Answering examination questions

Look at the number of marks

The marks should tell you about how long to spend on a question. A rough guide is a minute for every mark. The number of marks will indicate how many different points are required in the answer. If only one mark is available only one idea or one answer is required; if three marks are available then three different points are needed.

Look at the space allocated for the answer

If only one line is given then the answer required is short, e.g. a single word, a short phrase or a short sentence. Some questions will require more extended writing and so four or more lines will be allocated.

Read the question carefully

It is often easier to answer the question you would like to answer rather than the one that has actually been set! Circle or underline the key words. Are you choosing from a list that has been given or do you have to remember the answer? Are you using the Periodic Table? Are you describing or explaining? Are you completing a table? (This is a very common mistake in examinations – candidates often forget to complete tables or diagrams because a space for the answer is not given with the question.)

Look at the front of the paper when doing calculations

You will need to remember most of the formulae you use but not all of them. Some formulae will be printed at the front of the examination paper.

Decide on the order in which you want to answer the questions

In your examination papers you will have to answer all the questions. This does not mean that you have to answer them all in the order they are printed on the paper. If you start with a question that you are confident you can answer you will feel much better about tackling some 'harder' questions later. If you miss any questions out don't forget to go back and do them later!

Drawing charts and graphs

You should be familiar with the use of pie charts, bar graphs and line graphs. Axes will often be given but on the higher tier papers you may have to choose your own axes.

Example 1 – Drawing a pie chart

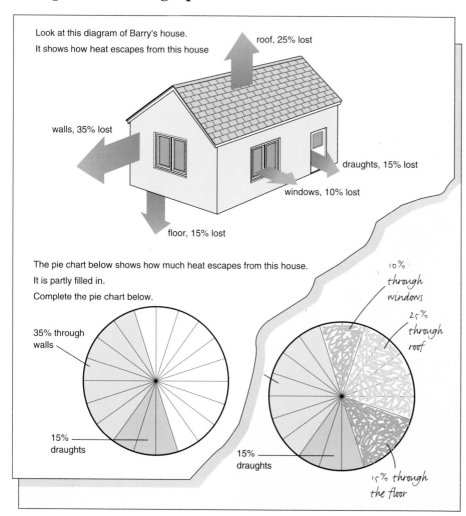

Look at this diagram of Barry's house.
It shows how heat escapes from this house

roof, 25% lost

walls, 35% lost

draughts, 15% lost

windows, 10% lost

floor, 15% lost

The pie chart below shows how much heat escapes from this house.
It is partly filled in.
Complete the pie chart below.

35% through walls

15% draughts

10% through windows

25% through roof

15% draughts

15% through the floor

Answer: Each segment of the circle represents 5% of the total heat that escapes. You can see this because the 15% as draughts covers three segments and the 35% through walls covers $7 \times 5\% = 35\%$. Of the 10 segments remaining, 'through the roof' should take 5 ($5 \times 5\% = 25\%$), 'through the windows' should take 2 ($2 \times 5\% = 10\%$) and 'through the floor' should take 3 ($3 \times 5\% = 15\%$).

Example 2 – Drawing a bar chart

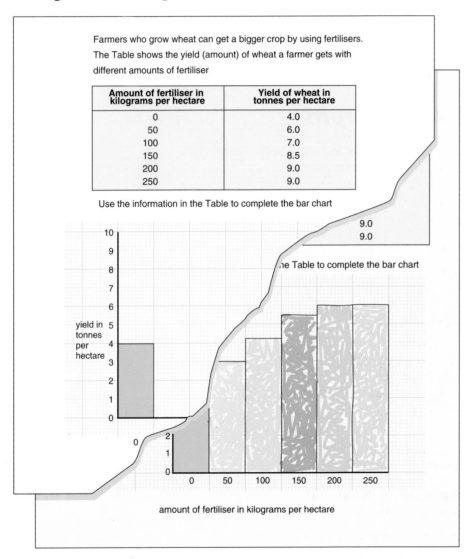

Farmers who grow wheat can get a bigger crop by using fertilisers. The Table shows the yield (amount) of wheat a farmer gets with different amounts of fertiliser

Amount of fertiliser in kilograms per hectare	Yield of wheat in tonnes per hectare
0	4.0
50	6.0
100	7.0
150	8.5
200	9.0
250	9.0

Use the information in the Table to complete the bar chart

amount of fertiliser in kilograms per hectare

Answer: The bar chart should be completed as shown. It is very important to draw the bars with a ruler. You will need to be accurate to within half a square to get the marks.

172

Example 3 – Drawing a line graph

Look at the Table.

It shows how much carbon dioxide is formed during the first 7 minutes.

Time (mins)	Total volume of carbon dioxide formed (cm³)
0	0
1	18
2	34
3	48
4	60
5	66
6	
7	

Plot these points on a line graph.

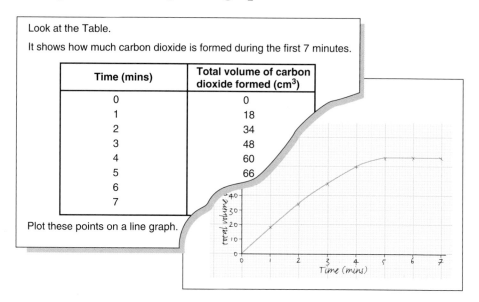

Answer: Use a sharp pencil and mark the points with a small cross. The crosses must be in exactly the right place to get the marks. You must then join up the points or you will lose marks. Nearly always the points will form a smooth curve (as in this example) or a straight line (a 'line of best fit' can be drawn). It is very rare to have to join the points in a 'zig zag' fashion.

Writing chemical equations

Chemical equations are used as a shorthand way of describing reactions. They show the starting materials (the reactants) and the finishing materials (the products). Chemical equations can be written in words (a word equation) or in symbols (a symbolic equation). When symbols are used the equation must be balanced.

Example 4 – Writing a word equation

Question: When petrol is burned in oxygen, carbon dioxide and water are formed. Write a word equation for this reaction.

Answer: The word equation is: petrol + oxygen → carbon dioxide + water
   Petrol and oxygen are the reactants; carbon dioxide and water are the products.

Example 5 – Writing a word equation

Question: A gas power station burns methane. When methane burns carbon dioxide and water are formed.

Answer: The word equation is: Methane + oxygen → carbon dioxide + water
   In this example you are expected to know that when the methane burns it will react with oxygen from the air.

Example 6 – Writing a symbolic equation

Question: Gas-fired power stations use natural gas. Natural gas contains methane (CH_4) and a small amount of hydrogen sulphide (H_2S). When hydrogen sulphide burns in oxygen it forms sulphur dioxide (SO_2) and water.

Answer: You will be expected to know that oxygen gas exists as O_2 molecules and that water is H_2O.

First write down the formulae for the reactants and the products;

$$H_2S + O_2 \rightarrow SO_2 + H_2O$$

The equation now needs to be balanced. In other words there must be the same number of hydrogen, sulphur and oxygen atoms on both sides of the equation. The important rule to remember is that balancing numbers can only be put in front of the formulae. The formulae themselves should not be changed.

	Reactants	Products
1 Count the atoms on each side	2H 1S 2O	2H 1S 3O
2 Increase the number of oxygen atoms on the reactants side.	$H_2S + 2O_2 \rightarrow$	$SO_2 + H_2O$
3 Count the atoms on each side again.	2H 1S 4O	2H 1S 3O
4 Increase the number of oxygen atoms on the products side. By putting $2H_2O$ the number of oxygen atoms will balance.	$H_2S + 2O_2 \rightarrow$	$SO_2 + 2H_2O$
5 Count the atoms on each side again.	2H 1S 4O	4H 1S 4O
6 Double the number of hydrogen atoms on the reactants side. This will also double the number of S atoms so the number on the products side will also need to be doubled.	$2H_2S + 2O_2 \rightarrow$	$2SO_2 + 2H_2O$
7 Count the atoms on each side again.	4H 2S 4O	4H 2S 6O
8 Increase the number of oxygen atoms on the reactants side.	$2H_2S + 3O_2 \rightarrow$	$2SO_2 + 2H_2O$
9 Count the atoms on each side again.	4H 2S 6O	4H 2S 6O

It balances! Although this process seems complicated each step can be done very quickly.

Doing calculations

In most cases you will need to remember the formula to be used. Where this is not the case the formula will be given on the front page of the examination paper. In some examples you will be able to substitute numbers in the formula and work out your answer directly. In other cases you will need to rearrange the formula. The important thing to remember is that you must show your working. You can score marks even if your answer is wrong.

Example 7 – Calculating without rearranging the formula

Methane was used to heat some water using a Bunsen burner

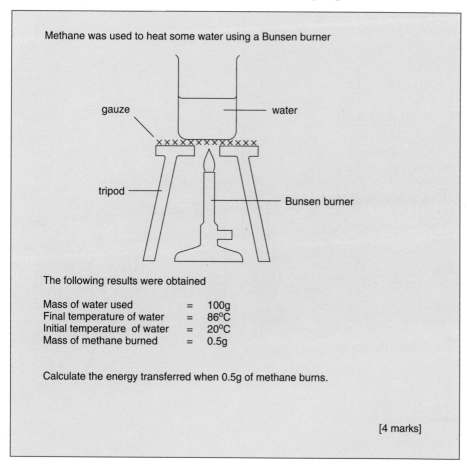

The following results were obtained

Mass of water used	=	100g
Final temperature of water	=	86°C
Initial temperature of water	=	20°C
Mass of methane burned	=	0.5g

Calculate the energy transferred when 0.5g of methane burns.

[4 marks]

Answer: In this example the formula you need will be given on the front of the examination paper.

1 Write down the formula:

energy transferred = mass × specific heat capacity × temperature rise
(1 mark)

2 Substitute values into the equation:

energy transferred = $100 \times 4.2 \times 66$ (1 mark)

3 Work out your answer:

energy transferred = 27 720 (1 mark)

4 Write down the units:

energy transferred = 27 720 J (1 mark)

Example 8 – Rearranging the formula

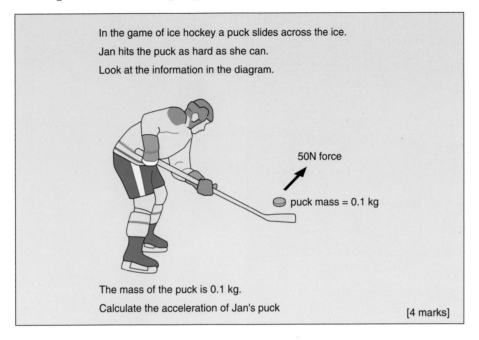

In the game of ice hockey a puck slides across the ice.

Jan hits the puck as hard as she can.

Look at the information in the diagram.

50N force

puck mass = 0.1 kg

The mass of the puck is 0.1 kg.

Calculate the acceleration of Jan's puck

[4 marks]

Answer: In this example you will need to remember the formula.

1 Write down the formula:

$F = ma$

R

p199

2 Rearrange the formula to make a the subject of the formula:

$a = \dfrac{F}{m}$ (1 mark)

3 Substitute the figures into the formula:

$a = \dfrac{50}{0.1}$ (1 mark)

4 Work out your answer:

$a = 500$ (1 mark)

5 Write down your units:

$a = 500$ m/s^2 (1 mark)

Looking at different types of question

The examination questions will be of a type called structured questions. These will be based on a particular part of a unit or chapter and will ask a number of related questions. The parts of the structured question can vary. They can require short answers (worth one mark) or longer answers involving extended prose.

Short answer – these require a single word or small phrase as an answer. They are used because they can test your knowledge of a lot of things very quickly.

Extended prose – these require longer answers, usually several sentences. They will test how well you can link different ideas together. They often require you to explain ideas in some detail and will test your understanding. In this type of question it is important to use technical terms correctly and to write clearly.

Example 9 – Short answer

Look at this list. Each one is a type of electromagnetic radiation

infra-red   ultra-violet   light   X-rays   microwaves

Choose from the list to fill in the gaps in the Table. Each answer may be used once, more than once or not at all.

Use	Type of radiation used
Watching television	
Detecting broken bones	
Getting a suntan	
Cooking food	
Remote control of a television	

[5marks]

Answer: In this question there are five parts and a list of five possible answers. Take care though, the question states that each answer may be used once, more than once or not at all. Do not assume that each possible answer will be used once. The answers are, from top to bottom: light, X-rays, ultra-violet, microwaves or infrared, infrared (1 mark each).

Example 10 – Short answer

A class is studying the plants and animals in a field.

Look at some of the equipment being used.

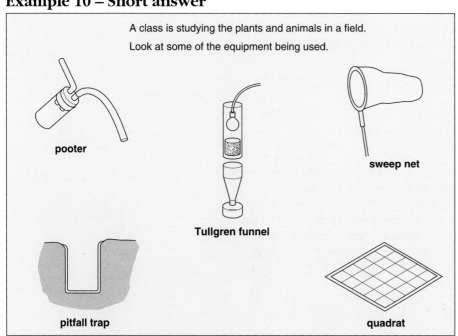

pooter

Tullgren funnel

sweep net

pitfall trap

quadrat

Complete each of the sentences below

Choose your answers from the diagrams.

(a) To collect from a tree trunk you would use a

. . . .

(b) To collect large ground beetles that come out at night you would use a

. . . .

(c) To collect butterflies resting on the grass you would use a

. . . .

(d) To help estimate the number of daisies in the field you would use a

. . . .

Answer: In this question five possible answers are given for the four questions. The answers are: (a) pooter (1 mark); (b) pitfall trap (1 mark); (c) sweep net (1 mark); (d) quadrat (1 mark).

Example 11 – Extended prose

Question: Rocks at the top of a mountain are broken into smaller pieces. After a long time the smaller pieces of rock become soil. This is done by weathering, erosion and transportation. Write about how rocks can be made into soil. (3 marks)

Answer: There are three marks for this question and the way it is written you are prompted to think about the processes of weathering, erosion and transportation. Water enters cracks in the rock and in cold weather it freezes, causing the rock to crack further or parts to break off (weathering – 1 mark); wind and rain cause small particles of rock to break off (erosion – 1 mark); the particles are then carried by streams (transportation – 1 mark) and become even smaller, eventually forming soil.

Example 12 – Extended prose

Question: Insulin is a hormone. What is the job of insulin? Explain fully. (3 marks)

Answer: In this example there is no prompting. However, there are three marks which suggests that three different ideas are needed. The hormone insulin is released in the body to reduce the amount of glucose present in the blood (1 mark). The glucose is converted into glycogen which is stored in the liver (1 mark). An excess of glucose in the bloodstream will affect the brain and could cause a coma (1 mark).

Looking at structured questions

Structured questions will give you information in a number of ways: in text, diagrams, tables and graphs. You will need to interpret this information to answer the questions set.

Example 13 – Interpreting a food web

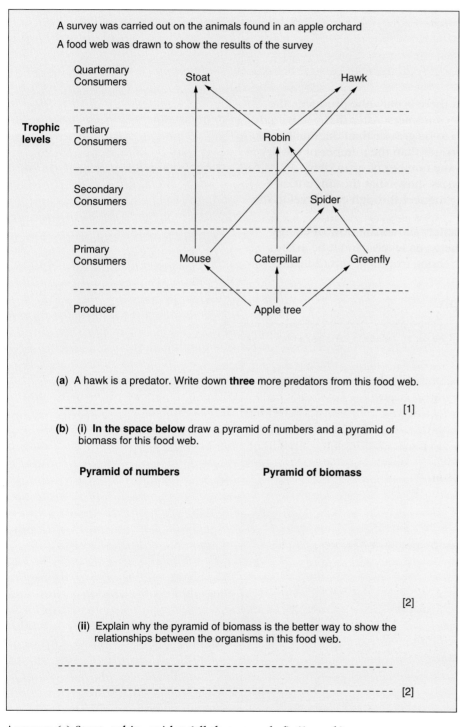

A survey was carried out on the animals found in an apple orchard

A food web was drawn to show the results of the survey

Quarternary Consumers — Stoat   Hawk

Trophic levels

Tertiary Consumers — Robin

Secondary Consumers — Spider

Primary Consumers — Mouse   Caterpillar   Greenfly

Producer — Apple tree

(a) A hawk is a predator. Write down **three** more predators from this food web.

———————————————————————————————— [1]

(b) (i) **In the space below** draw a pyramid of numbers and a pyramid of biomass for this food web.

Pyramid of numbers   **Pyramid of biomass**

[2]

(ii) Explain why the pyramid of biomass is the better way to show the relationships between the organisms in this food web.

————————————————————————————

———————————————————————————————— [2]

Answer: (a) Stoat, robin, spider (all three needed) (1 mark).

(b)

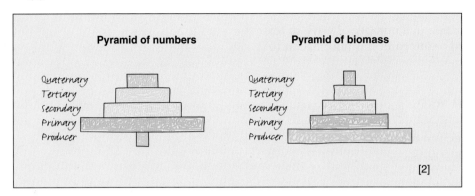

| | Pyramid of numbers | Pyramid of biomass |

[2]

(i) The pyramid of numbers shows that there is only one producer, the apple tree, but a large number of primary consumers. After that you would expect the number of primary consumers to be greater than the number of secondary consumers, which would be greater than the number of tertiary consumers, which would be greater than the number of quaternary consumers (1 mark). The pyramid of biomass shows that the amount of biomass decreases as you move from the producer through each level to the quaternary consumers (1 mark).

(ii) The pyramid of biomass more accurately shows the flow of energy through the web. As the energy transfer between levels cannot be 100% efficient the mass must decrease with increasing trophic levels (2 marks).

Example 14 – Interpreting a graph

The graph shows what happens to the speed of the car as it starts to roll down a track.

Look at the graph.

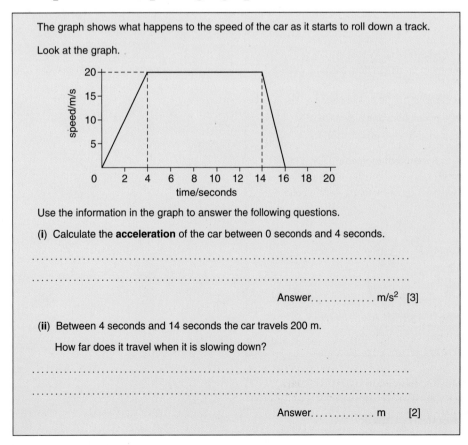

Use the information in the graph to answer the following questions.

(i) Calculate the **acceleration** of the car between 0 seconds and 4 seconds.

....

....

Answer.............. m/s^2 [3]

(ii) Between 4 seconds and 14 seconds the car travels 200 m.

How far does it travel when it is slowing down?

....

....

Answer.............. m [2]

Answer: (i) Acceleration = change in speed / time (1 mark)
  $a = 20/4$ (1 mark)
  $a = 5$ m/s^2 (1 mark)
  (ii) Distance travelled is the area under the line.
  Distance travelled when slowing down = $^1/_2 \times 2 \times 20$ ($^1/_2$ base $\times$ height)
(1 mark)
  Distance = 20 m (1 mark)

Example 15 – Interpreting a diagram

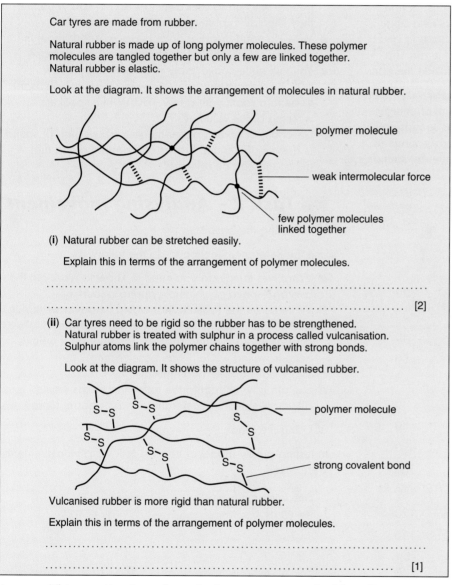

Car tyres are made from rubber.

Natural rubber is made up of long polymer molecules. These polymer molecules are tangled together but only a few are linked together. Natural rubber is elastic.

Look at the diagram. It shows the arrangement of molecules in natural rubber.

— polymer molecule

— weak intermolecular force

— few polymer molecules linked together

(i) Natural rubber can be stretched easily.

  Explain this in terms of the arrangement of polymer molecules.

  ....

  .... [2]

(ii) Car tyres need to be rigid so the rubber has to be strengthened. Natural rubber is treated with sulphur in a process called vulcanisation. Sulphur atoms link the polymer chains together with strong bonds.

  Look at the diagram. It shows the structure of vulcanised rubber.

— polymer molecule

— strong covalent bond

Vulcanised rubber is more rigid than natural rubber.

Explain this in terms of the arrangement of polymer molecules.

  ....

  .... [1]

Answer: This question is testing whether you can use the idea of intermolecular forces to explain simple physical properties.

  (i) There are few links between the polymer molecules and the intermolecular forces are weak (1 mark). On stretching the weak forces can be broken and the polymer molecules can slide over each other (1 mark).

  (ii) In this case the intermolecular forces are strong (covalent bonds) and so they will not break easily. The rubber will resist stretching (1 mark).

Extension tasks

Task 1 – Sounds

Hearing is one of the five main senses. We use sound to carry messages and to sense our surroundings. Sound travels as a pressure wave. In the ear, it makes a small thin piece of skin – called the eardrum – vibrate to and fro in time with the changes of pressure in the air. The vibrations are sensed by nerve cells deep inside the ear.

The human ear is very sensitive, and can hear very quiet sounds that actually carry only a tiny amount of energy. Bright light can damage the eye – and loud sounds can damage the ear. We measure the loudness of sounds in decibels (dB). The table shows how loud different sounds are.

Loudness	Sound you hear	Sound level (dB)
silence	limit of your hearing	0
quiet	ordinary breathing	10
	faint whisper	20
	turning newspaper page	30
moderate	inside a car, windows shut	40
	ordinary conversation	50
	normal TV listening level	60
	television adverts	70
loud	busy street traffic	80
	pneumatic drill	90
	underground train	100
extremely loud	jet plane taking off	110
	makes a tickling feeling in ear	120
	thunder overhead	130
dangerous to hear	near speakers at rock concert	140
	military jet taking off	150
	space rocket at lift off	160

a You drop a pin and it hits the floor. Estimate the sound level in dB.

b Look at the list of sounds in the table. Which is the loudest that you have heard? Describe what it felt like at the time.

c Tractor drivers and road workers wear ear muffs. Most people who go to rock concerts do not. Do you think they should? Explain your answer.

d Why do you think that doctors are worried about the fact that many young people use personal stereos?

e You live quite comfortably in a room lit by a few 100 W electric lamps. Why would it be less pleasant to be in a room with a few 100 W hi-fi speakers working at full volume?

f Describe, or invent, experiments to show that: (i) sound is a wave; (ii) sound waves carry energy; and that (iii) sound can be reflected.

Task 2 – Analysing movement

1 Checking the basics.

Use the Reference Section to do the following:

a What two things do you need to know to work out the *average speed* of a vehicle during a journey.

b Write down the formula that would help you work out: (i) the final speed after a vehicle has been steadily accelerating for a few seconds; (ii) how far it would have travelled while it was accelerating.

c What does acceleration mean?

d Explain how changing the following things would affect an object's acceleration: mass, shape, force?

2 Using the ideas.

In testing a new model of car, the following measurements were taken.

time from start to finish (seconds)	speed (metres/second)
0	0
2	6
4	12
6	18
8	24
10	28
12	30
14	30
16	30

a Draw a graph of the speed against time. Mark on your

graph: (i) the part which shows a steady acceleration. (ii) the part which shows a steady speed.

b Use the table, or the graph, to work out: (i) the change in speed in the first 6 seconds, (ii) the rate (in metres per second squared) at which the car accelerated.

c A car is designed so that it can *decelerate* faster than it can *accelerate*. Give a reason for this.

d Is the force that can be exerted by the car's brakes larger or smaller than the force that the engine can produce? Give a reason for your answer.

e The test car had a mass of 800 kg. Use the value of the acceleration calculated above to work out the effective force produced by the engine. (Note: force = mass × acceleration.)

f The designers want the brakes to stop the car from a speed of 30 m/s in a time of 3 seconds. Work out the braking force that this would need.

g Would it be safer to design the car so that it could stop from this speed in a time of 0.5 seconds? Give reasons for your answer.

h Give two safety features you would look for in a well-designed car. Explain, using your knowledge of physics, how any one of the features helps to make the car safer.

▇ Task 3 – The greenhouse effect

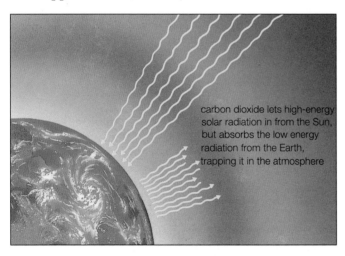

carbon dioxide lets high-energy solar radiation in from the Sun, but absorbs the low energy radiation from the Earth, trapping it in the atmosphere

Greenhouse gases allow the Sun's rays to pass relatively freely through the atmosphere to warm the surface of the Earth, but they prevent the Earth's heat from being radiated back into space.

The greenhouse gases are carbon dioxide, the chlorofluorocarbons (CFCs), methane, nitrous oxide and, in the lower atmosphere, ozone. Carbon dioxide is the largest single contributor to the greenhouse effect, accounting for more than half the expected rise in temperature by the year 2030. The amount of CO_2 in the atmosphere has increased by more than a quarter since the late 18th century and the rate of increase is itself increasing – half the total increase has taken place since 1950. The combustion of fossil fuels and other industrial releases are now pumping more than 5 billion tonnes of CO_2 into the atmosphere each year.

This is more than three times the amount in 1950.

Most scientists now agree that if the CO_2 in the atmosphere doubled, it would cause a rise in temperature at the Earth's surface of between 1.5 °C and 5.5 °C. The last major change in temperature on Earth was at the end of the last Ice Age. That change was only 3–4 °C. The fear is that the rise due to the greenhouse effect will cause a complete change in the global climate.

No single nation accounts for the bulk of the world's production of CO_2, but the USA, China and the USSR together produce more than half of it. In Britain, generating electricity in power stations powered by fossil fuels produces 30 per cent of the carbon dioxide that the U.K. produces.

There are several mysteries about the greenhouse effect. One is that only about half the CO_2 pumped into the atmosphere stays there. We know that some of it is taken up by the surface waters of the oceans – but we do not know how much the sea could absorb, or exactly how it does it.

If the seas stay cool the air will not warm up very much. But if the seas warm up so will the atmosphere. And because of the inertia in the system, air temperatures will continue to rise for many years after any rise in ocean temperature.

Another unpredictable consequence is what effect warming up the sea will have on its ability to hold carbon dioxide. If this makes it give out some of its CO_2, then a small rise in temperature will lead to a vicious upward spiral in which the world gets hotter and hotter.

[Adapted from an article in the *Independent*, 17th October 1988.]

a What gases are causing the greenhouse effect?

b What part of the Sun's radiation is the main cause of the heating effect?

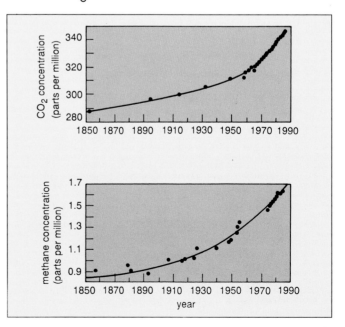

c Why has there been such an increase in CO_2 emissions into the atmosphere since about 1950?

d Plants are able to take in CO_2. They use it to help them grow, in turn giving out oxygen. (i) What is this process called? (ii) What other human activity, not mentioned in the above passage, may be helping to increase the proportion of CO_2 in the atmosphere?

e Methane (CH_4) is a gas produced by the action of bacteria on waste organic material (decaying plants, etc.). Most of it comes from cows as part of their digestive process. Some comes from *termites* – insects that build large nests out of partly chewed wood.

Describe more fully what happens in one of these examples of methane production.

f Explain what the author means by 'a small rise in temperature will lead to a vicious upward spiral in which the world gets hotter and hotter'.

Task 4 – Energy from chemicals

1 The data gives the quantity of energy given out when 1 kilogram of each substance is burned.

	Petrol	Sugar
Energy	42 MJ	17 MJ
Cost	42p	57p

(1 MJ is 1 000 000 joules)

a Which substance gives the most energy per penny?

b Why is sugar not used as a fuel for cars?

c What else must a good fuel be able to do as well as produce a lot of energy?

d Suggest two reasons why the body uses sugar (in the form of glucose) as a fuel for muscles and cells.

2 a Draw the apparatus you would use to collect a sample of liquid water from the exhaust gases given off by a small petrol engine in the laboratory.

b What are the 'contrails' (vapour trails) from a jet airliner cruising high in the sky made of? Where has this substance come from? Why don't the contrails form when the aircraft is flying low?

c You can lift your arm from waist to shoulder, quite slowly, in about a second. The muscle action is fuelled by the reaction between glucose and oxygen in the cells. This reaction is speeded up by a series of enzymes in the cells, which are very good catalysts. In fact, they speed up the reaction by as much as 1 000 000 000 times.

Calculate how long it would take you to lift your arm if these enzymes weren't there. Give your answer to the nearest year.

If using a calculator use:
1 hour is 3600 seconds
1 day is 24 hours
1 year is 365 days

If not using a calculator use the approximations:
1 hour is 3333 seconds
1 day is 25 hours
1 year is 333 days

3 A group of students were investigating fuels and did an experiment to measure how much energy the gas used in camping stoves could supply. Their results are listed below.

Mass of gas container before use	233.5 g
Mass of gas container after use	231.5 g
Mass of water heated	0.4 kg
Temperature of water before heating	20 °C
Temperature of water after heating	60 °C

a Draw a diagram showing the equipment they might have used for this experiment, and how it would be set up.

b What mass of gas was used?

c What was the rise in temperature of the water?

d Use the formula:

$$\text{heating energy} = \text{mass of water} \times \text{rise in temperature} \times 4.2$$

to check that the energy in kilojoules supplied to the water by the burning gas was 67.2 kJ.

e This energy was supplied by the mass of gas that you calculated in part (b) above. Scale up your answer to part (d) to calculate how much energy would be supplied by a kilogram (1000 grams) of gas.

f The calorific value of the gas (butane) is said to be 50 000 kJ per kilogram. Suggest a reason why the students got a different value.

Task 5 – The rock cycle

Use the Reference Section and the large diagram about the rock cycle in chapter 6, Rocks and Metals, to help you to answer the following questions.

a What are sedimentary rocks?

b What are igneous rocks?

c How are metamorphic rocks made?

d What part does the Sun play in helping to make new rocks?

e Where do volcanoes get their energy from?

f Explain the difference between erosion and transport as parts of the rock cycle.

g Why are these processes called a cycle?

Task 6 – Cells

a Draw a diagram of a simple animal cell. Label the main parts. Then draw labelled arrows showing whether the following things go into or come out of the cell: oxygen, carbon dioxide, water, food.

b Write clear, accurate and interesting sentences containing each of the following words (one sentence for each): bolus, duodenum, enzyme, villus, alveolus, diffusion.

c You can use a diagram to help you answer this question. The human heart contains four chambers: (i) What are their names? (ii) What other parts of the body are they connected to? (iii) Which chambers take blood into the heart, and which push blood away from the heart? (iv) In each case, say what the differences are between the blood entering and the blood leaving the heart.

d Human beings are mammals. All mammals have a double circulatory system. (i) What does double circulatory system mean? (ii) Simpler animals – like a fish – have a single circulatory system. What are the advantages of a double system?

Task 7 – Ouch!

a Suppose you touch something that is very hot. You move your hand away very quickly! Use some or all of the words in this list to help you answer the following questions: response, stimulus, skin, relay neurone, effector, spinal cord, axon, receptor, central nervous system, sensory neurone, motor neurone, brain.

b What organ of the body senses the fact that the object you touch is hot?

c Moving your hand away is a reflex action. List in their correct order the parts that nerve impulses go through from the time you touch the hot object to the time you move your hand.

d Is this reflex action a cranial reflex or a spinal reflex? Explain the difference.

e Do plants have senses? If you think so, list as many plant senses as you know.

f Plan an experiment to investigate one of the following: (i) whether plants respond to light; (ii) whether plant growth is affected by the force of gravity.

g What are the two main ways in which the human body controls itself? Describe each one clearly and compare

them with the way a plant (i) responds to light and (ii) controls what happens in reproduction.

Task 8 – The wild wood

Read the following passage then answer the questions about it.

There was no Moon, and in the middle of the wood you couldn't see your hand before your face. Silent on a low branch, the tawny owl swivelled her head, using her large eyes to scan the forest floor. It was autumn, and there was a rich smell of decay as the damp leaves rotted. It was the time of year when the tangled underground threads of the fungi colonies began to reproduce. The floor of the clearing was dotted with a variety of toadstools and mushrooms.

The owl ignored the hawk moth fluttering across the clearing – leave that to the bats! She focused her keen eyes on a movement in the layer of dead leaves. A caterpillar arched its way through some newly fallen leaves, and began to munch into a rich and juicy one. The sound – and the scent – attracted the attention of another animal. It lifted its thin nose out of its burrow and sniffed. Sure of the direction, it ran with surprising speed and grabbed the

caterpillar in its sharp teeth. The vole used its forepaws to hold the struggling victim and made short work of it. It moved a few steps and then froze. It did this by instinct – and it was just as well. The owl's eyes lost the vole against the dark background of the dead leaves. They were 'programmed' to sense movement.

But the owl waited patiently. When the vole moved again the owl swooped. The vole neither saw nor heard the silent wings of death. There was a brief flurry as the sharp talons dug into the warm body and the vole screamed until it was torn to pieces by the powerful beak, to be swallowed bones and all.

a Name one predator and one prey animal named in the passage.

b Which of the organisms mentioned is a decomposer? Explain your answer.

c The passage describes one small part of an *ecosystem*. What is an ecosystem?

d All living things need energy, and we can think of energy as *flowing through* an ecosystem. Trace the energy flow that ends up (for a time at least) in the owl.

e Draw a food web for the organisms mentioned in the passage.

f Draw a rough pyramid of numbers for caterpillars, voles and owls.

g One year, a gamekeeper puts down poison which kills off most of the voles and similar small rodents. What happens to the caterpillars/moths and the owl? You can give the answer in words, or draw a graph showing how the populations of these animals change over the next few years.

■ Task 9 – Biological recycling

R

p226
p227

The diagrams on pages 226 and 227 in the Reference Section show the main biological cycles in nature. Choose one of them and write a short description of what happens and why the cycle is important for human life on Earth.

■ Task 10 – A mixed bag

Use the Index and the Reference Section to help you to answer the following questions.

1 What are the main types of pesticides? Why are they used and what are the possible dangers if they are over-used?

2 Draw diagrams showing:
a How a prism can act as a mirror.
b A circuit in which two lamps can be connected to the same power supply and be controlled separately by two switches.
c The differences between arteries and veins.
d How the populations of greenfly and ladybirds might change together over a fairly long time if there was a sudden increase in the numbers of greenfly to start with (hint: ladybirds eat greenfly).
e The arrangements of molecules in a dilute solution compared with a strong solution.

3 How does electroplating work?

4 How did nitrates get into the soil (for growing crops) before the large-scale factory production of nitrates, which only began about 60 years ago?

5 Copy out the following passage and fill in the missing words. Underline these words, or write them in a different colour ink. Choose from the words listed at the end – but not all of the words are given and some are wrong.

To start with, the energy in coal came from the _____. We can't use this energy unless the coal is burned – this means it combines with _____. This chemical reaction is _____. In a power station, the energy is first transferred to _____ and so increases its pressure so that it can drive _____. As these turn, they spin large coils of wire at high speed. The coils spin in a _____ field, and so generate electricity.

Unfortunately, most of the energy produced by burning the coal is _____ . It goes into water in the _____ towers. Eventually this energy just raises the _____ of the surroundings very slightly. In other words, it _____ out. This means that a power station has an _____ of only about 35%.

Word list: *energy, efficiency, turbines, armature, Sun, magnetic, electric, temperature, cooling, exothermic, endothermic, steam.*

6 a Explain what rate of reaction means.
b What are the four main factors that decide how quickly a chemical reaction occurs?
c Choose *one* factor and explain what effect it has on the rate of reaction.

Reference
Section

Safety rules

1 **Think safe!**

2 **Read/listen to instructions.**

3 **Move carefully.**

4 **Beware of poisons – do not eat or drink in laboratories.**

5 **Save eyes – wear eye protection whenever you handle chemicals.**

6 **Work cleanly – mop up spillages and do not put solids or paper into sinks.**

7 **When in doubt, check!**

This section covers the basic investigating, measuring and testing skills that are useful in any kind of practical science. It also includes some more advanced techniques which have special uses.

INVESTIGATING

Techniques for investigations on plants

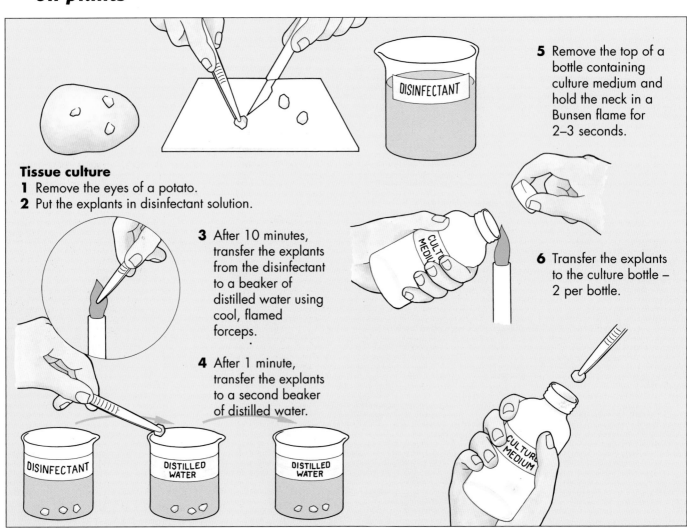

5 Remove the top of a bottle containing culture medium and hold the neck in a Bunsen flame for 2–3 seconds.

Tissue culture
1 Remove the eyes of a potato.
2 Put the explants in disinfectant solution.

3 After 10 minutes, transfer the explants from the disinfectant to a beaker of distilled water using cool, flamed forceps.

4 After 1 minute, transfer the explants to a second beaker of distilled water.

6 Transfer the explants to the culture bottle – 2 per bottle.

DISINFECTANT

DISINFECTANT   DISTILLED WATER   DISTILLED WATER

CULTURE MEDIUM

Reference

Detecting starch in leaves

1 Dip a leaf in boiling water for about a minute.

2 Turn off the Bunsen flame.

3 Put the leaf into a test tube containing ethanol.

4 Put the test tube into hot water.

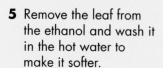

5 Remove the leaf from the ethanol and wash it in the hot water to make it softer.

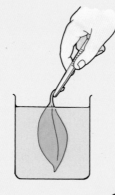

6 Carefully spread the leaf out on a white tile and then put dilute iodine solution all over it.

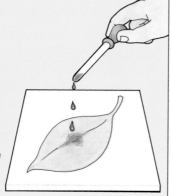

7 The parts that turn blue contain starch.

Ecology field work

Collecting insects

Beating tray

This is a standard-sized sheet or tray which is held under a tree or a bush which is then shaken. Small creatures fall onto the sheet and can be collected. A pooter is a useful tool to collect them.

A pooter

The large tube is held over an insect; the other is used to suck up the insect.

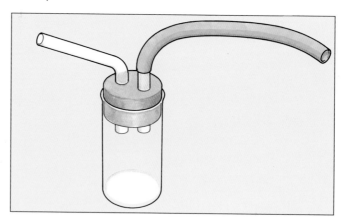

Pitfall trap

Used to collect ground insects. Sink a clean jam jar into the ground so that the top is level with the soil. Cover the mouth of the jar with a stone or wood roof to keep the rain out of the jar. You can bait this jar with meat to attract scavengers. Inspect the trap regularly.

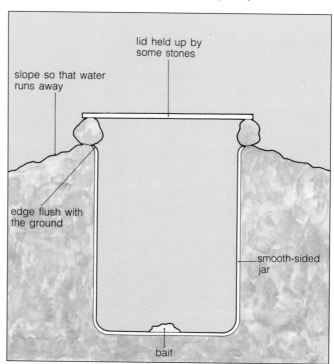

lid held up by some stones

slope so that water runs away

edge flush with the ground

smooth-sided jar

bait

Reference

Tullgren funnel

This is used to collect small soil animals. A soil or leaf-litter sample is placed on a sieve under a lamp. The heat from the lamp drives the animals through the sieve down a funnel into a pot containing 60% ethanol. The ethanol kills the animals, so stopping the carnivores from devouring the rest.

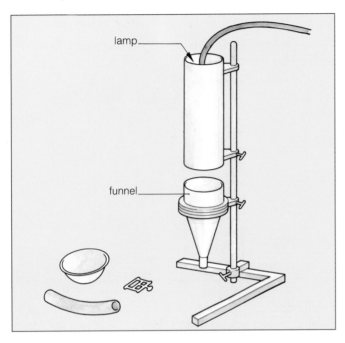

Sweep net

Used to catch small flying insects. You use a sweep net by waving it to and fro in front of you over the plants. Check the net regularly to see what you have caught.

Sampling plants

Kick sample

This special net is used to take a sample of the wildlife from a stream bed.

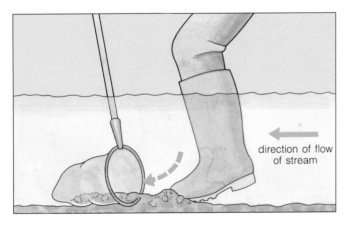

Quadrat

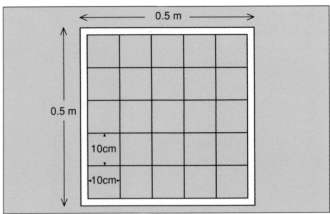

To compare different areas, you must take a standard sample. The type of sample depends on the nature of the area. The standard sample is taken by using a quadrat. This is a square metal or wooden frame, usually 0.25 m^2 or 1 m^2, but the quadrat can be bigger – it depends on what you are studying. A tree survey requires at least a 10 m^2 quadrat; an investigation into daisies on the lawn would need a 0.25 m^2 one.

Often the quadrat is used at random – throwing into a general area. Sometimes you want to study along a line through an area. Then, the quadrat can be placed at regular intervals along this line to sample the vegetation and animal life. If the area covered by the quadrats, and of the habitat, is known, the total number of individuals in the whole habitat can be calculated.

Worked example using a quadrat

A 1 m^2 quadrat is used 20 times and the total number of daisies enclosed is 100. Estimate the population of daisies in the field if its area is 1000 m^2.

Number of daisies: = 100

Area of 20 quadrats: $20 \times 1 = 20$ m^2

Number of daisies in 1 m^2: $\dfrac{100}{20}$ = 5 daisies per m^2

Number of daisies in 1000 m^2: $1000 \times 5 = 5000$

Sampling using quadrats works best if:

- The quadrat is randomly placed in the habitat, i.e. you do not see an area of daisies and deliberately put the quadrat over it.
- The organism being examined is evenly spread throughout the habitat, i.e. if all the individuals are grouped in just one or two areas, a low estimate can be obtained if none of the quadrats is placed over them.
- A reasonable number of samples is taken, i.e. recording individuals in a single quadrat is not going to be very representative of a whole field.

Capture and recapture

This is a method that allows you to estimate the size of large populations of organisms living in one area. It involves the following stages:

1 Capture – Catch and count a sample of the organism.
2 Mark – Mark each organism with paint, a ring or a tag.
3 Release – Release the organisms back into their habitat.
4 Recapture – After 24 hours or more, collect another sample of the organism.
5 Calculate

$$\text{Estimated total population} = \frac{\text{number in sample 1} \times \text{number in sample 2}}{\text{number of marked individuals in sample 2}}$$

Worked example of capture and recapture
To estimate the number of woodlice inhabiting a stone wall, a student captures a sample and marks them with a dark spot of paint.

Number of woodlice marked with paint: 100
Number of woodlice caught 24 hours later: 100
Number of sample 2 with paint spots: 5

$$\text{Estimated total population:} = \frac{100 \times 100}{5}$$
$$= 2000$$

Collecting gases

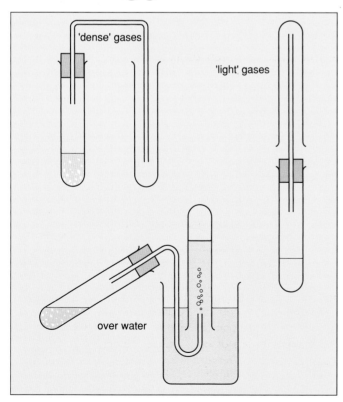

Titration

Add the acid a little at a time, whilst shaking the flask to make sure the chemicals mix. Carefully watch the colour of the indicator in the flask. The reaction is complete when the indicator shows that the liquid in the flask is at neutral pH.

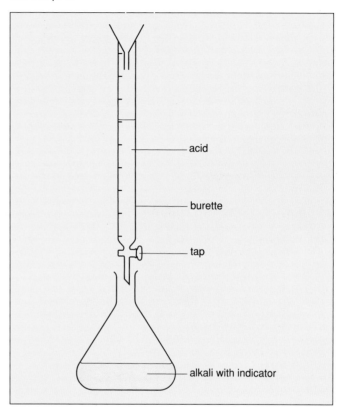

Distilling

Distilling is a way of separating a mixture of two or more liquids. It relies on the fact that the liquids will boil at different temperatures.

Simple method

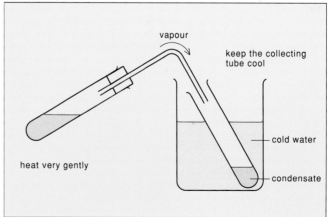

More complicated method using a still/condenser

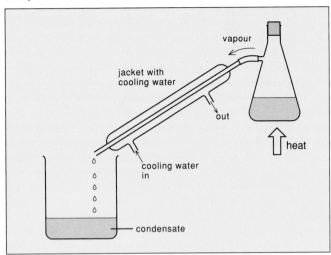

Using a fractionating column

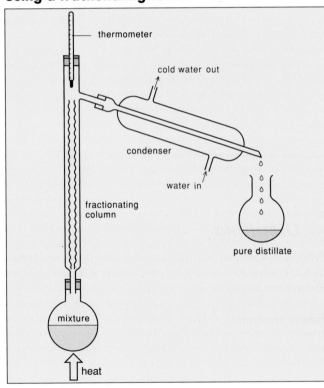

Dropping funnel

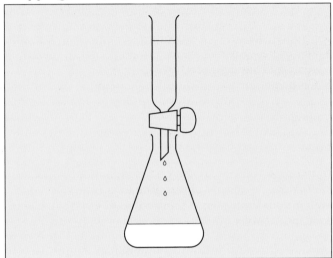

Evaporating

Slow method

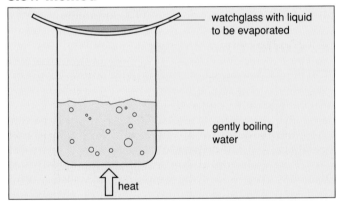

Quick method

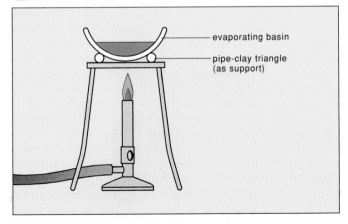

MEASURING

Temperature

Use the right kind of thermometer; *glass* thermometers are useful for liquids and the air, but should not be pushed into the soil.

A *maximum-and-minimum* thermometer can record the highest and lowest temperatures reached during a period of time.

Wind speed

Measured with an anemometer

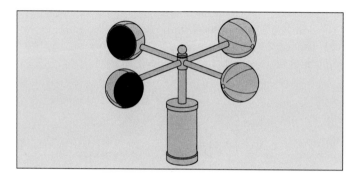

Acidity

Measured with either a pH meter or by using indicator (solution or paper).

A simple test for the pH of soil:

1 Take a small sample of soil and dry it carefully.
2 Put the dry soil into a test tube, add distilled water and shake.
3 Let the solid settle until the water is clear.
4 Add indicator solution (or use paper) and compare the colour with a pH chart.
(Note: For a more accurate result use a special Soil Testing Kit.)

Turbidity

1 Place a cross painted on a white metal disc at the bottom of a large measuring cylinder.
2 Pour in water until you *just* can't see the cross.
3 The higher this water level, the clearer the water must be.

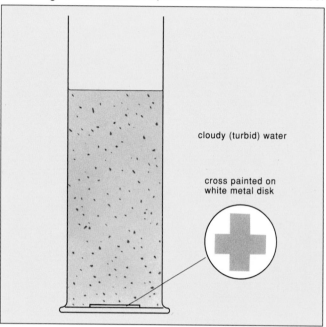

cloudy (turbid) water

cross painted on white metal disk

Measuring water use by leaves

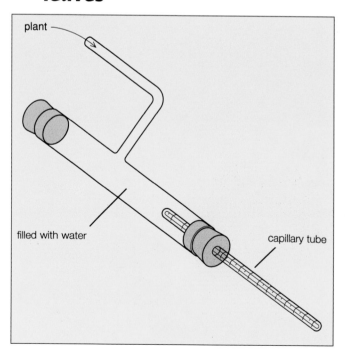

plant

filled with water

capillary tube

A sealed system on a top-pan balance

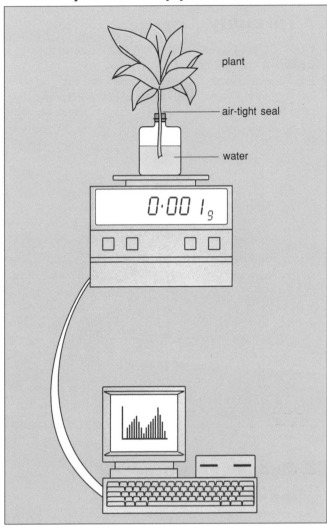

plant

air-tight seal

water

0·001 g

Fuels

Measuring energy output

First decide whether you are going to compare equal volumes of the fuels or equal *masses*. Weigh or measure the volumes of the fuel samples accordingly.

Decide on a standard mass of water (50–200 grams) which is placed in a standard container (a metal can or beaker). Measure the temperature of the water before you heat it.

Burn the fuel samples, in turn, in such a way that the energy they release is used to heat up the water, and measure the *final* temperature the water reaches after all the fuel is burned.

Calculate the *rise* in temperature produced by burning the fuel. The larger the temperature rise, the more energy the sample of fuel was able to provide.

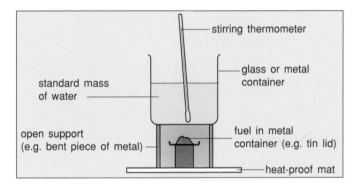

stirring thermometer

glass or metal container

standard mass of water

open support (e.g. bent piece of metal)

fuel in metal container (e.g. tin lid)

heat-proof mat

A rough value for the energy supplied by the fuel, in joules, can be calculated using the formula:

$$\text{energy supplied} = \text{mass of water (in grams)} \times \text{rise in temperature} \times 4.2$$

Note: Unless you can be sure that all the energy went into the water, the comparison is not very accurate. It is quite difficult to stop the surroundings being heated by the fuel.

Measuring lung capacity

Blow into a rolled-up plastic bag, specially made as a cylinder and marked off in litres

Measuring voltage and current

The diagram shows how the instruments are placed in a circuit to measure the resistance of a lamp (in *ohms*) and the power (in *watts*) that the lamp needs to make it work.

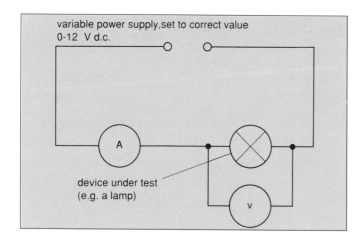

variable power supply,set to correct value
0-12 V d.c.

A

device under test
(e.g. a lamp)

V

Measuring resistance

$$\text{resistance} = \frac{\text{voltmeter reading}}{\text{ammeter reading}} \qquad R = \frac{V}{I}$$

Measuring electrical power

power = voltmeter reading × ammeter reading

For example, if the voltmeter reads 6 V and the ammeter 0.5 A:

$$\text{resistance} = \frac{6}{0.5} = 12 \text{ ohms,}$$

$$\text{power} = 6 \times 0.5 = 3 \text{ watts.}$$

Measuring energy

Electrical energy

Use the formula:

electrical energy = voltage × current × time
$$E = VIt$$

(E in joules, V in volts, I in amperes and t in seconds.)

By definition, a *volt* is the potential difference between two points when a current of 1 ampere flowing between them produces 1 joule of energy each second. In most applications, this is produced as heating energy.

Measuring work and energy

Work and energy are measured in the same unit: the joule.

The word work is used scientifically to mean the quantity of energy transferred by means of applying a force, such as

● lifting something against the force of gravity,
● slowing a bicycle by using the force of the brakes,
● accelerating a car by using the force from its engine.

The work done for the energy transferred is calculated using the formula:

$$\text{work} = \text{force} \times \begin{array}{l} \text{distance moved in the} \\ \text{direction of the force} \end{array}$$

$$W = Fd$$

(W is in joules, F is in newtons and d in metres.)

Measuring power

Power is the rate at which work is done, or the rate at which energy is being used. It is calculated by dividing the work done by the time taken to do it:

$$\text{power} = \frac{\text{work done}}{\text{time taken}} \qquad P = \frac{W}{t}$$

Power is measured in watts, if work is in joules and time is measured in seconds: work = joules per second.

Measuring efficiency

The efficiency of a system measures how good it is as an energy converter:

$$\text{efficiency} = \frac{\text{energy output}}{\text{energy input}} \times 100\%$$

No system, machine or process has an efficiency greater than 100%. That would mean that energy had been created. That can't be done. Energy can only be transferred from something else that already has energy. The energy output cannot be greater than the input.

Some typical efficiencies:

System	Efficiency (%)
car engine	25
steam engine (train)	10
diesel engine	40
electric motor (large)	90
power station	33
human muscle	85
bicycle	27
central heating:	
gas-fired boiler	75
oil-fired boiler	70
coal-fired boiler	60
photosynthesis:	
wheat	1
sugar cane	2.5
food animals:	
beef cattle	0.6
fish	20

Reference

Heating energy

Use the formula:

$$\frac{heating}{energy} = mass \times temperature\ rise \times specific\ heat\ capacity$$

$$H = mTc$$

The energy needed to heat an object depends on its mass (how much of it there is), the rise in temperature produced, and the substance the object is made of. Some materials need more energy to heat them through 1°C; water needs 4.18 kilojoules (kJ), while copper needs only 400 joules. This quantity is called the *specific heat capacity*.

Substance	Specific heat capacity (J/kg K)
water	4180
aluminium	900
copper	400
iron	475
polystyrene	1300
glass	600

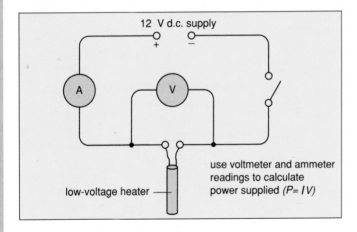

Detecting radioactivity

The standard way is to use a Geiger counter. For safety reasons this equipment may not be used by students under 16 years old.

Measuring stress

When a force or load is applied to a structure, the force is shared out over the area involved. Thus a useful idea is stress.

$$stress = \frac{force}{area}\ or\ \frac{load}{area}$$

$$S = \frac{F}{A}$$

Measure force as above, then measure or calculate the area (A) on which the force acts:

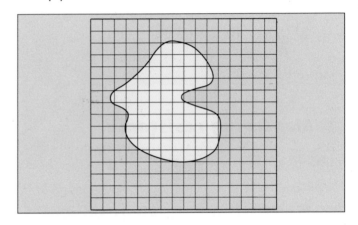

1 Trace outline.
2 Count the squares: e.g. 60 squares, each square 1 cm² therefore area = 60 cm².
3 The area of a rectangle or square is width × height.
4 The area of a circle is πr^2, where r is the circle's radius.

Measuring strain

Strain measures the effect of a stress, e.g. the change in length per unit length, the angle bent or twisted through per unit length.

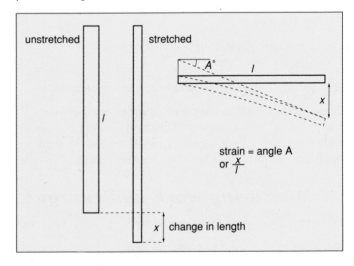

$$strain = \frac{change\ in\ length}{unstretched\ length} = \frac{x}{l}$$

Measuring volume and density

Measure the mass (by weighing). Calculate the density by using the formula:

$$\text{density} = \frac{\text{mass}}{\text{volume}}$$

Measuring speed

You can measure average speed by measuring the time taken to cover a measured distance:

$$\text{average speed} = \frac{\text{distance}}{\text{time}}$$

Use a ticker-timer and tape to measure speed over short distances and times.

Connect the ticker-timer to a low-voltage supply (check the value first, and whether it is an a.c. or d.c. operation). As the tape moves through the timer, the timer marks it with a dot 50 times a second. If the tape is fixed to a moving object, it will produce a record of how the object moved.

The space between the dots shows how far the tape moved in a fiftieth of a second.

50 spaces = 1 second

10 spaces = $\frac{1}{5}$ second (a 'tentick')

Note: Count the spaces, not the dots. The tape can be cut up into tenticks and stuck to a baseline to make a graph showing how the object moved. This is a *speed–time* graph.

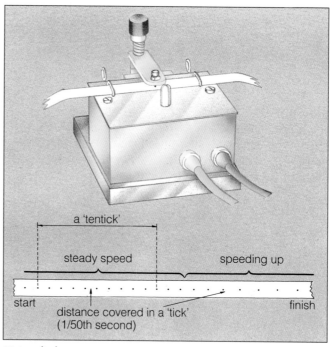

Using light gates

If you use light gates linked to a computer, it is easy to measure the average speed of the object as it passes through the light gate. Measure the length of the object that obstructed the light gate. The computer can tell you for how many seconds the object obstructed the light gate. Use the equation above to calculate the object's average speed.

Measuring acceleration

You need to measure two speeds, each one over a fairly short time interval. Measure one at the beginning and the other near the end of the movement. Subtract one from the other to find the *change in speed*. Divide this by the time elapsed between taking the two speeds. The result is the acceleration (*the change in speed in a certain time*).

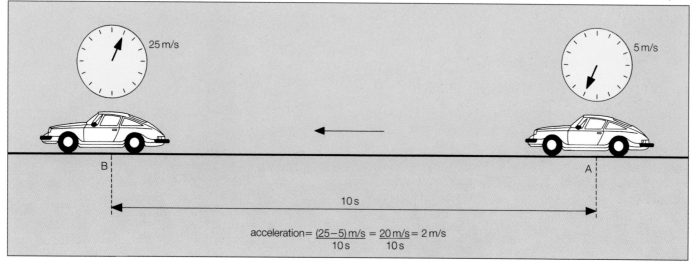

$$\text{acceleration} = \frac{(25-5)\,\text{m/s}}{10\,\text{s}} = \frac{20\,\text{m/s}}{10\,\text{s}} = 2\,\text{m/s}$$

Identifying metals

You can use a flame test or the sodium hydroxide test.

Flame test

Dip a splint into the solution or powder being tested. Put the dipped end into a clear blue Bunsen flame, near the bottom. The flame will become coloured, and the colour produced shows what metal is present.

Metal	Colour
calcium	brick red
copper	green
potassium	lilac
sodium	yellow

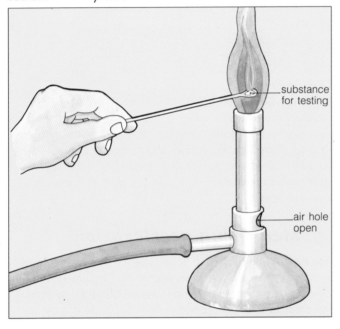

substance for testing

air hole open

Sodium hydroxide test for metals in compounds

Dissolve the metal compound and put some of the solution in a test tube. Add one or two drops of sodium hydroxide solution. Note the colour of any precipitate that may be formed. Then add more sodium hydroxide ('to excess'). Use the table below to work out what metal was in the compound.

Precipitate colour after adding 2 drops of sodium hydroxide	Effect of adding more sodium hydroxide	Metal in compound (metallic ions)
pale blue	no change	copper
green	no change	iron(II)
brown	no change	iron(III)
white	no change	calcium
white	disolves to colourless solution	zinc, lead or aluminium

Detecting water

The simple tests for water are:

● For large quantities: measure the boiling point (100 °C for pure water).
● For small quantities: touch the liquid with dry cobalt chloride paper; this will change from blue to pink if water is present.

Physics formulae

The magic triangle

This is an easy way to rearrange many simple formulae.
The formula must have three quantities. One of the
quantities must be multiplied by or divided by another of
the quantities. For example, the magic triangle can be
used to rearrange: $R = V/I$, $P = IV$ or $v = f\lambda$.

Constructing the triangle

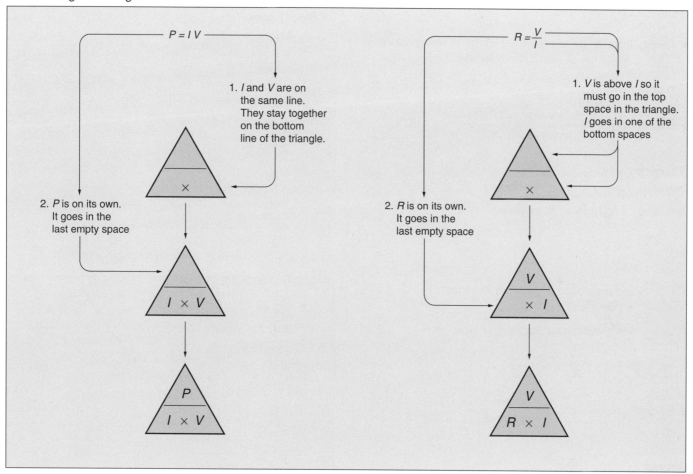

Using the triangle

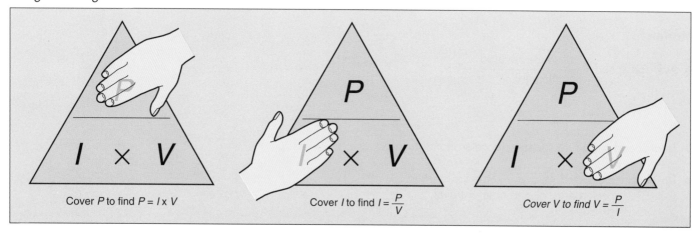

Cover P to find $P = I \times V$

Cover I to find $I = \dfrac{P}{V}$

Cover V to find $V = \dfrac{P}{I}$

Reference

Energy and power
- Potential energy = mgh (h is the change in height)
- Kinetic energy = $\frac{1}{2}mv^2$ (v is the speed of a mass m)

- Power = $\dfrac{\text{energy}}{\text{time}}$

- Electrical power (in watts):
  $P = VI$
- Energy transferred in time t by current I under potential difference V:
  $E = VIt$
- Energy transferred to create a change in temperature (T) of a mass (m) of substance with specific heat capacity c:
  $E = mcT$

- Efficiency = $\dfrac{\text{useful energy transferred}}{\text{energy supplied}} \times 100\%$

Electricity
(See also, Energy and power, above)

Definition of resistance, R, in ohms:

- $R = \dfrac{V}{I}$

- Combined resistance of resistors in series:
  $R = R_1 + R_2 + R_3 + \dots$
- Combined resistance of resistors in parallel:

  $\dfrac{1}{R} = \dfrac{1}{R_1} + \dfrac{1}{R_2} + \dfrac{1}{R_3} + \dots$

- Charge (in coulombs) = $\dfrac{\text{current}}{\text{(amperes)}} \times \dfrac{\text{time}}{\text{(seconds)}}$

  $Q = It$

Waves
- Speed = frequency × wavelength
  $v = f\lambda$

Motion

- Average speed = $\dfrac{\text{distance covered}}{\text{time taken}}$

  $v = \dfrac{d}{t}$

- Final speed = starting speed + (acceleration × time)
  $v = u + at$
- The distance covered, d, if you know the starting speed, u, acceleration, a, and time of travel, t:
  $d = ut + \frac{1}{2}at^2$

- Force = mass × acceleration
  $F = ma$
- Impulse = change of momentum
  $Ft = mv$

Graphs of motion

Distance–time graphs
The steepness shows the speed.

(a) Steady speed.

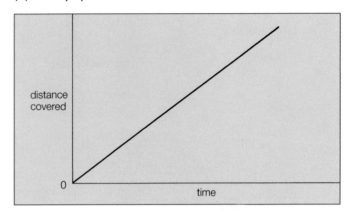

(b) Steady acceleration (steadily changing speed).

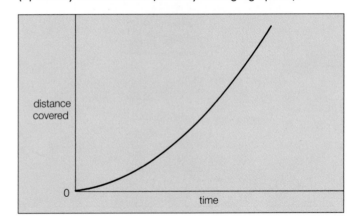

Speed–time graphs
The steepness shows the acceleration

(a) Steady speed.

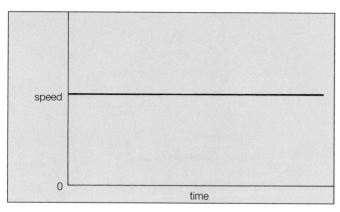

(b) Steady acceleration.

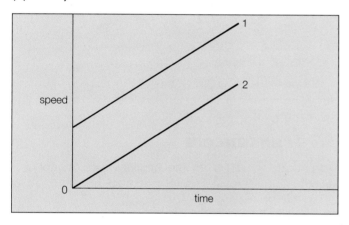

Line 1. Already moving when the time starts.

Line 2. At rest when the timing starts.

Laws of motion ('Newton's laws')

1 A force is needed to change the movement of an object; otherwise the object will keep still or keep moving steadily in a straight line.
2 If an unbalanced force does act on an object, it will make the object accelerate and/or change its direction of movement.
3 Two objects are always needed to produce a force, and the force acts equally on both.

The gas laws

If you hold your finger over the end of a bicycle pump and then push the plunger, the walls of the pump will feel warmer (and so will your finger!).

If a volume of gas is heated, the gas expands or its temperature increases.

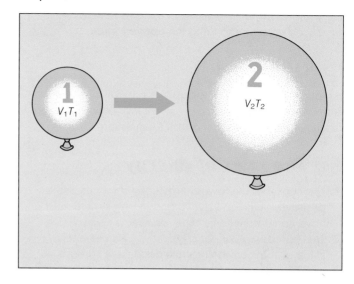

These results are described by the gas formula. It says that for a fixed mass of gas:

$$\frac{PV}{T} = \text{constant}$$

P is pressure, V is volume, T is temperature in kelvin. Kelvin temperatures start at absolute zero, -273 °C.

At constant temperature
At constant temperature, the volume of a gas is *inversely proportional* to its pressure. This means that if you double the pressure, the volume of the gas halves. Another way of looking at this is to say that the volume multiplied by the pressure remains constant:

$$P_1 \times V_1 = P_2 \times V_2$$

At constant volume
At constant volume, the pressure of a gas is *proportional* to its temperature in kelvin. This means that if you double the temperature, the pressure of the gas doubles. Another way of looking at this is to say that the pressure divided by the temperature remains constant:

$$\frac{P_1}{T_1} = \frac{P_2}{T_2}$$

At constant pressure
At constant pressure, the volume of a gas is proportional to its temperature in kelvin:

$$\frac{V_1}{T_1} = \frac{V_2}{T_2}$$

Hooke's law

An object obeys Hooke's law if it is elastic and stretches (or compresses) evenly with force, i.e. if the change produced is proportional to the applied force.

Ohm's law

An object obeys Ohm's law if its electrical resistance stays the same whatever the current that flows through it (assuming that the object doesn't get hotter).

The laws of energy

1 The conservation law: energy cannot be created or destroyed – the energy we find in one system must have come from some other system.
2 The 'spreading out' law: whenever we use energy, some of it becomes unusable because it spreads out to warm up the surroundings.

Power rating of some common devices

A unit of electrical energy is 1 kilowatt-hour (3.6 megajoules).

Device	Typical power rating	What you get for 1 unit
one-bar electric fire	1 kW	1 hour's heating
radiant heater	3 kW	20 minutes' heating
kettle	2 kW	10 litres of boiling water
lamp	100 W	light for 10 hours
colour TV set	160 W	6 hours' use
cassette player	50 W	1 day's play
hi-fi system	100 W	10 hours' listening
electric iron	500 W	2 hours' use
food mixer	100 W	60 cake mixes
toaster	900 W	70 slices of toast
refrigerator	200 W	1 day's use
vacuum cleaner	500 W	2 hours' cleaning
instant shower	3 kW	1 shower

Wiring a plug

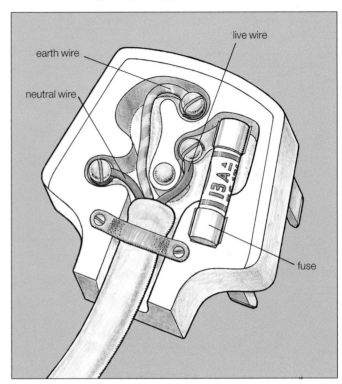

Transducers

Transducers convert a physical quantity (such as light or sound) into an electrical signal, and back again.

Moving-coil microphone

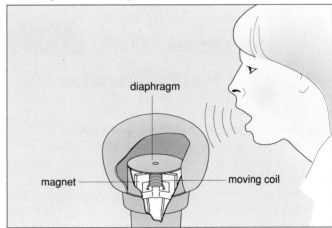

Telephone earpiece

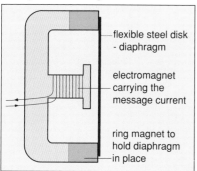

- flexible steel disk - diaphragm
- electromagnet carrying the message current
- ring magnet to hold diaphragm in place

Loudspeaker

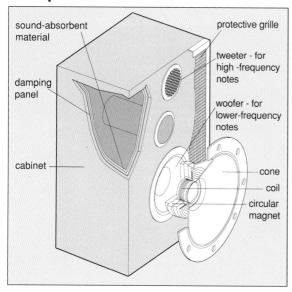

- sound-absorbent material
- damping panel
- cabinet
- protective grille
- tweeter - for high-frequency notes
- woofer - for lower-frequency notes
- cone
- coil
- circular magnet

▨ *Pitch, loudness and quality of sounds*

You can get an idea of how sound waves vary by using a cathode ray oscilloscope (CRO) to look at the signals from a microphone. The picture on the CRO is called a *trace*.

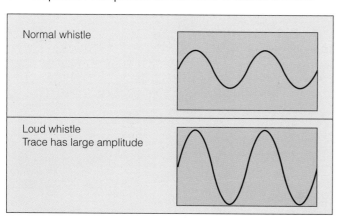

Normal whistle

Loud whistle
Trace has large amplitude

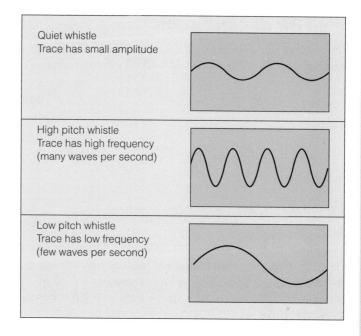

Quiet whistle
Trace has small amplitude

High pitch whistle
Trace has high frequency
(many waves per second)

Low pitch whistle
Trace has low frequency
(few waves per second)

Even when the loudness and pitch stay the same, you can still tell the difference between the sound from a violin and the sounds from other instruments.

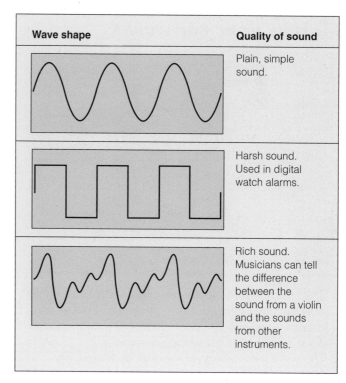

Wave shape	Quality of sound
	Plain, simple sound.
	Harsh sound. Used in digital watch alarms.
	Rich sound. Musicians can tell the difference between the sound from a violin and the sounds from other instruments.

The decibel scale

The decibel scale measures the loudness of sound as it reaches your ear. A loudness of 140 dB causes pain.

Loudness	Sound you hear	Sound level (dB)
silence	limit of your hearing	0
quiet	faint whisper	20
moderate	ordinary conversation	50
loud	busy street traffic	80
extremely loud	jet plane taking off	110

Every time you increase the power (energy per second) of the sound by 10 times, the loudness increases by 10 dB. A pneumatic drill produces sound waves with a loudness of 90 dB. These waves transfer 1000 times as much energy each second as sound waves from a TV programme (60 dB). There are 3 steps of 10 dB between 60 dB and 90 dB. This is an increase of $10 \times 10 \times 10 = 1000$ times the power.

How your ear works

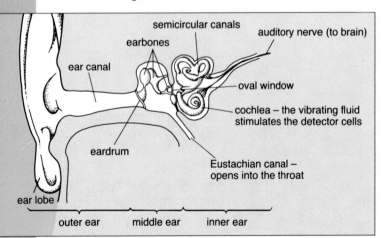

1 The *ear drum* is a piece of skin that is stretched tightly over the end of the *ear canal*. It vibrates like the skin of a drum when sound waves reach it. It is connected to three small bones called the ear bones.
2 The ear bones are joined together by hinges. The bones work like levers enlarging the vibrations and transmitting them to the *oval window*.
3 The vibrations reach the *cochlea*, which is shaped like a snail shell. Inside the cochlea there are detector cells that pick up vibrations of different frequencies. They also sense how loud the sound is.
4 The detector cells send signals to the brain along the hearing nerve.

The electromagnetic spectrum

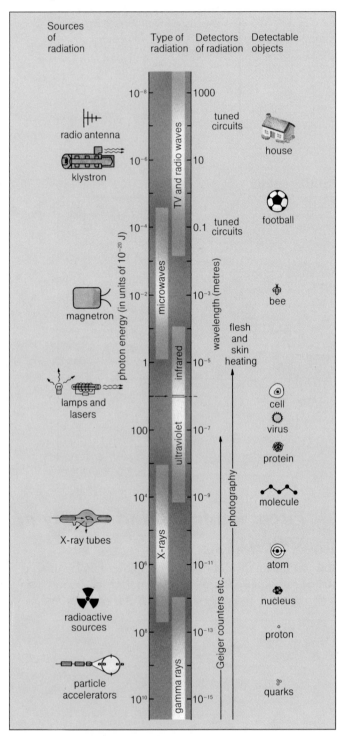

Electromagnetic waves

Electromagnetic waves (light waves) travel through a vacuum. An electromagnetic wave is a transverse wave, that has vibrating electric and magnetic fields moving along together.

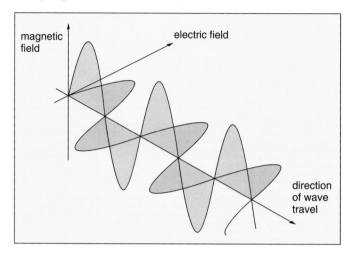

Lenses and their uses

Weak positive lens

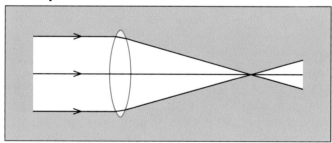

Strong positive lens

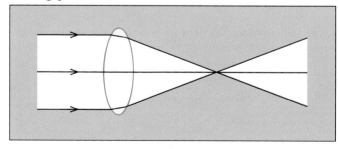

Negative lens

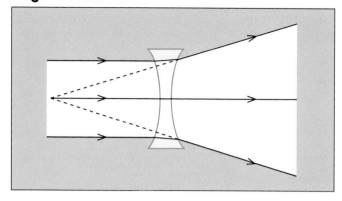

Eye

Light is focused by both the cornea and the eye lens. The eye lens changes shape to alter its strength.

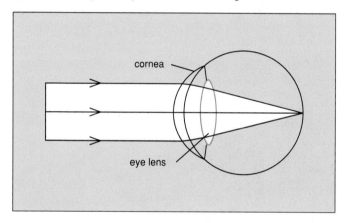

Camera

The lens can be moved backwards and forwards to focus the image on the film.

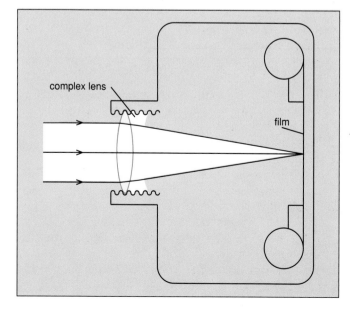

■ *Reflection*

When light is reflected, the angle of incidence equals the angle of reflection.

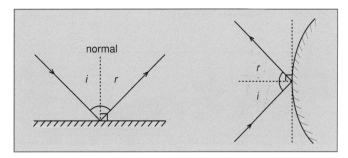

When you look into a mirror you see an image that appears to be behind the mirror. This is called a *virtual* image because it is not really there. The mirror fools your brain. Your brain thinks that rays of light are travelling in straight lines directly to your eye from the virtual image behind the mirror.

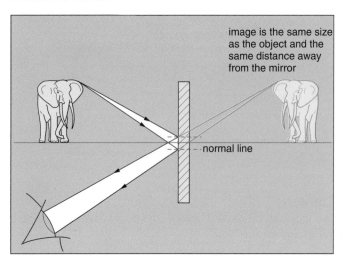

image is the same size as the object and the same distance away from the mirror

normal line

Concave mirror

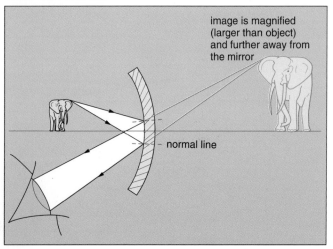

image is magnified (larger than object) and further away from the mirror

normal line

Convex mirror

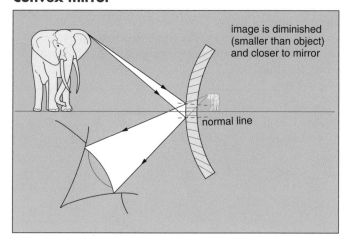

image is diminished (smaller than object) and closer to mirror

normal line

■ *Refraction*

Light changes direction when it goes from one material to another if the light does not enter at a right angle to the surface.

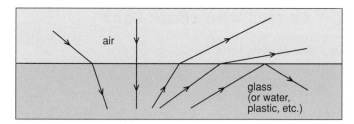

air

glass (or water, plastic, etc.)

As light goes from a less dense to a more dense material (say, air to glass), its direction changes to make a larger angle to the surface. The reverse happens when light goes the other way (e.g. water to air) As the angle changes, light leaves closer and closer to the surface. Eventually it cannot leave at all and *total internal reflection* occurs.

Total internal reflection in a light-carrying fibre

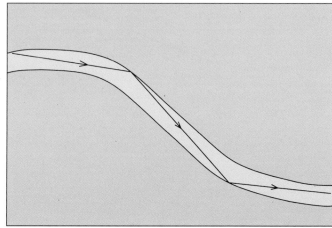

Reference

Prism deviating a ray of light

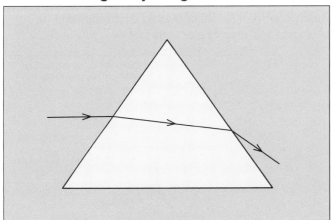

Prisms used as mirrors

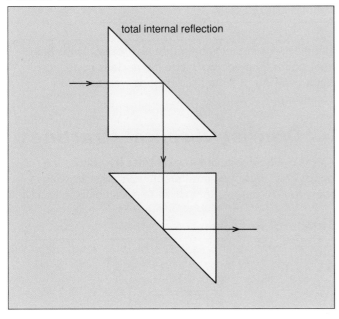

Real and apparent depth
An optical illusion caused by refraction.

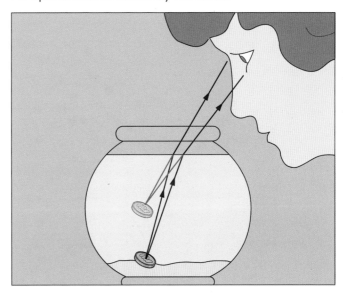

Reference

Solid, liquids, solutions and gases

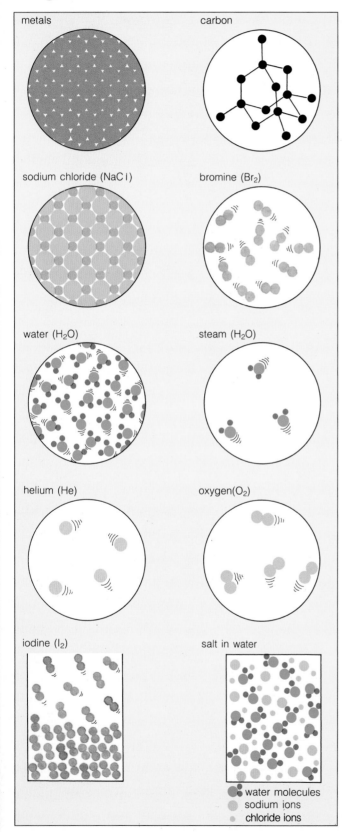

metals

carbon

sodium chloride (NaCl)

bromine (Br$_2$)

water (H$_2$O)

steam (H$_2$O)

helium (He)

oxygen (O$_2$)

iodine (I$_2$)

salt in water

water molecules
sodium ions
chloride ions

A simple model of an atom

Atoms consist of a central nucleus of protons and neutrons, and a set of electrons that orbit this nucleus.

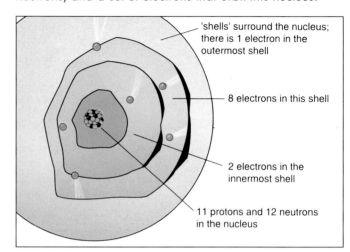

'shells' surround the nucleus; there is 1 electron in the outermost shell

8 electrons in this shell

2 electrons in the innermost shell

11 protons and 12 neutrons in the nucleus

The electrons in atoms are more like fuzzy clouds than neat points. They do not circle the nucleus in neat orbits, but a drawing of three fuzzy clouds would be very confusing.

Drawing chemical structures

Atoms are held together in molecules by bonds. The bonds can be shown in different ways. The drawings show four representations of an ethene molecule (C$_2$H$_4$).

Structural formula

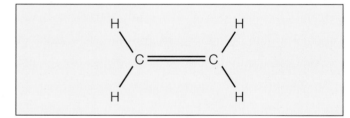

Simple diagram

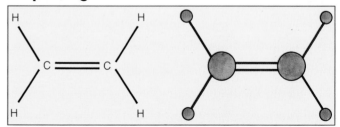

Reference

'Ball-and-stick' model

But the sticks don't really exist of course! A more realistic model is 'space filling'.

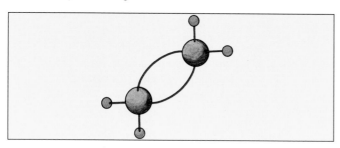

Solid models

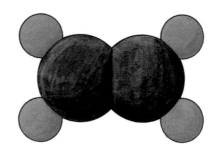

The Periodic Table

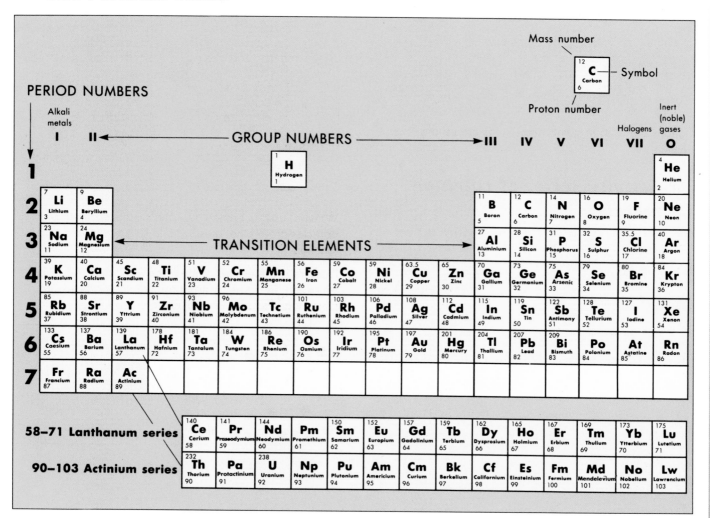

Reference

Ions

An electron has a negative charge and a proton has a positive charge. A neutron has no charge at all. If these positive and negative charges are not balanced out in a molecule or atom, it will have extra positive or negative charge(s). This is called an ion. The table shows the charges on some ions.

Positive ions (cations)		Negative ions (anions)	
ammonium	NH_4^+	bromide	Br^-
hydrogen	H^+	chloride	Cl^-
copper(I)	Cu^+	iodide	I^-
potassium	K^+	hydroxide	OH^-
sodium	Na^+	nitrate	NO_3^-
silver	Ag^+	carbonate	CO_3^{2-}
calcium	Ca^{2+}	oxide	O^{2-}
magnesium	Mg^{2+}	sulphate	SO_4^{2-}
copper(II)	Cu^{2+}	sulphite	SO_3^{2-}
iron(II)	Fe^{2+}	sulphide	S^{2-}
zinc	Zn^{2+}	phosphate	PO_4^{3-}
aluminium	Al^{3+}		
iron(III)	Fe^{3+}		

Cations are usually metals and anions are usually non-metals.

Activity series of common metals

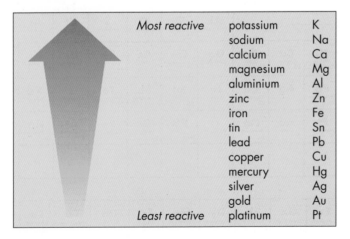

Most reactive	potassium	K
	sodium	Na
	calcium	Ca
	magnesium	Mg
	aluminium	Al
	zinc	Zn
	iron	Fe
	tin	Sn
	lead	Pb
	copper	Cu
	mercury	Hg
	silver	Ag
	gold	Au
Least reactive	platinum	Pt

Factors involved in rates of reaction

What decides how quickly chemical changes can take place?

Concentration is a measure of how much chemical is packed into a solution. By increasing the concentration of the reactants, the reacting particles are more likely to meet. In a dilute solution, there are fewer particles and they are further apart, so they are less likely to meet.

Reaction rates are speeded up by making sure that particles meet more often and/or with enough energy to react. This is done by:

- making the solutions more *concentrated*;
- using *higher temperatures*;
- using a *catalyst*;
- increasing the *surface area* of any solids (e.g. making the solids into fine powders, thin plates or wires).

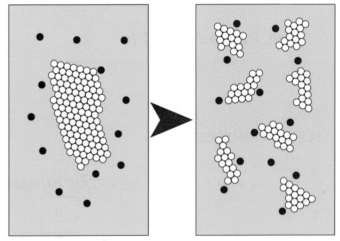

When a lump is broken into smaller pieces, more of its particles are on the 'outside' and so are exposed to a reaction.

Pressure is a measure of the force with which a gas is squeezed. In a gas at high pressure, the particles are closer together and more likely to bump into each other.

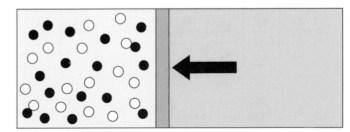

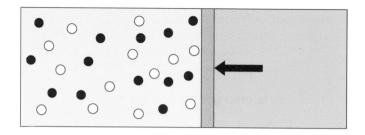

In a gas at lower pressure, the particles are further apart and are less likely to meet.

Electrochemistry

When a salt (sodium chloride, copper sulphate, etc.) dissolves in water, its ions become separated. This produces an *ionic solution*.

When this solution is made part of an electric circuit, the ions move. Positive ions (cations) go to the negative plate (*cathode*). Negative ions (anions) go to the positive plate (the *anode*). The solution is called an *electrolyte*. This effect is used in electroplating.

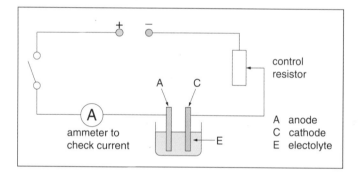

Common chemicals

This table shows some commonly found chemical compounds. It gives their 'household' names and their formulae.

Name	Common name	Formula
aluminium oxide	alumina	Al_2O_3
ammonia		NH_3
ammonium chloride		NH_4Cl
ammonium nitrate	'Nitram' fertiliser	NH_4NO_3
calcium carbonate	limestone, chalk	$CaCO_3$
calcium chloride		$CaCl_2$
calcium hydroxide	slaked lime	$Ca(OH)_2$
calcium oxide	quicklime	CaO
carbon monoxide		CO

Name	Common name	Formula
carbon dioxide		CO_2
cobalt(II) chloride		$CoCl_2$
copper(II) chloride		$CuCl_2$
copper(II) oxide		CuO
copper(II) sulphate		$CuSO_4$
hydrogen chloride		HCl (g)
hydrochloric acid		HCl (aq)
hydrogen fluoride		HF (g)
hydrogen peroxide		H_2O_2
hydrogen sulphide		H_2S
iron(II) oxide		FeO
iron(III) oxide		Fe_2O_3
magnesium carbonate		$MgCO_3$
magnesium chloride		$MgCl_2$
magnesium oxide	magnesia	MgO
manganese(IV) oxide	manganese dioxide	MnO_2
nitric acid		HNO_3
nitrogen monoxide		NO
nitrogen dioxide		NO_2
potassium chloride		KCl
potassium hydroxide	caustic potash	KOH
potassium manganate(VII)	potassium permanganate	$KMnO_4$
potassium nitrate	saltpetre	KNO_3
silicon(IV) oxide	silicon dioxide, silica	SiO_2
sodium carbonate	soda ash, washing soda	Na_2CO_3
sodium chloride	salt	$NaCl$
sodium hydrogencarbonate	sodium bicarbonate	$NaHCO_3$
sodium hydroxide	caustic soda	$NaOH$
sodium nitrate		$NaNO_3$
sodium sulphate		Na_2SO_4
sulphur dioxide		SO_2
sulphur trioxide		SO_3
sulphuric acid		H_2SO_4
water		H_2O
zinc oxide		ZnO

Reference

Alkanes

The alkanes are a group of carbon compounds of the general formula C_nH_{2n+2}.

Name	Formula	Melting point (°C)	Boiling point (°C)
methane	CH_4	−182	−161
ethane	C_2H_6	−183	−88
propane	C_3H_8	−188	−42
butane	C_4H_{10}	−138	−1
pentane	C_5H_{12}	−130	36
hexane	C_6H_{14}	−95	69
heptane	C_7H_{16}	−91	99
octane	C_8H_{18}	−57	126
nonane	C_9H_{20}	−51	151
decane	$C_{10}H_{22}$	−30	174
dodecane	$C_{12}H_{26}$	−10	216
eicosane	$C_{20}H_{42}$	37	344

Fuels

Fuels are chemicals which can be used as a source of energy – the energy is usually released when the chemicals are burned with oxygen.

Fossil fuels

These are the remains of living organisms (which may be plants or animals) that lived many millions of years ago. They have been converted into complicated mixtures of hydrocarbons, which are compounds of hydrogen and carbon.

Renewable fuels

These are fuels made from plants or from animal wastes. Unlike fossil fuels they are not 'used up', but can be made as long as animals and plants live and grow on Earth.

- **Wood**: the main cooking fuel of the world. Although it is renewable, in many parts of the world it is being used up faster than it can grow.
- **Biogas**: this is methane, CH_4. It is produced by the action of bacteria causing decay on many organic wastes, such as agricultural waste (e.g. sugar cane leaves), animal and human dung, household waste in rubbish tips, etc. Biogas is widely used in China, and also by some local councils in the UK, who are burning the methane from decaying rubbish to provide hot water for district heating.

- **Biological ethanol**: ethanol is alcohol, and is produced when yeasts grow in sugar solution. Mixed with petrol it can be used to power car engines, and is made on a large scale in Brazil from sugar cane, 'Gasohol'.
- **Renewable energy**: wind, wave and solar energy.

Nuclear fuels

These are radioactive elements that provide energy in power stations (and nuclear bombs) as a result of physical changes deep inside the atom (in the nuclei). They are not 'fuels' in the ordinary chemical sense, there is no combination with oxygen or any other kind of chemical reaction. The elements used in power stations are plutonium and uranium.

Fuels and pollution

All fuels cause pollution when used. The chemicals produced when hydrocarbon fuels (coal and oil) are burned are water and carbon dioxide. If the fuels contain other substances (such as sulphur) then other polluting substances are released (such as sulphur dioxide, which dissolves in water to make sulphuric acid – and so 'acid rain'). Water is harmless, but carbon dioxide is building up in the atmosphere. The result will be a gradual warming up of the Earth due to the *greenhouse effect*.

Carbon monoxide is a deadly poisonous gas produced when a fuel is not properly burned. If there is a shortage of oxygen, the hydrocarbon fuel will produce carbon monoxide (CO) instead of carbon dioxide (CO_2).

Reference

The uses of crude oil

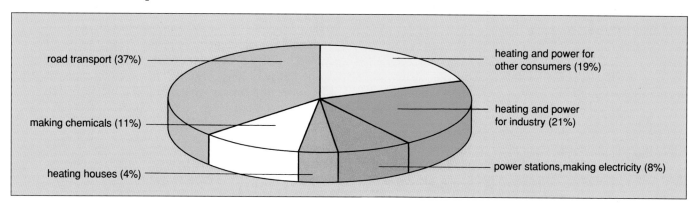

road transport (37%)

heating and power for other consumers (19%)

heating and power for industry (21%)

making chemicals (11%)

heating houses (4%)

power stations, making electricity (8%)

The lifetime of resources

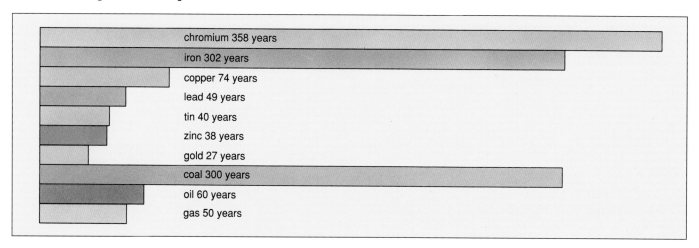

chromium 358 years
iron 302 years
copper 74 years
lead 49 years
tin 40 years
zinc 38 years
gold 27 years
coal 300 years
oil 60 years
gas 50 years

Minerals

Mineral	Formula	Annual production (kilotonnes in 1992)	Main product
haematite (iron ore)	Fe_2O_3	516 000	steel
bauxite (impure aluminium oxide)	various aluminium hydroxides, sulphides and complex hydrocarbons	106 520	aluminium
porphyry copper (pyrites, bornite, chalcopyrite)	CuS, Cu_5FeS_4, $CuFeS_2$	9254	copper
sphalerite (zinc blende)	ZnS	7133	zinc
galena, cerussite	PbS, $PbCO_3$	2980	lead
cassiterite	SnO_2	258	tin
wolframite	$(Fe,Mn)WO_4$	52	tungsten

Reference

213

Geology

The major types of rock

Sedimentary rocks

These are made from particles eroded from other rocks that have been deposited, usually in sea water, where rivers that carried the particles ended. Some were laid down in lakes, others in deserts as wind-blown sediments.

Sedimentary rocks often contain fossils. These are the remains of an animal or plant that has been preserved in the rock. The original material has usually been changed chemically so that wood, bones, flesh, shells, etc. have been changed into a mineral of some kind.

Igneous rocks

Igneous rocks were formed from a hot liquid material called *magma* that comes from deep inside the Earth. Surface flows of magma are called *lavas*. Magma that cooled inside the Earth formed rocks that have unique properties (e.g. large crystals). Associated landforms are *sills*, *dikes* and *bosses*. Volcanoes also produce material that is thrown into the air, forming piles of material that may eventually form hard rock.

Metamorphic rocks

These are rocks that have been changed, usually by high temperatures and pressures when igneous material flowed over or through them.

A simple key for identifying rocks

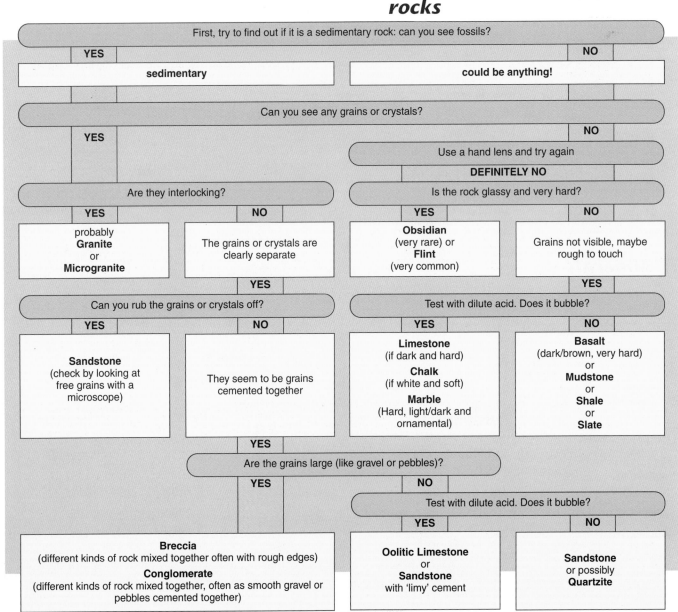

First, try to find out if it is a sedimentary rock: can you see fossils?

YES	NO
sedimentary	**could be anything!**

Can you see any grains or crystals?

YES — Are they interlocking?

- YES: probably **Granite** or **Microgranite**
- NO: The grains or crystals are clearly separate — YES — Can you rub the grains or crystals off?
  - YES: **Sandstone** (check by looking at free grains with a microscope)
  - NO: They seem to be grains cemented together — YES — Are the grains large (like gravel or pebbles)?
    - YES: **Breccia** (different kinds of rock mixed together often with rough edges) / **Conglomerate** (different kinds of rock mixed together, often as smooth gravel or pebbles cemented together)
    - NO: Test with dilute acid. Does it bubble?
      - YES: **Oolitic Limestone** or **Sandstone** with 'limy' cement
      - NO: **Sandstone** or possibly **Quartzite**

NO — Use a hand lens and try again — DEFINITELY NO — Is the rock glassy and very hard?

- YES: **Obsidian** (very rare) or **Flint** (very common)
- NO: Grains not visible, maybe rough to touch — YES — Test with dilute acid. Does it bubble?
  - YES: **Limestone** (if dark and hard) / **Chalk** (if white and soft) / **Marble** (Hard, light/dark and ornamental)
  - NO: **Basalt** (dark/brown, very hard) or **Mudstone** or **Shale** or **Slate**

Faulting, folding and erosion

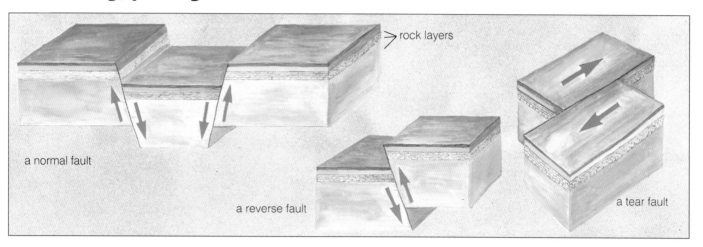

rock layers

a normal fault

a reverse fault

a tear fault

Fault

A geological structure formed when one section of rock moves past another. The fault is the plane along which the rocks slide.

The arrows show how the rock slabs may have moved.

Fold

This describes the effects produced when rocks are squeezed sideways.

The rocks are laid down under the sea in horizontal layers.

Slow, tectonic, Earth movements fold the rocks.

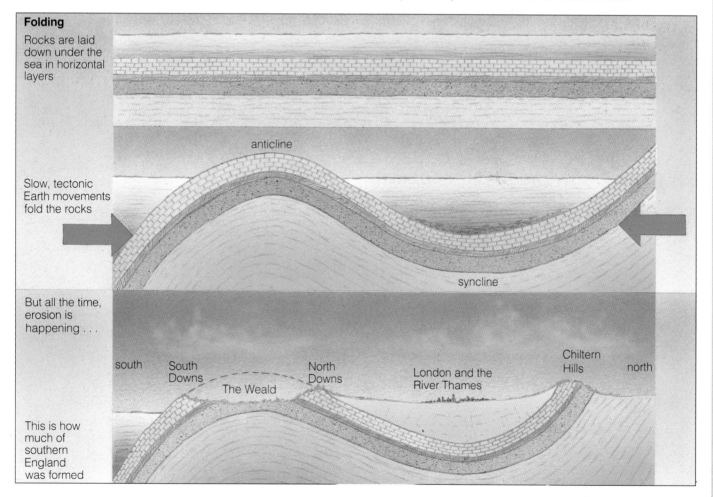

Folding

Rocks are laid down under the sea in horizontal layers

Slow, tectonic Earth movements fold the rocks

anticline

syncline

But all the time, erosion is happening . . .

south   South Downs   North Downs   London and the River Thames   Chiltern Hills   north

The Weald

This is how much of southern England was formed

Erosion

Any process that wears away rocks is called erosion: water, ice, wind, etc. Rain water is slightly acidic because of dissolved carbon dioxide and modern pollutant gases. Some rocks are easily dissolved, e.g. limestone.

Radioactive dating

The radioactivity of rocks decreases with time at a known rate so the ages of rocks and fossils can be found by measuring the radioactivity in them.

The greenhouse gases

	Carbon dioxide (CO_2)	Methane (CH_4)	Chlorofluoro-carbons (CFCs)	Nitrous oxide (N_2O)	Surface ozone (O_3), i.e. close to the Earth's surface
annual increase (%)	0.5	1	6		
time taken to break down (years)	7	10	15 000	170	2–3 weeks
how strongly it traps energy (compared with carbon dioxide)	1	30	10–20 000	150	2000
total contribution to greenhouse effect (%)	50	18	14	6	10
source	burning, especially fossil fuels	breakdown of organic chemicals by bacteria without enough oxygen, e.g. in rice fields, burning fuels, in intestines of cows and sheep	coolants in fridges and air conditioners; also used in foam and aerosol sprays	made by bacteria in the soil and the breakdown of nitrate fertilisers; burning fossil fuels and wood	around 75% of surface ozone is made when sunlight affects car exhaust fumes

Changes in the Earth's climate

1. Global temperature: for the past 150 000 years

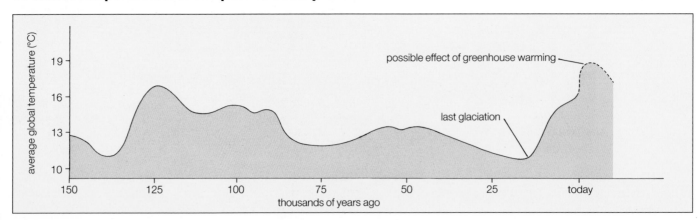

2. European temperature: the past 1000 years

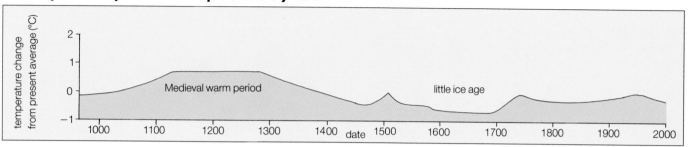

3. Global atmospheric CO_2: the past 200 years

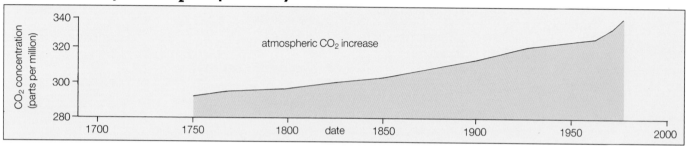

▉ *Acid rain*

Living cells

The microscopic units of life

Many different types of cell make up the bodies of living organisms.

A typical cell has a nucleus surrounded by living material called cytoplasm. The *cytoplasm* contains all sorts of small structures with their own jobs to do in keeping the cell alive and working. The cell contents are all kept together by a very thin *membrane*. The *nucleus* controls the chemical activities of the whole cell. The membrane is pierced by tiny pores which allow substances like oxygen and food and carbon dioxide to pass into and out of the cell cytoplasm.

Different types of cell are *specialised* in structure to carry out different functions or jobs. You can see some examples of different animal cells in the illustrations.

Cells in the blood

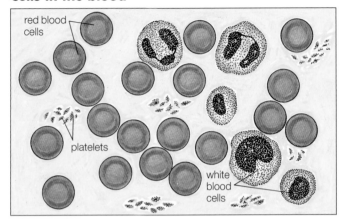

An animal cell

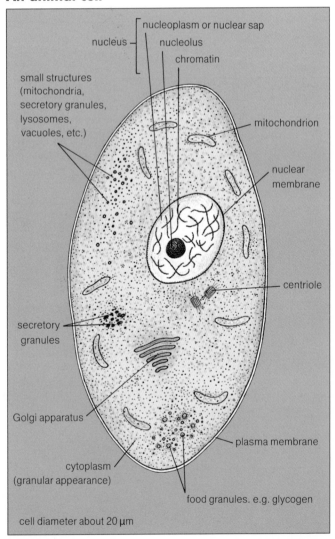

A human sperm cell

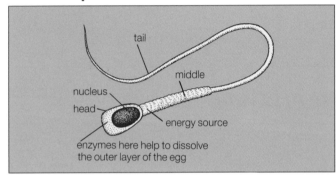

A human egg cell

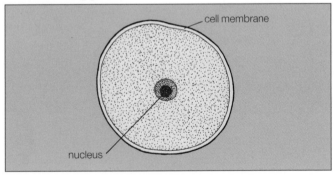

Organs in the human body

When similar cells are grouped together to do a single job, they are called a *tissue*. When different tissues are grouped together, we call this an organ. The diagram shows the main organs in the human body.

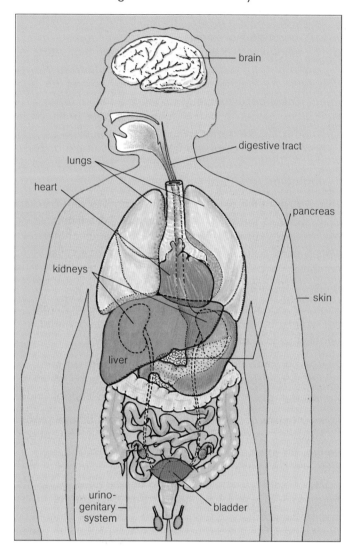

Organs work together in *systems*.

The central nervous system

Conditioned reflexes

These are reflex actions triggered off by a 'learned' stimulus. They are the basis for 'training' in animals, and in humans.

Conditioned reflexes were first discovered by a Russian scientist called Ivan Pavlov in 1902. He knew that dogs always salivate (produce saliva) when they see or smell food and that this was a normal reflex. Every time Pavlov fed the group of dogs in his laboratory he rang a bell. After much repetition the dogs would salivate at the sound of the bell. There was no need for food to be present at all. Pavlov had set up a conditioned reflex in the dogs. They had become conditioned to salivate on hearing the bell.

Types of nerve fibre

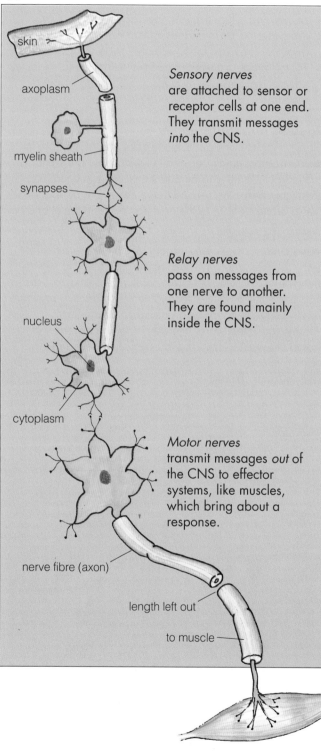

Sensory nerves are attached to sensor or receptor cells at one end. They transmit messages *into* the CNS.

Relay nerves pass on messages from one nerve to another. They are found mainly inside the CNS.

Motor nerves transmit messages *out* of the CNS to effector systems, like muscles, which bring about a response.

Cranial nerves are attached directly to the brain and serve the head and face. *Spinal* nerves are joined to the spinal cord and communicate with the rest of the body. These large nerves contain many smaller nerve fibres conducting impulses in different directions. Nerves inside the spinal cord relay information to and from the brain.

- *Sensory* nerves are attached to sensor or receptor cells at one end. They transmit messages into the CNS.
- *Relay* nerves pass on messages from one nerve to another. They are found mainly inside the CNS.
- *Motor* nerves transmit messages out of the CNS to effector systems like muscles, which bring about a response.

Passing messages on

Nerve impulses or signals move from one nerve fibre to another across small gaps called *synapses*. The signal is carried across the gap as a tiny amount of a chemical. The chemical causes the second nerve cell to fire off electrical pulses along its fibre to the next nerve cell in the chain.

Each nerve cell is linked at the synapse with several other nerve cells, so that if one system fails there are others to carry the message on. The synapse also helps to 'damp' the system. If insufficient chemical is released across the gap at the synapse, the second nerve cell fails to respond. The message is not passed on and so unimportant information is therefore 'filtered out' of the system. We would not want to respond to every stimulus we receive!

The human brain

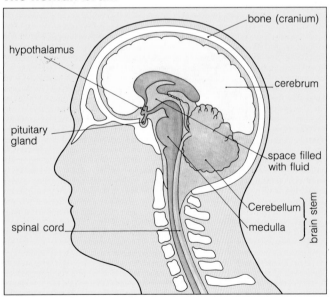

The brain is made of several distinct parts that do different jobs. The brain is protected by the cranium or skull, in which it floats in a special fluid.

- *Medulla* – controls important but basic and automatic functions, e.g. the control of breathing and heart rate.
- *Cerebellum* – controls and coordinates movement and balance. Much of this is automatic but we also have to learn how to do it properly, for example in walking, or riding a bike, or playing a sport. Some people are better at this than others. The cerebellum coordinates fast, accurate movements.
- *Hypothalamus* – a small part of the brain that seems to control some basic body needs, such as thirst and hunger. It is also the control centre for some of our emotional behaviour, e.g. anger and sexual drive.
- *Pituitary gland* – this small lobe at the base of the brain controls the release of special chemicals called hormones from other organs and tissues of the body.
- *Cerebrum* or *cerebral hemispheres* – the largest part of our brains.

The surface of the cerebrum is full of grooves and cracks to increase its surface area. Most of the 14 billion cells of the nervous system are located here and each of these cells is able to link up with 25000 other nerve cells! No computer yet built – or even planned – has a relay capacity as large as this.

The cerebrum is the seat of consciousness, it deals with our senses, it controls speech, holds our memory, and enables us to think. It is the site of intelligence.

The cerebrum is made of two parts, the left and right cerebral hemispheres. The right half of the brain controls the left half of the body and the left controls the right side.

Different parts of the hemispheres carry out different jobs or functions, as you can see in the illustration. The speech centre, for example, is located in the left hemisphere, whereas the centre that responds to music is found on the right-hand side. Complex learning behaviour is located in the surface of both hemispheres called the cerebral cortex. Surprisingly, a lot of the brain does not seem to be used for anything, which explains why people with quite large parts of their brain damaged by accident or injury appear to function quite normally.

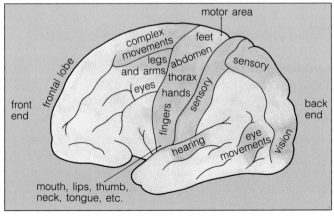

The digestive system

Enzymes

Name of enzyme	Where released	Part of gut releasing enzyme	Type of food digested	Products of digestion
salivary amylase	mouth	salivary gland	starch	maltose and glucose
pepsin	stomach	stomach (gastric) glands	protein	amino acids
pancreatic amylase	small intestine (duodenum)	pancreas gland	starch	maltose and glucose
trypsin	small intestine (duodenum)	pancreas gland	protein	amino acids
lipase	small intestine (duodenum)	pancreas gland	fats	fatty acids and glycerol

All of the chemical reactions inside living cells are catalysed and controlled by enzymes. Without enzymes, these reactions would not proceed rapidly enough to maintain the essential processes of life.

Digestive enzymes speed up the chemical digestion, or breakdown, of food inside the gut.

What are carbohydrates, proteins and fats made of?
Carbohydrates come in three forms:

- complex sugars, e.g. starch, which consists of many single glucose sugars joined together in a long chain;
- double sugars, e.g. maltose sugar, which consists of two glucose molecules joined together;
- single sugars, e.g. single molecules of glucose sugar.

The complex and double sugars in food have to be digested by the gut into single sugars before they can be absorbed through the wall of the intestine and into the blood. Any single sugars taken in as food are small enough to be absorbed straight away.

Fats consist of three fatty acid molecules joined to a single molecule of glycerol. Fats must be broken down by enzymes into separate fatty acid and glycerol molecules before they can be absorbed into the blood.

Proteins are large molecules consisting of many different amino acids joined together in a long chain. Proteins must be digested or broken down into these single amino acid molecules, which are then absorbed into the blood.

Food energy – needs
This chart shows the amounts of different kinds of nutrients needed by men and women of different ages in the daily diet. The amounts are called *the recommended daily amounts*.

Recommended daily amounts of nutrients
Units used in the table: g (gram); mg (milligram, 1×10^{-3}g); µg (microgram, 1×10^{-6}g); MJ (megajoule, 1×10^6J).

| | Energy (MJ) | Protein (g) | Minerals | | Vitamins | | | | |
			Calcium (mg)	Iron (mg)	A (µg)	B1 (mg)	B2 (mg)	Niacin (mg)	C (mg)
males									
1 year old	5.0	30	600	7	300	0.5	0.6	7	20
9–11 years	9.5	57	700	12	575	0.9	1.2	14	25
12–14 years	11.0	66	700	12	725	1.1	1.4	16	25
15–17 years	12.0	72	600	12	750	1.2	1.7	19	30
18–34 years									
desk worker	10.5	63	500	10	750	1.0	1.6	18	30
very active	14.0	84	500	10	750	1.3	1.6	18	30
females									
1 year old	4.5	27	600	7	300	0.4	0.6	7	20
9–11 years	8.5	51	700	12	575	0.8	1.2	14	25
12–14 years	9.0	53	700	12	725	0.9	1.4	16	25
15–17 years	9.0	53	600	12	750	0.9	1.7	19	30
18–34 years									
desk worker	9.5	54	500	12	750	0.9	1.3	15	30
very active	10.5	62	500	12	750	1.0	1.3	15	30
pregnant	10.0	60	1200	13	750	1.0	1.6	18	60

Reference

221

Use of foods by the body

Carbohydrates are used to provide energy. Glucose sugar is the main source of energy through respiration for essential life processes. Excess carbohydrate in the diet is stored as glycogen or converted into fat for storage.

Fats are also used to provide energy. They actually provide more energy than carbohydrate, but too much fat is hard to digest and a high-fat diet is thought to be unhealthy. Excess fat is stored under the skin and around large organs like the heart and kidneys.

Proteins are not normally used for energy. Proteins are needed for growth (to make new living tissue). They are also essential for repair of damaged tissue and to replace cells that are constantly being worn away, e.g. skin cells. Only in extreme starvation when no fat or carbohydrate is available are the proteins of the body respired to release energy.

▉ *The excretory system*

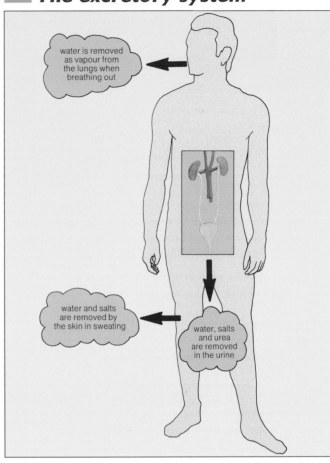

water is removed as vapour from the lungs when breathing out

water and salts are removed by the skin in sweating

water, salts and urea are removed in the urine

▉ *Nutrients present in 100 gram of food (approximate values)*

Food	Energy (kJ)	Protein (g)	Carbohydrate (g)	Fat (g)	Iron (mg)	Vitamin C (mg)
bacon, grilled	1670	28	0	31	1.3	0
beans, baked	270	5	15	0.5	1.4	0
beef, grilled	930	31	0	11	3.0	0
butter	3050	0.5	0	82	0.2	0
cabbage, boiled	70	1.5	2	0	0.4	20
chapati	1400	8	50	13	2.3	0
chips	1000	3.5	34	10	0.8	10
chocolate	2200	8	59	30	1.6	0
cornflakes	1500	8	82	0.5	7	0
curry, chicken	1000	10.7	2	21	1.8	1
fish, fried	850	20	8	10	0.5	0
hamburger, fried	1100	20	7	17	3.1	0
lettuce	40	1	1	0	0.9	15
margarine	3050	0	0	80	0	0
milk	250	3.3	5	4	0	1
orange juice	170	0.5	9	0	0.3	50
peanuts	2400	24	9	50	2	0
potatoes, boiled	350	1.5	20	0	0.3	11
samosa	2400	6	19	54	1	3
spaghetti	1450	12	74	2	2.1	0
toast, white	1250	10	65	2	2.2	0
yoghurt	200	5	6	1	0.1	0.2

Reference

1 Human urinary system

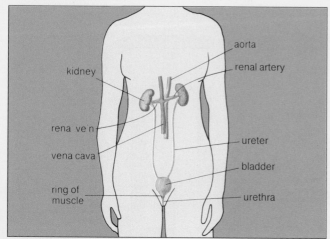

kidney
aorta
renal artery
rena ve n
vena cava
ureter
bladder
ring of muscle
urethra

2 Section through human kidney

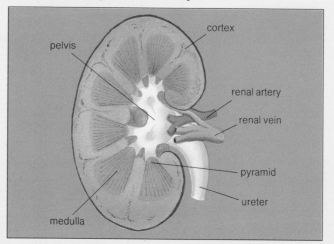

pelvis
cortex
renal artery
renal vein
pyramid
ureter
medulla

How the kidney works

The working unit of the kidney is the *nephron* or kidney tubule. You can see a diagram of the nephron in the illustration opposite.

What happens in the kidney nephron?

1 Blood enters the kidney in the renal artery, which splits into smaller blood vessels.

2 Blood plasma – the liquid part of blood – containing water, salts, glucose sugar, and urea waste, is filtered out of the blood at each *glomerulus*. This is called *ultrafiltration* because it happens at high pressure.

3 The filtered liquid, called the *glomerular filtrate*, enters the kidney tubule at the *Bowman's capsule*.

4 As the liquid flows down the tubule, useful substances such as glucose sugar and some of the salts and water are reabsorbed into the blood. This is called *selective reabsorption* because only *some* of the substances are reabsorbed back into the blood.

5 Harmful wastes like urea, and some water and salts, remain inside the kidney tubules. This liquid, called *urine*, flows towards the collecting ducts in the pelvic region of the kidney.

6 The collecting ducts join up to form the *ureter*, which transports urine to the *bladder*.

7 The bladder stores the urine until it can be discharged from the body.

8 Filtered blood, cleansed of urea waste, leaves the kidney via the renal vein.

By changing the amount of water and salts that are reabsorbed along the tubule, the kidneys are able to control the amounts of these substances in the blood and the body.

If the body has excess water we release watery pale yellow urine in large amounts. If the body is suffering from a lack of water, more water is reabsorbed in the kidney tubules. More concentrated, dark yellow urine is produced in smaller amounts.

3 The action of the nephron

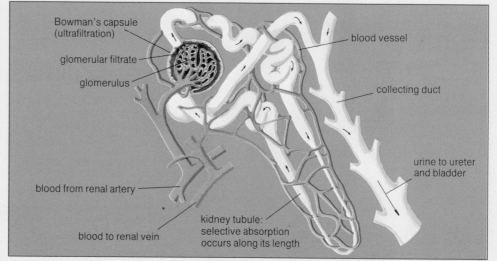

Bowman's capsule (ultrafiltration)
glomerular filtrate
glomerulus
blood vessel
collecting duct
urine to ureter and bladder
blood from renal artery
blood to renal vein
kidney tubule: selective absorption occurs along its length

The cardiovascular system

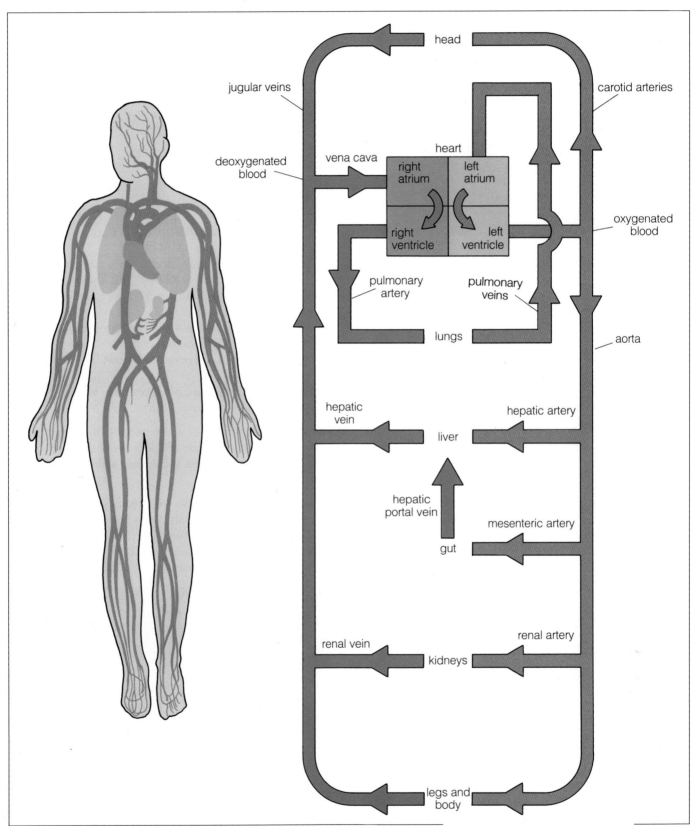

Blood clotting

The clotting of blood involves a series of complex chemical changes. The process must not be allowed to happen inside the body. A clot, or *thrombosis*, formed inside our blood vessels might block the supply of blood to a vital organ – with fatal consequences.

To stop this happening, our blood contains chemicals that prevent clotting. These are called *anticoagulants*. They are given to patients who are undergoing surgery. One commonly used anticoagulant is Heparin.

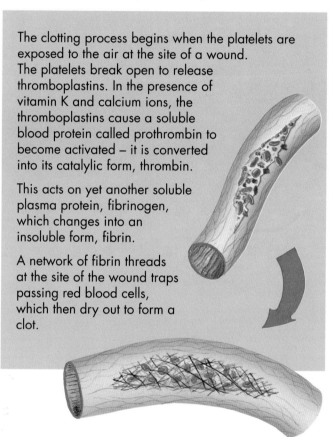

The clotting process begins when the platelets are exposed to the air at the site of a wound. The platelets break open to release thromboplastins. In the presence of vitamin K and calcium ions, the thromboplastins cause a soluble blood protein called prothrombin to become activated – it is converted into its catalylic form, thrombin.

This acts on yet another soluble plasma protein, fibrinogen, which changes into an insoluble form, fibrin.

A network of fibrin threads at the site of the wound traps passing red blood cells, which then dry out to form a clot.

Biological recycling

In the natural world, substances are being recycled all the time. The oxygen you breathe in will have come from a plant feeding by photosynthesis. Other plants will take up the carbon dioxide you breathe out.

Human beings and the things they do, may change or interfere with these natural cycles.

● Intensive farming may release all sorts of harmful chemicals into the soil.
● Burning fossil fuels in our power stations puts millions of tonnes of carbon dioxide and other gases into the air every year.
● Cutting down the rain forests at a rate of one hundred acres a minute could change the weather patterns of the world.

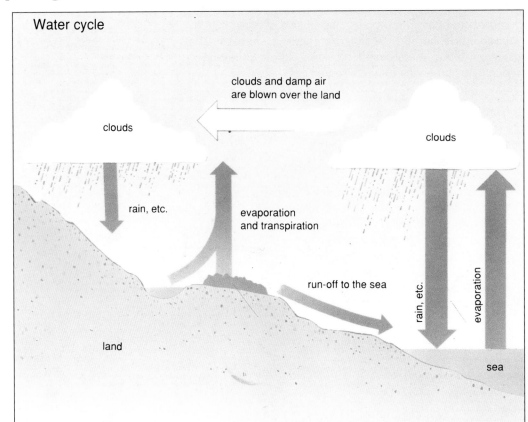

Water cycle

clouds and damp air are blown over the land

clouds

clouds

rain, etc.

evaporation and transpiration

run-off to the sea

rain, etc.

evaporation

land

sea

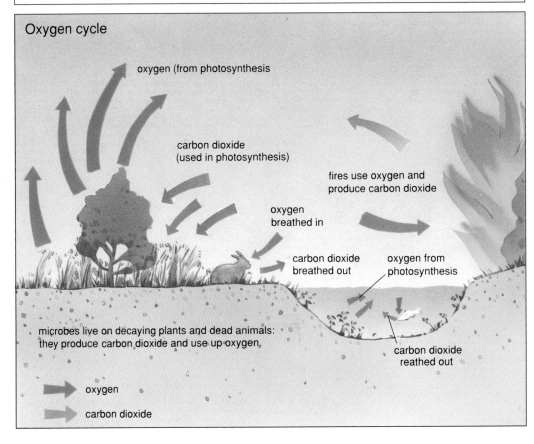

Oxygen cycle

oxygen (from photosynthesis

carbon dioxide (used in photosynthesis)

fires use oxygen and produce carbon dioxide

oxygen breathed in

carbon dioxide breathed out

oxygen from photosynthesis

microbes live on decaying plants and dead animals: they produce carbon dioxide and use up oxygen.

carbon dioxide reathed out

oxygen

carbon dioxide

Reference

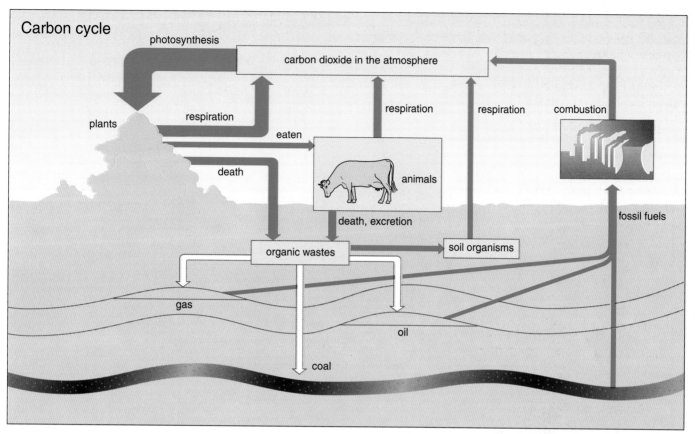

Carbon cycle

photosynthesis

carbon dioxide in the atmosphere

plants

respiration

eaten

respiration

respiration

combustion

death

animals

fossil fuels

death, excretion

organic wastes

soil organisms

gas

oil

coal

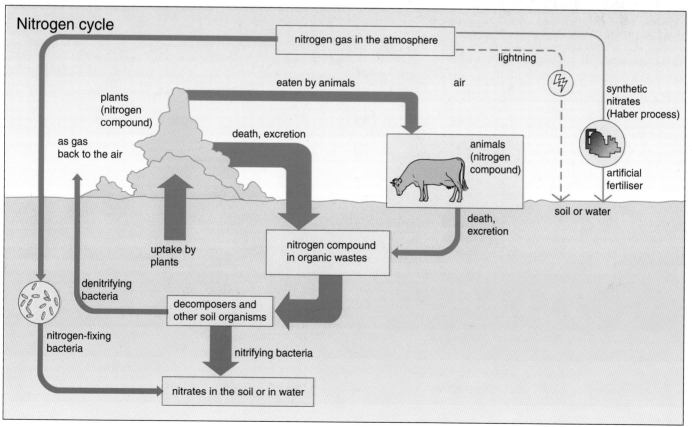

Nitrogen cycle

nitrogen gas in the atmosphere

lightning

eaten by animals

air

synthetic nitrates (Haber process)

plants (nitrogen compound)

death, excretion

animals (nitrogen compound)

as gas back to the air

artificial fertiliser

soil or water

death, excretion

uptake by plants

nitrogen compound in organic wastes

denitrifying bacteria

decomposers and other soil organisms

nitrogen-fixing bacteria

nitrifying bacteria

nitrates in the soil or in water

Reference

Ecology

Ecology is the study of living organisms and how they cope with the world in which they live. There are several special terms that ecologists use.

● *Ecosystem* is the term used to describe a habitat and the community of living organisms living in it.
● The *habitat* is where an organism lives, obtains its food and shelter, reproduces and so on.
● A *community* is all the plants and animals in a particular habitat.

● The *environment* is everything around a living creature that could possibly affect it. The habitat of a rabbit for example is grasssland, but its environment would include the weather, the nature of the soil and so on.
● A *food chain* is a simple way of showing the feeding relationships within a community. Every food chain begins with plant material, followed by the animals that feed on the plant and so on.

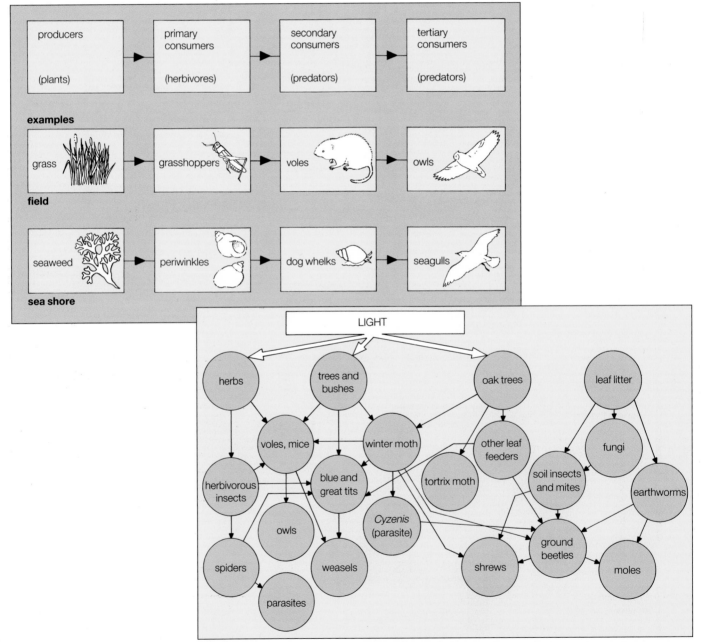

● A *food web* shows all the feeding relationships in a community.

- A pyramid of numbers shows the number of animals and plants at each stage in the food chain.

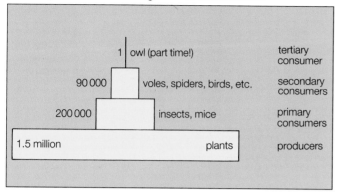

- A *pyramid of biomass* shows the mass of the organisms at each stage in the food chain.

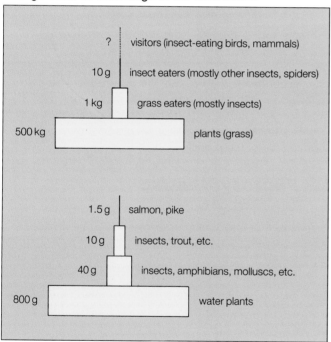

- A *pyramid of energy* shows how much energy is in each part of a food chain.

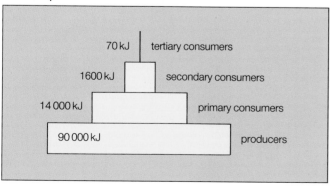

Plant growth hormones (auxins)

The movement of plants towards light is called phototropism. The mechanism of phototropism was revealed over a span of 50 years.

Charles Darwin

Darwin is most widely known for his theory of natural selection, but he was also a good experimenter. He carried out experiments on the developing shoots – called *coleoptiles* – of grass seedlings.

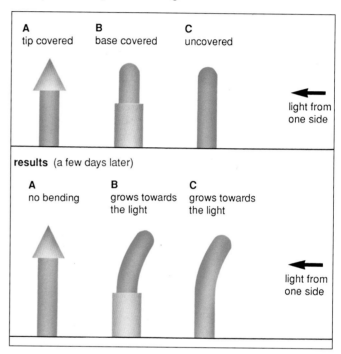

In 1880, Darwin proved that it was only the tip of the shoot that was sensitive to light.

Peter Boysen-Jensen

Thirty years later, in 1910, the Dutch biologist Boysen-Jensen found out how the information about the direction of the light is passed to the rest of the shoot.

Reference

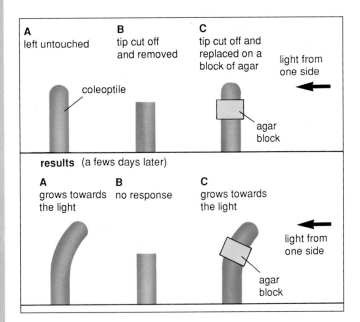

A
left untouched

B
tip cut off
and removed

C
tip cut off and
replaced on a
block of agar

coleoptile

light from
one side

agar
block

results (a fews days later)

A
grows towards
the light

B
no response

C
grows towards
the light

light from
one side

agar
block

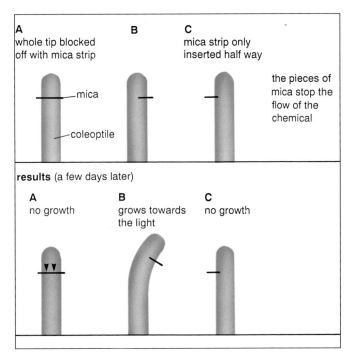

A
whole tip blocked
off with mica strip

B

C
mica strip only
inserted half way

mica

the pieces of
mica stop the
flow of the
chemical

coleoptile

results (a few days later)

A
no growth

B
grows towards
the light

C
no growth

Agar is mostly water, so Boysen-Jensen concluded that the tip must send a message that is able to move through water. In other words a *chemical* messenger – auxins. Further experiments using mica to block the auxins, showed that they passed down only the dark side of the shoot.

Later experiments showed that the auxins could be collected in agar blocks and used to make stem cells grow longer. Finally, radioactive labelling allowed scientists to trace the route that the auxins took via the shaded side of the plant.

Photosynthesis

Plants get their food from sugars and other organic chemicals that they make for themselves. They do this by

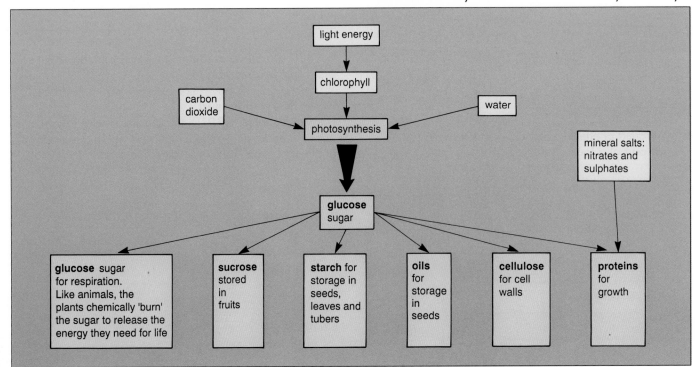

light energy

chlorophyll

carbon
dioxide

photosynthesis

water

mineral salts:
nitrates and
sulphates

glucose
sugar

glucose sugar
for respiration.
Like animals, the
plants chemically 'burn'
the sugar to release the
energy they need for life

sucrose
stored
in
fruits

starch for
storage in
seeds,
leaves and
tubers

oils
for
storage
in
seeds

cellulose
for cell
walls

proteins
for
growth

Reference

taking in carbon dioxide and water, and using these in reactions that require energy from light. These reactions are called photosynthesis.

The complete process can be summarised as:

$$\text{carbon dioxide} + \text{water} \xrightarrow[\text{chlorophyll}]{\text{light energy}} \text{glucose sugar} + \text{oxygen}$$

Or as a chemical equation:

$$6CO_2 + 6H_2O \xrightarrow{\text{light energy}} C_6H_{12}O_6 + 6O_2$$

Fertilisers

Most of the chemicals a plant uses come from the air (carbon dioxide and oxygen) or the soil (water). But to make use of these basic materials, plants take up other chemicals from the soil, especially nitrates, phosphates, calcium and magnesium. A fertile soil, able to grow good crops, must have a good supply of these minerals.

When a farmer grows crops on the same soil for many years, these essential minerals get used up. In a natural environment, of course, old plants die and rot, so the minerals go back into the soil. On farms, however, the plants are removed for human or animal food, and the minerals are not recycled unless the animal and plant wastes (sewage and manure) are ploughed back into the soil as *natural* fertiliser.

Modern farming rarely ploughs back natural manure because it is expensive to keep and handle, and not easy to get if the farm doesn't keep animals. *Artificial* fertilisers are used instead. These are chemicals specially made to contain the right balance of essential minerals. The quality of these fertilisers is tightly controlled. They may contain two or more of the following:

Element	Compound	Source
nitrogen	ammonium nitrate	Haber process (nitrogen taken from the air)
phosphorus	phosphate	rocks
potassium	potash, potassium chloride	rocks
calcium	calcium carbonate, calcium hydroxide (lime)	rocks
magnesium	magnesium carbonate	rocks

Artificial fertilisers are usually combinations of nitrates, phosphates and potassium salts, so they are called *NPK* fertilisers. Each plant's need for minerals is different, so there are many different types and proportions of chemicals for the farmer to choose from.

Economics of fertilisers

Fertilisers are expensive, and misuse will mean a low profit. If a field loses 10% of its nitrates at the critical time (at a fertiliser cost of £10), the farmer might lose 1 tonne (£100) of wheat.

This table shows the costs of producing a hectare of wheat crop (about 7.0 tonnes):

seed	£45
fertiliser	£85
sprays (herbicide, pesticide)	£75
labour	£120
machinery (wear, fuel)	£150
rental/rates	£135
overheads	£30
total costs	£640
selling price	£742
net profit	£102

absorption: the way in which a substance is taken into one area from another, e.g. glucose is absorbed into the blood from the small intestine.

acceleration: how much something's speed increases every second. Acceleration = change in speed / time taken to change.

activation energy: the energy needed to start a chemical reaction

adrenalin: a hormone produced by the adrenal glands. Prepares the body for 'fight' or 'flight'.

air resistance: drag caused by something moving through air.

alimentary canal: tubular part of the digestive system that passes from the mouth to the anus.

alkane: a hydrocarbon where the carbon atoms are bonded together by single bonds only.

alveoli: small sacs found in the lungs. They form the area of gaseous exchange.

ampere: the unit of current. The electric charge that flows during one second.

amplitude (wave): the maximum change of the medium from normal, e.g. the height of a water wave above the level of calm water.

amylase: a digestive enzyme that helps convert starch into maltose and glucose.

anus: a ring of muscle at the end of the alimentary canal. Controls loss of faeces (indigestable food) from the body.

arteries: the blood vessels that carry blood away from the heart.

atom: the smallest particle of an element. The atoms of different elements are made from different numbers of protons, electrons and neutrons.

auxin: a chemical made by plants (a plant hormone) that affects the way they grow.

biochemical (reaction): a chemical reaction in a living thing.

biomass: the mass of all the organisms in a population, community or habitat.

boiling: changing a heated liquid into a gas at the boiling point. Boiling happens throughout the liquid.

boiling point: the temperature of a boiling liquid – the highest temperature that the liquid can reach and the lowest temperature that the gas can reach.

bolus: a ball of food that passes along the alimentary canal.

bond: one particle attracts another and sticks to it using a force.

bronchioles: part of the respiratory system. Tiny tubes that join bronchi to alveoli.

bronchus: part of the respiratory system. Two tubes that link trachea (windpipe) to bronchioles.

Brownian motion: the jerky movement of small particles floating in air or water. The motion is due to the constant collision of the surrounding, unseen air or water particles.

burning: the reaction of a substance with oxygen with a large transfer of heat energy out to the surroundings.

capillaries: tiny blood vessels that exchange materials with surrounding tissues.

carbon cycle: the processes that recycle carbon in the environment. Involves photosynthesis, respiration, decay, burning, etc.

catalyst: a chemical that is added to speed up a reaction, but remains unchanged at the end.

central nervous system: the brain and spinal cord.

chemical change: a change that is not easily reversed because new substances are made.

chemical digestion: the breakdown of large food molecules into smaller ones by enzymes.

chemical reaction: *see* chemical change.

circulatory (system): the heart and blood vessels (arteries, veins, capillaries).

colon: part of the large intestine. Water and mineral salts are absorbed from it into the bloodstream.

combustion, complete: the chemical change of a fuel burning in oxygen to make carbon dioxide and water.

combustion, incomplete: the chemical change of a fuel burning in a limited supply of oxygen to make carbon monoxide and water.

community: all of the organisms that live in a particular habitat.

compression: a region where particles are squashed together.

concentration: amount of chemical dissolved in 1 litre (dm^3) of solvent.

condensation: the changing of a gas to a liquid.

conduction, heat: transferring energy from particle to particle through a substance.

conductors, heat: substances that conduct heat very well.

consumer: an organism (usually an animal) that eats another to get its energy. Primary consumers (herbivores) eat plants. Secondary/tertiary consumers (carnivores) eat animals.

convection: hot fluid expanding and rising above cooler fluid.

coulomb: the unit of electric charge.

crest: the highest part of a wave.

critical angle: *see* total internal reflection.

deceleration: how much something's speed decreases every second. Deceleration = – change in speed / time taken to change.

decompose: when a chemical breaks down into new chemicals.

decomposer: an organism (usually bacteria and fungi) that eats (breaks down) dead and decaying organisms.

denature: changing the shape of an enzyme, by high temperatures or incorrect pH, so that it no longer works.

density: the mass, in kilograms, of one metre cube of a substance.

diaphragm: sheet of muscle that helps in breathing. It is located under the lungs.

diffraction: waves spreading into the shadow when they pass an edge.

diffusion: molecules moving from an area of high concentration to an area of low concentration.

digestion: food breaking down into smaller particles.

dispersion: splitting white light into colours.

drag: a friction force caused by something moving through a fluid (liquid or gas).

duodenum: part of the small intestine. Links the stomach to the ileum. Substances from the pancreas and gall bladder are added to the food here.

ecosystems: a group of organisms and the environment they live in.

effective collision: a collision of particles where enough energy is able to be transferred to break the bonds within the molecules and make new bonds.

effectors: muscles or glands that are stimulated in response to information picked up by the body.

egestion: loss of faeces (indigestable food) from the body.

elastic: describes materials that go back to their original shape and size after you stretch them.

electric current: flowing electric charge.

electromagnetic spectrum: the 'family' of electro-magnetic radiations (radio, microwave, infrared, visible light, ultraviolet, X-rays, gamma rays.) They all travel at the same speed in a vacuum (3×10^8 m/s).

emulsification: the way in which bile changes large fat droplets into smaller ones. Bile lowers the surface tension of fat causing it to break up. It is not a chemical change.

endocrine gland: a gland that produces hormones.

endocrine system: the group of organs (glands) in the body that produce hormones.

endothermic: a type of reaction in which energy is transferred in from the surroundings as heat.

enzyme: a chemical that speeds up certain reactions in biological systems, e.g. digestive enzymes speed up the chemical digestion of food.

eutrophication: an increase in mineral levels in rivers and lakes usually caused by pollution with fertilisers or sewage.

evaporation: liquid changing into a gas at a temperature lower than the boiling point.

exhalation: breathing air out of the lungs.

exocrine gland: a gland that produces substances and secretes them into ducts (tubes) e.g. sweat glands, tear glands.

exothermic: a type of reaction in which energy is transferred out to the surroundings as heat.

extension: the increase in length when something is stretched.

fluid: any liquid or gas.

food chain: a simple feeding relationship between a series of organisms, e.g.
plant → herbivore → carnivore.

food web: all the feeding relationships within a habitat.

force: a push or a pull, measured in newtons (N).

fossil fuel: fuel made from the remains of decayed animal and plant matter compressed over millions of years.

fraction: a collection of hydrocarbons that have similar molecular masses and boil at similar temperatures.

fractional distillation: separating fractions of a mixture by distilling. The process depends on the differences in boiling points of the fractions.

fractionating column: the column in which fractional distillation takes place, where crude oil is boiled and the fractions are cooled at different heights in the tower.

freezing: changing a liquid to a solid at the melting point.

frequency: the number of vibrations per second.

friction: the force that resists when you try to move something.

fuse: a special wire that protects an electric circuit. If the current gets too large, the fuse melts and stops the current.

gall bladder: stores bile made by the liver.

gametes: the sex cells of living organisms, e.g. sperm, ova.

gamma rays: *see* electromagnetic spectrum.

gaseous exchange: the way in which oxygen and carbon dioxide are 'swapped'. In the lungs oxygen passes into the blood and carbon dioxide passes out of the blood. In the rest of the body oxygen passes out of the blood into the cells, and carbon dioxide passes into the blood.

gland: an organ that makes a substance which is passed outside of it, either in the blood or through a duct (tube).

gradient: slope of a curve.

haemoglobin: red pigment found in red blood cells that can carry oxygen.

herbicide: a chemical used to kill harmful plants ie a weedkiller.

homeostasis: fine control of the internal environment of the body, so that it stays almost constant. For example, control of sugar level in the blood.

hormones: chemicals produced in the body by endocrine glands which control the way it works.

hydrocarbon: a compound made of carbon and hydrogen only.

hydrolysis: the chemical breakdown of a substance due to the action of water.

ileum: part of the small intestine. Digested food is absorbed from the ileum into the bloodstream.

image: what you see when you look at an object through a mirror, lens or the interface between two mediums (e.g. air and water).

impervious (rock): a rock that will not allow liquids or gases to pass through it.

impulse, mechanical: the effect of a short push. Impulse = force × time that the force was pushing.

impulse, neural: the message carried by a nerve cell.

infrared: *see* electromagnetic spectrum.

ingested: to take food into the mouth, i.e. to eat.

inhalation: breathing air into the lungs.

insecticide: a chemical used to destroy insects that destroy crops.

insulators, heat: substances that do not conduct heat very well.

interference: waves combine with each other as they collide.

intermolecular bonds: forces between molecules attracting them together weakly.

intramolecular bonds: forces within the molecule holding the atoms together strongly.

inversely proportional: two things are inversely proportional to each other if one thing doubles when the other thing halves.

iris: the coloured part of your eye. It expands and contracts to change the amount of light getting into your eye through the pupil.

kinetic energy: energy that something has because it is moving. Kinetic energy = $\frac{1}{2}mv^2$.

law of energy, first: energy cannot be created or destroyed.

law of energy, second: some energy always becomes unusable whenever energy is transferred.

long sight: an eye defect. A person with long sight cannot focus on close objects.

longitudinal wave: a wave where the motion of the medium is parallel to the direction of the wave.

loudness: how loud (or soft) a sound appears to your ear.

lymphocytes: white blood cells that produce antibodies which fight infection.

mass: the amount of matter, usually measured in kilograms. Gravity makes large masses weigh more than small masses.

mechanical digestion: the breakdown by muscle action or bile of large particles of food into smaller bits.

melting: changing a solid into a liquid at the melting point.

menstruation: the loss of blood and tissue that happens at the beginning of a females reproductive cycle, i.e. a period.

microwaves: *see* electromagnetic spectrum.

molecule: a group of two or more atoms strongly bonded together.

momentum: fast objects and massive objects need a lot of force to stop them – they have a large momentum. Momentum = mass × velocity.

motor neurone: a nerve cell that carries an impulse from the central nervous system to an effector (a muscle or gland).

mouth: the start of the alimentary canal.

multicellular: made of many cells.

nastic response: a response to a general stimulus, e.g. opening of some flowers when it gets light.

nervous (system): coordinates some activities of the body. The nervous system is made up of brain, spinal cord and nerves.

neurone: a nerve cell.

non-renewable fuel: fuel that cannot be made again in a short time span.

normal: a line drawn at 90° to a mirror or the boundary between two mediums. You use the normal line to measure the angles of light rays.

nucleus, atomic: the tiny centre of an atom made from protons and neutrons.

nucleus, cell: part of a cell. Controls the activities of the cell.

oestrogen: a female sex hormone. Controls secondary sexual characteristics and development of the uterus.

off-peak electricity: electricity, produced by power stations at night, that can be bought cheaper than usual.

optic nerve: carries impulses from the eye (retina) to the brain.

organisms: living things, i.e. bacteria, plants, fungi, animals.

organs: part of an organism that contains a number of tissues and has a certain function (job) to do.

ovary: 1. organ in plants that makes ovules (eggs) and may develop into a fruit. 2. organ in female vertebrates that makes ova (eggs) and sex hormones.

ovulation: the release of an ovum from the ovary of a vertebrate animal.

ovum: the female reproductive cell in vertebrates (unfertilized egg).

oxidation: when a chemical has reacted with oxygen.

oxygen cycle: the cycle of chemical reactions in the natural environment that convert oxygen to other chemicals and back again to oxygen via photosynthesis in plants.

pancreas gland: a gland that has two parts: the endocrine part produces the hormones insulin and glucagon – the exocrine part produces digestive enzymes.

payback time: the number of years it takes for the money you save on reduced heating bills to equal the money you spent on insulating your house.

period: *see* menstruation

peristalsis: the muscular action that squeezes a bolus of food along the alimentary canal.

phagocytes: white blood cells that eat invading organisms.

photochemical (reaction): a reaction affected by light.

photons: particles of light and other electromagnetic radiations. Sometimes radiation behaves like waves, sometimes like particles.

photosynthesis: a reaction that plants carry out to make food.

physical change: a change in chemicals that is easily reversed and does not involve the making of new chemical bonds.

pitch: whether a note sounds high or low to your ear.

pituitary gland: a small but important gland on the lower surface of the brain. It releases many different types of hormones.

plasma: the liquid part of the blood.

plastic: describes materials that do not go back to their original shape and size after you stretch them.

population: the number of organisms of a single species.

power: the energy transferred in one second. Measured in watts.

predator: a carnivorous animal (secondary/tertiary consumer) which hunts other animals for food.

pressure: the effect of a force spread out over an area. Pressure = force / area.

prey: animals that are hunted by predators.

primary sexual characteristics: the external features seen at birth which help tell males and females apart.

producers: organisms, usually plants, that make their own food.

progesterone: a female sex hormone. It allows the uterus to develop and stops ovum release.

proportional: two things are proportional to each other if one thing doubles when the other thing doubles.

quality, sound: a particular 'flavour' that a sound has because it was produced by a certain instrument.

radar: a form of microwaves, *see* electromagnetic spectrum.

radiation, heat: infrared radiation given out by all things. Infrared rays from hot objects carry more energy than those from cold objects.

radiation: energy that travels in straight lines, e.g. electromagnetic rays.

radio waves: *see* electromagnetic spectrum.

rarefaction: a region where particles are stretched further apart than normal.

rate (of reaction): how fast a reaction goes in a given interval of time.

receptor: part of the body, usually a sense organ, that picks up information about the body and its surroundings.

rectum: last part of the large intestine. Stores faeces (indigestable food).

reduction: when a chemical reacts losing oxygen.

reflection: when waves bounce off a mirror. The angle of incidence is the same size as the angle of reflection.

reflex: a rapid reaction to a stimulus by a nervous pathway.

refraction: when waves change direction because they have gone into a different medium. They change direction because their speed changes.

reproductive (system): the organs involved in producing offspring.

respiration: the reaction by which all living organisms get the energy they need from food.

response: the way that an organism reacts to a stimulus.

retina: part of the back of the eye that contains cells sensitive to light.

saliva: the liquid secreted into the mouth. In humans it contains water, mucus and salivary amylase (the starch digesting enzyme).

secondary sexual characteristics: the changes that occur at puberty to the bodies of girls and boys. They are the outward signs of puberty.

sediment: the collection of small particles of rock that have beeen worn down by weather and transported by rivers to a place where they are pushed together.

seismic waves: waves that travel through rocks. Earthquakes produce seismic waves.

sensory neurone: a nerve cell that carries impulses from a sense receptor to the brain or spinal cord.

short circuit: an extra, unwanted branch of an electric circuit. It bypasses other parts of the circuit and causes a large current to flow.

short sight: an eye defect. A person with short sight cannot focus on far away objects.

solute: the chemical that dissolves in a solvent.

solvent: the chemical that dissolves a solute to make a solution.

specific heat capacity: the heat capacity of 1 kilogram of a substance. Specific heat capacity = heat capacity / mass. The heat capacity of a substance is the amount of energy (in joules) needed to raise the temperature by 1 °C.

spectrum: the 'rainbow' of colours that make up white light (red, orange, yellow, green, blue, indigo and violet).

speed: how far something moves every second. Average speed = distance travelled / time taken.

stimulus: the information that causes a receptor to pass a message on to the rest of the nervous system.

surface area: the total area of the outside of an object. Particles of chemical reactants can bombard only the surface of an object.

suspension: a liquid that contains very small paricles of solid that are held throughout the liquid without dissolving or settling as a sediment.

systems, body: groups of organs with a general job to do e.g. reproductive system, digestive system.

testes: the male organs that make sperm. In vertebrates, the testes also make sex hormones such as testosterone.

testosterone: a male sex hormone. It controls secondary sexual characteristics and the development of sperm.

thermostat: a temperature operated switch used to control electric appliances

thorax: the chest area. In most vertebrates, the thorax contains the heart and lungs.

tissues: groups of cells with a common structure and function (job).

total internal reflection: when all the light trying to get out of a medium is reflected back in. It happens when the angle of incidence of a ray (going out of the medium) is greater than the critical angle.

tracers: radioactive substances that doctors use to find out about the inside of a patient's body. They put the tracer inside the patient's body and measure the radiation.

trachea: part of the respiratory system. Commonly called the windpipe.

transverse wave: a wave where the change of the medium is at 90° to the direction of the wave.

tropism: response to a stimulus from a certain direction, e.g. the growth of a plant towards light.

trough: the lowest part of a wave.

ultrasound: sound that humans cannot hear because its pitch is too high.

ultraviolet: *see* electromagnetic spectrum.

veins: the blood vessels that carry blood towards the heart.

ventilation: the active process of breathing air into and out of the lungs.

volt: the unit of voltage. The energy carried by one coulomb of electric charge.

voltage: the energy carried by electric charge.

water cycle: a cycle of physical reaction where water is changed by energy from the sun into water vapour which condenses to form clouds which then convert the water droplets back to rain.

wave equation: $v = f \times \lambda$ more commonly written as: wavespeed = frequency × wavelength.

wavefront: the front of a wave. It is a straight line for a plane wave.

wavelength: the pattern repeat distance of a wave, e.g. from one crest to the next.

weight: the force of Earth's gravity pulling on a mass. Weight (in newtons) = 10 × mass (in kilograms).

work: the amount of energy transferred by a force moving something.

x-rays: *see* electromagnetic spectrum.

Reference

Reference

Reference

Reference

The authors and publishers are grateful to the following for permission to reproduce the copyright material on the pages indicated:

(T, top; B, bottom; C, centre; L, left; R, right)

Ancient Art and Architecture Collections 104 TL, 104 TR
Ace Photo Agency/Mugshots 6 BC, Howard 6 CL, Burns 6 C, Smith 77 R, Mauritius 82 L, Macia 101
Ajax News and Feature Service/Eastland 77 L
Allsport UK/Mortimore 48 T, Cole 48 R, Mortimore 53 L
Aviation Picture Library/Brown 104 BR
John Birdsall Photography 21 T, 21 B, 41, 58 T, 58 L, 68 C, 69 R, 84 TL, 127 TR
Anthony Blake Photo Library 68 BR, 79
British Petroleum Company 91, 92
Collections/Shout 15 B
EEV 16 (2)
Environmental Picture Library/Bond 39 T
Mary Evans Picture Library 97
Ford Motor Company 58 B
G.C.S.E. Science Review 161 B, 162 T
The Garden Picture Library/Howes 68 BL, 68 BC
Geoscience Features Picture Library 104 BL, 105 TL, 105 TR, 105 B, 106 L, 106 R, 112 TR, 112 BR
Peter Gould 117 T
Hansen Planetarium Pictures 90 TL
Holt Studios International 157, 159, 160 T, 160 B, 162 L, 164
ICCE Photo Library/Steele 35 L, Wakeford 39 C, Steele 96, Agren 98 TL, Purcell 98 TR, 150 (Canadian Mountains), 150 (coral reef)
Andrew Lambert Photographs 35 R, 39 B, 40, 43 T, 43 B, 44 L, 44 R, 45 R, 59, 71 T, 71 B, 74 T, 74 B, 83 B, 84 BR(2), 99 B, 111 R, 112 BL, 114 L, 114 R, 142, 146
Frank Lane Picture Agency/Wharton 84 TR, 150 (rocky beach), 156
Life Science Images/Boardman 116, 120 (aloe ferox), 132 CR
London Features International/Fowler 69 L
Microscopix/Syred 120 (bacteria), 121 CR
MRP Photography 90 BL
National Medical Slidebank 14 L, 15 T, 18 L, 18 R, 25 B
National Power 98 C(2)
New Scientist 96 B
Peter Newark's Pictures 104 CR, 161 T
Oxford Scientific Films/Watts/Parks 6 T(inset), Tipling 6T, Kamal 68 T, Zahl/Photo Researchers 99 T, 120 (kingfisher), 120 (spider), 120 (fungus), 121 T, 138 (2), London Scientific Films 132 BR, 136 TL, 136 TC, 136 TR, 136 BL, 136 BC, Morris 136 BR, 150 (rainforest, tundra, meadow, woodland), Cox 151, 162 R, 163
Professional Sport/Livesey 20, 36, 50 T
Quadrant Picture Library/Auto Express 48 B, 53 R
Rex Features/Dixon 50 B, Alpha Diffusion/Sipa 90 CR, 109 L, Sipa 145 T
Science Photo Library/NASA 6 CR, Parker 15 C, 27, 31, Clark 32, Menzel 45 L, Morgan 64, Plailly 75, Hart-Davis 82 R, Fraser 83 T, NRSC 90 TR, Gohier 109 R, Heseltine 111 L, 120 (fetus), 123 TR, 129 TR, 137, 145 B
Frank Spooner Pictures/Gamma/Barritt 141
UCL Medical Physics Department 14 BC
Volvo Car UK 57
C. James Webb 147
Wednesbury Tube 117 B